A109-
symbols = p113

Managerial Statistics

KERMIT O. HANSON

ASSOCIATE DEAN
COLLEGE OF BUSINESS ADMINISTRATION
UNIVERSITY OF WASHINGTON

GEORGE J. BRABB

ASSOCIATE PROFESSOR, DEPARTMENT OF
ACCOUNTING, FINANCE, AND STATISTICS
UNIVERSITY OF WASHINGTON

Managerial Statistics

SECOND EDITION

Prentice-Hall, Inc., ENGLEWOOD CLIFFS, N.J.

Library of Congress Catalog Card Number: 61–11813

Third printing . . . . March, 1964

PRINTED IN THE UNITED STATES OF AMERICA

55031-C

Preface to the second edition

This edition includes numerous significant revisions which have been incorporated within the "business planning and control" framework of the first edition. These revisions include new illustrations, reorganized presentation, and some completely new material.

Additional sources of data are included in Chapter 2. The treatment of sampling in Chapter 3 has been expanded considerably. Measures of central tendency and dispersion, formerly presented in two chapters, are introduced in Chapter 4. An introduction to the concepts of probability and inference in Chapter 5 constitutes one of the major changes in this edition. The emphasis upon forecasting is retained in Chapters 6, 7, and 8, which deal, respectively, with index numbers, time series analysis, and correlation. The importance of effective communication of statistical information is stressed in Chapters 9 and 10, which contain many tables and charts carefully selected from business reports; a discussion of the construction and interpretation of semi-logarithmic (ratio) charts is included in Chapter 10. Chapter 11 presents an enlarged coverage of the statistical techniques which may be employed to facilitate internal administrative control of business operations. Finally, Chapter 12 describes a managerial statistics program for both a large and a small business, thereby integrating the material presented in the preceding chapters.

The authors have attempted to achieve a desirable blend of descriptive, analytical, and interpretative material. Designed as an introductory text for the first semester (quarter) course in business statistics, it is directed more toward future business administrators ("consumers") than toward professional statisticians ("producers"). Chapters which are essentially descriptive should be regarded as "reading" chapters—to be assigned to students for reading and examination purposes, but to be allocated a minimum amount of time for classroom lecture and discussion. Classroom time thus freed could be devoted to the more difficult analytical and interpretative sections of the book. It has been the authors' experience that this approach has stimulated student interest in statistics and has led to an increased proportion of business students enrolling in advanced courses in statistics.

The authors are deeply grateful to the numerous associates and colleagues who have reviewed sections of this edition in its several stages. Special acknowledgment is due Professors Stephen H. Archer, Philip J. Bourque, and Robert C. Meier for their critical review of the chapters on sampling and statistical inference. Dale McFarlane rendered invaluable service in performing and checking arithmetic calculations, reading portions of the text, and a host of other assignments. Diane Mack was most cooperative and efficient in typing much of the manuscript. The authors are particularly grateful to Betty L. Brabb for her splendid assistance on many phases of the text revision.

We are indebted to Professor Sir Ronald A. Fisher, F.R.S., Cambridge, and to Dr. Frank Yates, F.R.S., Rothamsted; also to Messrs. Oliver and Boyd, Ltd., Edinburgh, for permission to reprint part of Table III from their book *Statistical Tables for Biological, Agricultural and Medical Research.* Our appreciation is extended to Professor Gregor Selba of the Graduate Institute of the Liberal Arts, Emory University and to Professor Alfred Thimm of Union College for their reading of the manuscript and many helpful suggestions. We are also indebted to Prentice-Hall, Inc. and Houghton Mifflin Company for permission to reprint the table of areas under the normal curve found in Appendix B.

Kermit O. Hanson
George J. Brabb

Contents

1 *Introduction*

The importance of the management function in business administration has grown tremendously during the twentieth century. This development, which has been particularly phenomenal during the past generation, has come about as the result of the gigantic growth of industry. The size and complexity of business organizations has necessitated an increasing amount of attention to the formulation of plans and budgets and to the administrative control of operations. The owner-operator of a small business could possess firsthand knowledge of details of his entire operation. This is not so with businesses owned by numerous stockholders, guided by boards of directors and managed by staffs of executives, none of whom can become intimately acquainted with the multiplicity of details concerning sales, production, inventories, finance, personnel, and administration.

In discharging their managerial functions business executives in all departments have become increasingly dependent upon accounting and statistical information. Accounting records and reports provide information concerning the revenues, costs, profits, losses, and financial condition of individual businesses. Accounting records are a prime source of data for statistical reports. Statistical data are also drawn from various administrative records and come from an almost infinite number of sources outside individual company records. Adequate accounting and statistical information which has been properly interpreted provides the foundation for sound business management.

Nature of managerial statistics

This text is designed to acquaint the reader with *statistics* useful to business management. Statistics is a word with at least two meanings. First, the word statistics refers to *meaningful numbers* such as the price of beefsteak, the amount of the national debt, or the average weekly hours per worker in manufacturing industries. These *meaningful numbers* are of interest to everyone, but they are of special interest to the statistician because they are the material with which he works.

The second meaning of the word statistics refers to the *processes* or *methods* by which meaningful numbers are collected, analyzed, and made to serve as guides to managerial decisions. Both these meanings are appropriate for the interpretation of the title and purpose of this book. Managerial statistics deals with data and methods which are useful to management executives in planning and controlling organizational activities. Statistical techniques which have only limited practical application to management problems have been excluded from this text. Similarly, little emphasis is placed upon theoretical or mathematical refinements which may be essential in training a professional statistician, but are unnecessary in training a business administrator.

Statistics as a managerial tool

SOURCES OF INFORMATION

Collection of data for management and control purposes originated with political states, hence, the term statistics. Undoubtedly, our own federal government is today the collector of the greatest volume of data and the employer of the greatest number of statisticians and statistical clerks. Much of the data collected by the government is useful to businessmen in planning future operations.

Trade associations and labor unions also engage in the collection of statistics. Private individuals and companies collect selected statistics on a continuing basis which they sell to various clients. Numerous research agencies specialize in market surveys and forecasts for private businesses. In addition, many business firms regularly maintain records of statistical information pertinent to their operations. One of the purposes of this text is to acquaint the student with the major sources of business information.

PRESENTATION OF DATA

Regardless of the source of the data, it must be carefully presented if it is to be fully utilized. Tabular and graphic devices can be used to aid in the description of the facts which the figures reflect. Narrative discussion of tables and graphs should be brief and concise, yet complete. Much of the value of a report is lost if significant findings are clouded or concealed by faulty presentation. An inadequate or inaccurate report used as a basis for decision-making can lead to the wrong decision and result in losses on operations.

FORECASTING

Planning is the first step in scientific management. All plans are based on forecasts. Formally or informally—knowingly or unknowingly—businessmen are making forecasts when they purchase inventories, when they purchase plant and equipment, when they engage personnel, in fact, whenever they perform any act in anticipation of the future. It never occurs to many businessmen that their numerous planning decisions reflect their intuitive forecasts. Businessmen cannot avoid making forecasts, they can only neglect to make as intelligent forecasts as possible. True, the most certain thing about the future is its unpredictability. However, some aspects of the future can be predicted more reliably than others. The wise businessman reduces the likelihood of error in his forecasts by carefully estimating the future impact of those factors which can be forecast with the greatest degree of accuracy. A forecast of general business conditions is usually a prerequisite to forecasts of sales for an industry or for a specific firm.

ADMINISTRATIVE CONTROL

Well-formulated plans are of little value if they are not effectively carried out. It behooves the business executive to exercise administrative control of his operations in an effort to correct controllable deviations from planned operations. For example, the trend of sales by products, territories, and salesmen is highly significant information. Executives must act rapidly to capitalize on favorable sales trends and also to adjust to unfavorable trends. Similarly, production costs should be subjected to critical analysis. Lack of control of production costs can easily result in a loss rather than a gain from business operations. Reduced costs increase unit profits just as surely as do increased selling prices.

When goods are produced by repetitive operations, statistical techniques may be employed to control the quality of the units produced. This is done by selecting small samples from the units produced and determining whether the characteristics of the samples conform to predetermined specifications. When production fails to meet required standards, immediate corrective action may be taken. Statistical quality control techniques also may be adapted to controlling repetitive clerical operations in the office.

Control must be exercised over inventories, overhead expenses, personnel, and financial matters. Audits of accounting records and business papers usually are based on samples. Samples also may be employed to measure the attitudes of employees, customers, and the public toward management policies and programs. If the operations plan has been expressed in dollars—that is, if all operations have been budgeted—internal statistics should be collected regularly and reported to management for control purposes.

Judgment, a prime factor

Knowledge of managerial statistics is not synonymous with possession of a crystal ball. Statistical formulas are not magical devices which always provide the "correct" solution. The successful businessman with years of experience is likely better able to forecast his firm's sales for the next year than is a college-trained statistician who is unfamiliar with the firm and with the industry of which it is a part. The business outlook for an individual firm may be quite different from the outlook for the industry, and both may vary from that of the economy as a whole. Statistical formulas can neither evaluate nor give cognizance to all the myriad factors which bear on the future. Nonetheless, a business executive familiar with the techniques of managerial statistics can better utilize his business knowledge in planning and controlling the affairs of his business. An intelligent forecast based on a sound analysis of the best available data is far superior to a forecast based on a combination of hunches and rumors.

A knowledge of business statistics provides an individual with an awareness of the many shortcomings of existing statistical sources and methods. This knowledge protects the individual against the all-too-frequent misuses of statistics; it also enables persons to obtain the maximum benefits from the proper application of statistical methods.

Questions and Exercises

1. What is the nature of managerial statistics?
2. What factor is largely responsible for the increased use of statistics by business executives?
3. How may statistics serve as a tool for management?
4. List those areas of business (administration, finance, sales, production, transportation, personnel, etc.) in which you believe statistics may be employed to good advantage. Can you list any areas in which you suspect statistics may be of little or no value to management?
5. Develop a habit of scanning financial journals or the financial page of a metropolitan daily paper. Prepare a list of regularly published information of a statistical nature.
6. Commence thinking about a business topic which you could select for a term research project. The topic may pertain to a region, an industry, a firm, or a function of business administration such as marketing, budgeting, or auditing. Further instructions will be provided at the end of Chapter 2.
7. Complete the problems in Appendix A.

2 *Sources of recorded data*

A wealth of data is readily available to the businessman who seeks facts upon which to base his management decisions. Furthermore, the majority of these data are available at little or no additional cost. The internal accounting, production, sales, personnel, and administrative records of a firm are valuable sources of data for statistical analysis. All too often these records are utilized only to fulfill the requirements for which they were initially designed—that is, for customary financial statements, income tax returns, reports for various regulatory authorities, and other miscellaneous purposes.

In addition to internal records, businessmen have ready access to many published sources of statistics which are frequently extremely useful. Trade associations publish data of interest to firms in the industries which they serve. The federal government is the largest collector and publisher of statistics. Much of the government's activity in this area is in response to public demand; all businessmen should be familiar with this service for which they pay taxes. There are also many private organizations which regularly publish statistics in specialized fields such as finance, construction, and marketing. These publications are available by subscription; many are also available at public libraries.

Occasionally a firm desires statistics which are not available in published form and can be obtained only by means of a survey. In such instances a firm may either (1) engage a private statistical organization to make a survey, or (2) assign the task of making a survey to employees of the firm. Many large organizations employ statisticians but also retain private research consultants; this somewhat parallels the practice of employing accountants and also retaining outside accounting firms for auditing and professional consultation.

The purpose of this chapter is to acquaint the reader with the major sources of recorded data which are of value to businessmen. Collection of data by sampling will be treated in Chapter 3.

Internal business records

ADMINISTRATIVE RECORDS

A well-organized and well-managed business is one in which policies, organization, and records are geared to one another. An organization must be developed in a fashion consistent with a firm's policies and must be staffed with personnel capable of implementing those policies. A firm's accounting system should be designed to reflect the results achieved by executives who are responsible for executing the policies and programs of the firm. Insofar as possible each type of account should be the responsibility of a single executive.

Annually, and frequently more often, many companies prepare budgets. Budgets are simply future plans of operation expressed in financial terms. The accounting system and supplementary records provide data for regular comparison of actual operations with planned operations. Deviations from planned operations require immediate analysis and corrective action if appropriate. The distinction between accounting and statistics is a fine one in this area. Accounting records are the source of data for statistical reports which measure the performance both of the firm as a whole and of the responsible executives.

The development of electric and electronic data-processing machines has greatly facilitated the use of accounting and administrative data for statistical control purposes. Data may be recorded by punching designated spaces in small cards, or in paper tapes, or as magnetic impulses on sensitized tapes. Such data sources may be the basic accounting records and can be processed by a variety of machines for specific purposes such as billing, sales control, inventory control, and many other purposes. Machines can add, subtract, divide, multiply, make simple decisions and print the data entered in the cards or tapes. Of great significance to the business analyst and statistician is the fact that machines also can sort and even analyze data according to the user's wishes. For example, sales data can rapidly be sorted by products, lines, territories, branch offices, salesmen, and other useful classifications. Differences in cost ratios, future potential, and probable profits can be determined. In most cases the cost of making such analysis on a continuing basis would be prohibitive if performed without the aid of specialized equipment.

The *Keysort* card system (made by the McBee Company) provides an ingenious and economical method for quickly sorting data into desired classifications. It is highly flexible and is ideally suited as an administrative tool for small businesses. Many large concerns also employ this system for those sorting operations which are not large enough to justify use of more expensive electrical equipment.

It is impractical to list or describe each of the various machines used in business data processing. Students of business administration should become familiar with the general capabilities of these machines; fortunately, a technical knowledge of "how" the machines operate is not essential to an understanding of "what" the machines can do.

SALES RECORDS

The ledger account entitled *Sales Revenue* reflects the total sales of a firm—the responsibility of the vice-president or officer in charge of sales. Similarly, there may be an account called *Field Sales Expense* which will include all sales expense for which the sales executive is responsible. Normally, sub-accounts will be provided for each major type of expense, such as salesmen's salaries, traveling expenses, and communication expense. These records are a valuable source of data for the analysis of sales revenue and expense. Although the primary classification of the above accounts is by individual responsibility, special sorting equipment facilitates reclassification of the data into several secondary classifications. Analysis of sales revenue and expense by products, lines, territories, branch offices, and salesmen enables management to capitalize on profitable operations and to eliminate unprofitable operations.

PRODUCTION RECORDS

Data contained in factory accounts and records can be reclassified and analyzed in much the same fashion as sales data. It is extremely important that management analyze expenses by products, processes, and departments. Analysis of inventories is required in order to prevent shortages which might lead to production stoppages and also to guard against accumulation of excess inventories which tie up large amounts of capital and which may lead to losses either because of a price break or because of deterioration or obsolescence.

PERSONNEL RECORDS

Companies which employ hundreds or thousands of employees urgently need good personnel records. Such records provide personal data and history which are important in planning promotions, replacements, and retirements. Classification of employees by significant age groups is essential in planning retirement programs and in determining the effect of national draft legislation during periods of war or emergencies. Personnel records also contain data on absenteeism, a serious factor which may result in costly slowdowns of operations.

summary

Internal accounting and administrative records are a prime source of data which may be subjected to statistical analysis. Electronic accounting machines greatly facilitate the classification and analysis of data required for statistical analysis of all phases of business operations which can be expressed quantitatively. In most instances these data have been recorded initially for financial statements, tax returns, or reports required by regulatory bodies. Hence, the utilization of these data for further statistical analysis provides a valuable and inexpensive by-product.

Published sources

Major sources of published data are government publications, trade association releases, financial journals, newspapers, and publications of private research organizations. A source may be classified as *primary* when the organization which published the data also collected them. A source may be termed *secondary* when the publishing agency is distinct from the collecting agency. For example, census data are collected and published by the Bureau of the Census, hence census volumes are primary sources of data. Publications which contain reprints, summaries, or reclassifications of data originally published in census volumes are secondary sources. Some publications, such as the *Survey of Current Business*, published monthly by the Department of Commerce, are primary sources for certain data and secondary sources for other data.

In general, it is better procedure to obtain data from primary sources than to rely on secondary sources. This is true because primary sources are likely to be more accurate and more detailed; terms are usually more fully defined, and procedures and forms used to collect the data may be illustrated. However, the high reputation of many organizations publishing secondary sources is sufficient to justify their use when primary sources are not readily available and when detailed information as to data, terms, or methods is not required.

CHECKING PUBLISHED SOURCES FOR ACCURACY AND VALIDITY

Data taken from any published source should be checked for accuracy (correctness) and validity (applicability) before they are used. Accuracy can be checked by cross-reference to other sources and by watching for figures which appear too large or too small in relation to the other figures. Care should also be taken to recognize and, where appropriate, to adjust for changes in classification such as length of the reporting period, definition of the reporting unit, or geographic area to which the data refer.

Validity of the data is more difficult to determine. Validity changes with the use which is to be made of the data. The manner in which the data have been collected and their exact definitions must be known. Income tax records would be an inappropriate source of information on very low income groups because of the omission of non-taxable incomes and of many incomes below the basic exemption rate.

LOCATING PUBLISHED INFORMATION

Although a wealth of published statistics is available, many persons fail to utilize these sources simply because they do not know of the existence of much of this information. Also, many persons feel incapable of, first, determining exactly what data they require, and, second, locating the data once their need has been determined. These problems are somewhat related; all may be solved by actual use of principal sources, such as census volumes. Ideas for application of data frequently occur after a person has discovered their availability.

Published sources can be classified in numerous ways. One such way is to classify them by the general type and diversity of information contained. Thus sources might be classified as:

1. Source Guides and Bibliographies,
2. General Reference Sources,
3. Specialized Sources.

SOURCE GUIDES AND BIBLIOGRAPHIES

A number of reference guides and bibliographies are available to aid experienced and inexperienced researchers alike.

How to Use the Business Library with Sources of Business Information, Second Edition, by H. W. Johnson and S. W. McFarland[1] is designed to train the reader in the use of the business library as well as to indicate a wide range of business information sources. A partial list of section headings indicates the materials covered.

How to Use the Library
Handbooks and Yearbooks
Pamphlets, Periodicals, and Reports
Directories
Business, Economic, and Financial Services
Government Publications
Aids for Small Business
Business Research and Reports

[1] H. W. Johnson and S. W. McFarland, *How to Use the Business Library with Sources of Business Information*, Second Edition, Cincinnati, South-Western Publishing Company, 1957.

Sources of Business Information, by E. T. Coman, Jr.[2] is designed to expedite the location of specific business information, including statistics. Its chapter headings are indicative of its scope:

1. Methods of Locating Facts
2. Basic Time-savings Sources
3. Locating Information on Firms and Individuals
4. The Business Scene
5. Statistical Sources
6. Financial Information
7. Real Estate and Insurance
8. The Literature of Accounting
9. Management
10. Marketing, Sales Management, and Advertising
11. The Human Factor—Industrial Relations
12. Basic Industries
13. Transportation by Railroad, Air, Motor Highway, and Water
14. Foreign Trade
15. A Basic Bookshelf

Government Statistics for Business Use, edited by P. M. Hauser and W. R. Leonard[3] describes statistics assembled by the several agencies of the federal government and emphasizes their availability to potential users. The editors have organized this text by major fields of industry, commerce, and finance; sections on prices, population, and labor are also included.

The *Statistical Abstract of the United States*, published annually by the Bureau of the Census, contains, in addition to vast quantities of data, an excellent bibliography of sources of statistical data. This bibliography covered thirty-four pages in the 1959 issue; included among the major classifications of sources were the following:

Agriculture
Business and Industry Index Numbers
Climate
Commodity Prices
Construction, Housing, and Real Estate
Consumer Incomes and Expenditures
Foreign Commerce and International Transactions
Forests and Lumber
Government
Insurance

[2] E. T. Coman, Jr., *Sources of Business Information*, Englewood Cliffs, N. J., Prentice-Hall, Inc., 1949.

[3] P. M. Hauser and W. R. Leonard, *Government Statistics for Business Use*, Second Edition, New York, John Wiley & Sons, Inc., 1946.

Labor
Manufactures
Minerals
Money, Banking, and Investments
National Income and Wealth
Population and Population Characteristics
Public and Private Debt
Public Lands
Public Utilities
Service Establishments
Vital Statistics, Health, and Medical Care
Wholesale and Retail Trade

Although it is unlikely that a single firm could profit from research in all of the above areas, it is difficult to conceive of a business which could not gain by intelligent analysis of selected series from the above list.

GENERAL REFERENCE SOURCES

Knowledge of a few major reference sources is an invaluable aid in locating information. Even when the desired information is not given in the reference source, references and bibliographies contained in these sources indicate where the information may be found.

General reference sources vary from dictionaries, encyclopedias, and almanacs to publications such as the *Statistical Abstract of the United States* and the major censuses published by the Bureau of the Census. Since this is a text on statistics (data analysis), the discussion below is limited to sources of numerical data.

Federal government sources. Principal among government sources are the major censuses issued by the Bureau of the Census of the Department of Commerce. The *Census of Population*, published every ten years and scheduled for publication of 1960 information in final form in 1960, 1961, and 1962, includes such data as the age, sex, marital status, school enrollment, residence, employment status, major occupation group, major industry group, and income of families and individuals, the number of married couples, families, and households, and other classifications.

The *Census of Housing*, also published every ten years and with 1960 data scheduled for publication in 1961 and 1962, has five major categories: occupancy characteristics, structural characteristics, condition and plumbing facilities, equipment and fuels, and financial characteristics of nonfarm dwelling units. Each of these categories has several subclassifications. For example, the equipment and fuels section contains data on electric lighting, heating equipment, heating fuel, kitchen sink, radio, refrigeration equipment, and television. Data in the *Census of Population* and *Census of Housing* are available for various geographic and municipal areas, some data being available for city blocks.

The *Census of Business*, last taken in 1958 and scheduled for publication in 1960 and 1961, will be taken again when funds are appropriated. Three major parts are retail trade, wholesale trade, and service trades. The retail trade section includes data on number of establishments, sales, payrolls, and personnel by kind of business; some additional data included are corporate status, credit arrangements, trucking facilities, merchandise line sales, and warehouse inventories. The wholesale trade and service trade sections also contain many classifications. Information is available for geographic divisions, states, metropolitan areas, and kinds of business.

The *Census of Manufactures*, last taken in 1958 and published in 1959 and 1960, will also be taken again when appropriations are made. It contains data on more than 6,000 products manufactured in the United States, including quantity and value of shipments, payrolls, employees, inventories, plant and equipment, size and type of establishments, and other data pertinent to manufacturing. Data are available for the United States, states, and industries.

The *Census of Agriculture* is taken every five years. Data for 1959 will be published by June, 1961. This census reports information on farms and farm property, population, land areas, number of farms, farm acreage, uses of land, value of farm property, cooperatives, farm receipts and expenditures, financial characteristics, types of products and livestock, and other agricultural data. These data are published for the United States, states, and counties.

The *Census of Mineral Industries*, last taken in 1958, provides a wealth of information on production, employment, prices, and other factors for the mineral industries. The *Census of Government*, last taken in 1957, provides detailed information on governmental units. Illustrations of how businesses can effectively use census data will be presented in later chapters of this text.

The *Statistical Abstract of the United States*, published annually by the Bureau of the Census, has already received mention. The 1958 issue numbered 1,040 pages—a veritable gold mine of statistical data.

A historical supplement to the *Statistical Abstract* containing about 8,000 series of widest general interest carries the series back to 1610. The supplement, *Historical Statistics of the United States from Colonial Times to 1957*, was published in 1960.

Agriculture Statistics is published annually by the Department of Agriculture. It is primarily a compendium of the most important statistical series relating to agriculture. Data are given for the United States, major regions, and states.

Minerals Yearbook is a comprehensive record of the production and marketing of minerals in the United States published annually by the Bureau of Mines of the Department of the Interior. It also provides information on foreign trade and the condition of the mineral industry in other countries.

Numerous publications containing statistical data are issued at various intervals during each year by various government agencies. Three of these which are best known and which cover a wide range of subjects are the *Survey of Current Business*, the *Federal Reserve Bulletin*, and the *Monthly Labor Review*.

The *Survey of Current Business* is published monthly by the Office of Business Economics, Department of Commerce. In addition to timely articles on business topics, each issue now contains 40 pages of statistical series, several of which are collected by private organizations. Major areas for which data are shown include:

Gross National Product and Its Components
Commodity Prices
Construction and Real Estate
Domestic Trade
Employment and Population
Financial Activities
International Transactions of the United States
Transportation and Communications Statistics
Statistics and Manufacturing by Major Industry

The Office of Business Economics also periodically publishes two major supplements to the *Survey of Current Business*. The supplement entitled *Business Statistics* is a comprehensive record, dating back to 1935, of business indicators which are brought up to date monthly in the *Survey of Current Business*. Over 2,600 different business series are included. The second supplement is entitled *National Income* and contains statistics pertaining to national income and gross national product for the period from 1929 to date. Also included are articles describing the nature of national income and product and the sources and methods of national income estimation. Usefulness of these data for forecasting purposes has gained increased recognition during recent years.

The *Federal Reserve Bulletin* is published monthly by the Board of Governors of the Federal Reserve System. This publication, which concentrates on financial data, has some overlap with the *Survey of Current Business*. Each issue contains about seventy pages of statistics, in addition to timely articles on finance, industry, and commerce. *Banking and Monetary Statistics*, published in 1943 by the Board of Governors of the Federal Reserve System, contains financial statistics series from their origin to 1935. Each of the 12 Federal Reserve Districts also publishes regular releases on business activity in its respective district.

The *Monthly Labor Review* is published monthly by the Bureau of Labor Statistics, Department of Labor. This publication contains many articles on current labor issues in addition to extensive statistics on (1) employment and payrolls, (2) labor turnover, (3) earnings and hours, (4) prices and cost of living, (5) work stoppages, and (6) building and construction. The section on prices and cost of living includes the well-known *cost of living index* or *consumer price index* which is officially designated as the *Index of Change in Prices of Goods and Services Purchased by City Wage-Earner and Clerical-Worker Families to Maintain Their Level of Living*.

The Bureau of Labor Statistics publishes at irregular intervals the *Handbook of Labor Statistics*. It is largely a historical summary and digest of articles, reports, and statistics published currently in the *Monthly Labor Review*.

Economic Indicators is prepared each month by the President's Council of Economic Advisers. Although it is officially prepared for the Joint Congressional Committee on the Economic Report, it receives wide distribution, including depositary libraries, and is available for sale by the Superintendent of Documents. Each issue reports the latest movements of the major economic indicators on (1) national output, (2) prices, (3) employment and wages, (4) production and business activity, (5) purchasing power, and (6) credit, money, and federal finance.

State and local government records. State governments compile and publish a variety of data which may be of value to businessmen.

States regularly publish reports on employment by industry classifications for all employment covered by social security legislation. Various taxing authorities provide data which can be used to estimate volume of activity; for example, total retail sales. Similarly, estimates of sales can be computed for gasoline, cigarettes, luxury items, and any other items which are subject to tax when sold. Also recorded are auto registrations and all other licenses issued. Public utilities publish data on the consumption of electricity, gas, water, and other services. County and city offices possess much information including data on real estate sales, building permits, and assessed valuations of property.

Private research organizations. A number of private organizations collect and publish business statistics, usually in a specialized field. Other agencies publish more general interest statistics. Among the latter is The National Industrial Conference Board which annually publishes *The Economic Almanac*, a large handbook of useful facts about business, labor, and government in the United States and other areas. The National Industrial Conference Board also publishes a *Basic Industrial Data* series, each issue of which is devoted to a specific industry. *The Commodity Year Book*, prepared and published by Commodity Research Bureau, Inc., contains several hundred pages of statistics on commodities ranging from alcohol to zinc.

The World Almanac, a well-known general statistical reference, is published annually by the New York *World-Telegram*. The Tax Foundation of New York annually publishes a volume entitled *Facts and Figures on Government Finance*; this publication includes a section on business, investment, and productivity. Several large banks throughout the nation regularly release statistics on business conditions. Local private agencies also have been organized to sell their services to clients in selected industries and/or geographic regions.[4]

United Nations publications. The UN publishes a wide range of reports on international trade, inflation, national incomes, vital commodities, and many other subjects. Its annual *Statistical Yearbook*, which relates to over 250 countries and territories, covers the following fields: population, manpower, agriculture, forestry, fishing, industrial production, mining and quarrying, manufacturing, construction, electricity and gas consumption, transport and communications, internal and external trade, balance of payments, wages and prices, national income, finance, public finance, social statistics, education and culture.

[4] Regularly published indicators of business conditions are discussed in Chapter 6.

SPECIALIZED SOURCES

In addition to the general sources listed above, there are innumerable specialized sources of more limited interest. Most of these are published by private organizations. A few are indicated below.

Trade association releases. Firms within many specific industries have organized trade associations. One of the functions of these associations is to collect statistical data on operations from member firms. Some of this data is made available only to members. However, numerous publications are made available to the public.

The *Life Insurance Fact Book* is published annually by the Institute of Life Insurance, an organization of legal reserve life insurance companies. The 1959 issue contained 125 pages devoted to statistics on a great many phases of life insurance company operations and finances. Many of the statistical series date back to 1900 and some of the current statistics are classified by states.

Automobile Facts and Figures is published annually by the Automobile Manufacturers Association. This publication contains statistics pertaining to virtually every facet of the automobile industry; also included are numerous statistics on highway and highway finances. The American Gas Association annually publishes *Gas Facts*, a statistical record of the gas utility industry in the United States. Similarly, Edison Electric Institute publishes an annual *Statistical Bulletin* for the electrical industry.

Trade associations in many other areas of business compile statistics which they release either annually or monthly or both. A business researcher should always contact appropriate trade associations when searching for trade or industry data.

Financial services and journals. Moody's Investors Service and Standard & Poor's Corporation each publish a great quantity of financial statistics. Moody's has published *Stock Survey* and *Bond Survey* weekly since 1936. Moody's *Manual of Investments* deals, respectively, with industrial, transportation, public utility, government and financial securities. Standard & Poor's publishes *Outlook for the Security Markets* weekly and *Current Statistics* on a monthly basis. Standard & Poor's *Trade and Securities Statistics* consists of a number of units including among others the *Security Price Index Record*, *Banking and Finance*, *Railroads*, *Public Utilities*, *Metals*, and *Current Statistics Combined with Basic Statistics*.

Some data compiled by Moody's and Standard & Poor's also appear regularly in the *Survey of Current Business* and the *Federal Reserve Bulletin.*

Other sources of current financial data are the *Commercial and Financial Chronicle*, *Barrons*, and the *Wall Street Journal*. Daily newspapers are also a source of current financial and business data.

Other private sources. A number of important sources have not been mentioned above. *Survey of Buying Power* is published annually by Sales Management, publishers of *Sales Management, The Magazine of Marketing*. This publication contains estimates of population, retail sales, wholesale sales, and effective buying income for states, counties, and cities. Retail sales estimates are made for five store groups: (1) food, (2) general merchandise, (3) furniture, household appliances, radios, (4) automotive, and (5) drug.

Dun and Bradstreet, Inc., each month publishes *Dun's Statistical Review*, containing data on building permits, trade indicators, business failures, and other business series. F. W. Dodge Corporation publishes construction statistics every month in the *Dodge Statistical Research Service*.

University bureaus of business research regularly publish statistical summaries of business trends in the states or areas which they serve. In addition, these bureaus occasionally publish comprehensive statistical abstracts, and also studies of specific industries or areas.

summary

Vast quantities of published data are available to businessmen. Much of this data may be obtained at no charge and almost all of it is available for reference at large public libraries. Large and small firms alike are becoming increasingly dependent upon statistics for management guidance. Knowledge of published sources will assist the businessman in the selection of appropriate data to aid in the formulation of policy decisions.

Questions and Exercises

1. How may data in internal business records be utilized for purposes of planning and control? Give several illustrations.

2. Distinguish between *primary* and *secondary* sources of published data. Why is this distinction important?

3. Review each of the statistical sources or guides which appear below. Prepare a list, noting for each source (1) the publisher, (2) date or dates of publication, and (3) the general nature and scope of content. This review may reveal sources of data for your term research project; it may also serve to suggest suitable topics to those students who have not selected specific topics as yet.
   (1) *Sources of Business Information*, by E. T. Coman, Jr.
   (2) *Government Statistics for Business Use*, edited by P. M. Hauser and W. R. Leonard
   (3) *Statistical Abstract of the United States*, by Bureau of the Census
   (4) *Survey of Current Business*, by U. S. Department of Commerce
   (5) *Business Statistics*, supplement to *Survey of Current Business*, by U. S. Department of Commerce
   (6) *Federal Reserve Bulletin*, by Board of Governors, Federal Reserve System
   (7) *Monthly Labor Review*, by U. S. Department of Labor
   (8) *Survey of Buying Power*, by Sales Management
   (9) *Life Insurance Fact Book*, by Institute of Life Insurance
   (10) *Automobile Facts and Figures*, by Automobile Manufacturers Association.
   (11) *Gas Facts*, by American Gas Association
   (12) *Statistical Bulletin*, by Edison Electric Institute
   (13) *Basic Industrial Data* series, by National Industrial Conference Board
   (14) *The Commodity Year Book*, by Commodity Research Bureau, Inc.
   (15) Major censuses published by the Bureau of the Census

4. Select a topic for a term research project. The range of possible topics is virtually infinite. However, most acceptable topics perhaps could be placed under one of the following broad classifications:
   (a) An analysis of the business and economic potential of a region, state, county, or city. This would involve collection, analysis and projection of data pertaining to major types of industry, markets, population, employment, and income.
   (b) An analysis of the business potential of an industry in a specific area. This study should reveal the characteristics of the firms within the industry, the growth or decline of the industry, the competition from the same industry in other areas, and the competition from other industries producing substitute products.
   (c) An analysis of the business potential of a specific firm. Local firms which may cooperate with student researchers make ideal topics. National concerns about which considerable information is

available in published form also make good topics. Analyses should reflect operating and financial trends and comparative standings of the firm within the industry as a whole and with its principal competitors.

(d) A report on the application of statistical techniques in marketing, budgeting, auditing, or other business administration functions. Projects of this nature would involve reading articles in professional and trade journals and portions of books on specialized topics. Visits to local firms employing managerial statistics should be made whenever possible.

Work on the term project should continue throughout the quarter or semester. Collection of data should be undertaken immediately. Ways in which those statistical techniques described in subsequent chapters may be applied to these data are indicated at the end of each chapter. Tables and charts should be designed to highlight significant findings. (See Chapters 9 and 10.)

A preliminary outline of the final report should be prepared as soon as possible. The outline should include the following parts:

I. Purpose of investigation
II. Scope and method of investigation
III. Presentation of findings
IV. Summary and conclusions
  A. General summary
  B. Tentative conclusions
  C. Limitations of investigation
  D. Recommended additional research
V. Bibliography

It is recognized that projects of the above nature cannot be given exhaustive treatment during a single school term. However, excellent training and experience can be gained in pursuing this research to the limit of available time. Since projects cannot be fully completed, Part IV, C and D in the above outline are very important.

5. How may users of published sources check published data for accuracy and validity?

Statistical Approach
(1) collect, study & present data relevant to the decision to be made
(2) to formulate a theory (or hypotheses) about the relation of facts to each other
(3) to predict or forecast the variables for future periods which are relevant to the decision which is to be made.
(4) to test or verify the prediction by observing what actually happens in the future period and to use this information to improve the theories of stage (2) & thereby the predictions of stage (3)

3 *Collection of data by sampling*

Internal records and published sources contain much of the information required for business planning and control purposes. However, businessmen frequently desire information which is not available in records or publications, such as information concerning the market for a product or service. This information often can be economically collected only by sampling. In addition, sampling methods are employed in auditing internal records, in testing quality of production, and in a variety of other applications.

Sampling is the process of collecting and analyzing a few data for the purpose of obtaining information about a large quantity of data. This large quantity of data is statistically referred to as the *population* or *universe*. By obtaining the reaction of a few consumers toward a product, a firm hopes to obtain an accurate picture of total consumer reaction to the product. By testing the tensile strength of a few lengths of wire, a firm hopes to secure an accurate measure of the tensile strength of a large quantity of wire. By selecting a few entries in a firm's accounting records, auditors hope to determine the degree of accuracy which may be expected throughout the records.

Sampling is obviously less expensive and less time consuming than a complete count or check of all data bearing on a particular problem. In many cases, where quality control tests involve destruction of the products, a 100 per cent test of production would be totally impractical. Consequently, sampling methods which produce reliable results are valuable additions to management's kit of tools.

The theory of sampling occupies a central position in statistical theory. The reason for assigning such importance to sampling theory is that it is seldom possible to study the entire group (population) about which knowledge is desired. It therefore becomes important to understand relationships between samples and populations and to be able to draw sufficiently accurate *inferences* about the true characteristics of a population based upon data from a small segment of that population. One basic problem is to choose a sample which is a small replica of the population. A second problem is to properly interpret the information derived from the sample. The first of these problems is the subject of this chapter. Later chapters deal with the problem of interpretation of sampling results.

Popular misconceptions about sampling

SIZE OF SAMPLE AND SIZE OF POPULATION

It is popularly supposed that if one wishes to sample a large population, a large sample is required. Conversely, it is supposed that to sample a small population a small sample is always adequate. The basic assumption is that a sample cannot be representative unless it contains some minimum percentage of the population, maybe five per cent, or ten per cent, or 20 per cent, etc. Actually, *there is practically no connection between the size of the population and the size of the sample*. The reason can be easily illustrated. If we are interested in sampling a homogeneous population in which every element has identical characteristics, how large a sample is required? If all items are identical, regardless of the number of items, one item will adequately represent the entire group. If, on the other hand, we are interested in sampling a heterogeneous population in which all items are completely different, only a complete census will give us a representation of the population.

In most sampling operations, the population to be sampled is neither completely homogeneous nor completely heterogeneous. The degree of homogeneity (or lack of same) is therefore a basic determinant of what is an adequate size of sample.

This is not meant to imply that size of sample is not important. An exercise in coin tossing can demonstrate effectively the importance of sample size. A perfect coin tossed into the air has equal probabilities of landing heads up or tails up. However, a sample of ten tosses may result in seven heads and three tails. A second sample may consist of four heads and six tails. Other combinations are likely to occur in additional samples. However, as these samples of ten are combined to form larger samples it will be found that the mathematical probability of an equal number of heads and tails is approximated. Differences among the several samples are referred to as *sampling variation* or *sampling error*. It will be observed that the variations among samples (*random errors of sampling*) decline as the size of the samples increases. Further, the difference between the true characteristics (in the case of coins, an equal percentage of heads and tails) of a mass of data and the characteristics of a sample drawn from that mass tends to decline as the size of the sample is increased.

How large a sample is needed to secure a desired degree of reliability? Mathematical tests of reliability are available. A complete discussion of these tests is beyond the scope of this book.[1] In general, the larger the sample, the higher the degree of reliability, although reliability does not increase in direct proportion with size. Rather, the reliability of a sample increases in proportion to increases in the square root of the number of items in the sample. For example, an increase in sample size from 25 (square root is 5) to 100 (square root is 10) reduces sampling error by half. To again reduce sampling errors by one-half it would be necessary to increase the sample size to 400 (square root is 20). Thus it becomes apparent that reduction of sampling error by increasing the size of the sample soon becomes a costly proposition; a decision must be made as to the point where slight gains in reliability fail to justify the necessarily increased costs of obtaining the larger sample.

RELIABILITY OF SAMPLE RESULTS

It is popularly supposed that a complete census *always* yields more accurate results than does a sample. Sample results are subject to

[1] A brief introduction to this topic appears in Chapters 4 and 5.

variation inherent in the sampling operation itself, *i.e.*, the variation in results between samples of the same size, independently selected in the same fashion, from the same population. Censuses are not subject to *sampling error*. However, samples and censuses are both subject to serious errors such as:

1. Failure to state the problem carefully and decide just what statistical information is desired.
2. Failure to properly define the population being studied.
3. Failure of the questionnaire to ask clearly, simply, and completely for information which can be acquired.
4. Using improper procedures in the collection of the desired information or failing to give clear and precise instructions and definitions.
5. Biases arising from nonresponse. (Nonrespondents usually have different characteristics than do respondents.)
6. Intentional and unintentional errors in response, or bias in response caused by interviewers.
7. Recording and computing errors arising during the collecting, editing, or tabulating of the data.

These *non-sampling* errors are more easily controlled when dealing with a small group of data than when dealing with a large group. The closer control over such errors, which is possible when using a sample, can make sample results *more* reliable than a complete census.

Types of samples

Although all samples are drawn for the same purpose—to obtain a reasonably accurate picture of a large mass of data—several types of samples have been developed to yield improved results in particular situations. Among the most widely used methods are: (1) simple random, (2) stratified, (3) area, (4) judgment, and (5) multiple sampling. Each of these methods is briefly discussed in the following paragraphs. In actual practice it is quite customary to combine various features of several of these methods to form a sampling method which meets the requirements of a specific problem.

SIMPLE RANDOM SAMPLE

Random as used here, does not mean "hit or miss." It means that each item in the universe being sampled has an equal opportunity of being selected in the sample. The sample of coin tosses described above was a random sample; heads and tails had equal opportunities of being selected. Random sampling yields good results if the universe sampled is homogeneous, that is, if the individual items which make up the universe are alike in nature and are subject to the same controlling forces. Combinations of numbers on dice are homogeneous unless the dice are loaded or manipulated. Names or numbers in a hat are homogeneous. Customers, however, are not homogeneous. Sex, age, education, and financial status are among major factors which cause customers to be a heterogeneous group. Similarly, eligible voters constitute a heterogeneous group. Simple random samples drawn from a heterogeneous group must be quite large in order to possess correct proportions of the several characteristics of the group. Expressed differently, simple random samples from such groups may not accurately reflect the characteristics of the population or universe from which they were selected.

STRATIFIED RANDOM SAMPLE

Fortunately, heterogeneous groups can often be subdivided into homogeneous groups or strata. A stratified sample is a combination of independent samples selected in appropriate proportions from homogeneous strata within a heterogeneous population.

Consider the case of a telephone company wishing to survey the attitudes of residential customers toward telephone services or rates. Let us assume that information already available indicates that customer attitudes vary by the type of service received. Customers receiving single-party service are known to possess more favorable attitudes than customers receiving two-party or four-party service. By dividing the total population of residential customers into cells or strata determined by the type of service received and sampling each stratum independently, a smaller sample can be used. This is because part of the differences in attitude (variability) in the population is known to be associated with type of service. Stratification by type of service will account for the variability *among* the strata and the sample selected must explain or reveal only the variability *within* strata. Each stratum is essentially a separate population and is sampled independently. Results from these independent samples are then combined according to the relative importance of the several strata in the population.

The nature of a particular investigation will determine the number of significant strata and the basis of stratification. Family income may be relatively unimportant in measuring the demand for basic necessities, such as bread and milk, but it obviously would be important in measuring the demand for expensive appliances and luxury items.

Among strata used in market research studies are occupational groups, age, sex, education, political preference, economic status, racial and religious groups, and residence by rural areas and cities of various sizes within each state. The nature of the questions asked in a particular poll determines the significant strata which should be used. Census data and other government reports have proven invaluable in determining the relative dimensions of the various strata.

When significant strata are well-defined and can be accurately measured, a random stratified sample is superior to a simple random sample because it is likely to be more representative of the population which is being sampled. Stratified samples can attain a given degree of accuracy with a smaller sample size than would be likely with simple random samples even though the latter happened to be drawn in a representative fashion. This is true because samples selected from populations comprised of widely diverse items must be larger than samples selected from populations whose items vary only slightly. Hence, classification of a population into strata containing items of similar characteristics reduces the size of samples required to insure a specified level of accuracy.

However, stratification may lead to serious error if the relative importance of the strata used is estimated incorrectly. When strata cannot be accurately defined and measured, a simple random sample will usually yield better results than a stratified sample.

RANDOM AREA SAMPLE

This type of sample pinpoints the geographic areas or locations in which items of information are to be obtained. This is done in an effort to obtain a more representative sample than would be likely if interviewers were relied upon to make the selections. For example, sample "censuses" of agriculture have been obtained by making a random selection of (1) states within each major agricultural region, (2) counties within each sample state, (3) townships within each sample county, (4) sections within each sample township, and (5) a quarter section within each sample section. Finally, all farmers whose residences were located on selected quarter sections would be interviewed. Some quarter sections would no doubt contain no farm residences whereas others might contain several. Most farmers so selected would be farming land beyond the boundaries of the quarter sections on which they resided. However, the area of the subject quarter sections would be important only to the extent that it determined the selection of a random sample of farmers to be interviewed. This method eliminates the bias which is difficult to control when field interviewers are permitted to select persons to be interviewed.

The area method may be employed effectively in cities. Successive random selection may be made of zones, blocks, and lots. Occasionally interviewers on a consumer or housing survey may be unable to find persons on a given lot at home or may be unable to secure their cooperation. In such instances, interviewers are often instructed to substitute residents of a specific adjacent lot. By specifying the substitute lots, interviewers are not permitted the option of introducing bias through substitution of the most inviting residence. Ideally, of course, callbacks should be made until the residents of the original lot are found at home.

JUDGMENT SAMPLE

A great many business problems do not yield readily to application of the above random sampling techniques. In most cases the universe is heterogeneous and imperfectly defined; time and cost factors may not justify attempts to develop and execute scientific sampling plans; populations may be small and contain a few atypical members. In such instances, the representativeness of samples selected is dependent upon the judgment of the individuals who select the sample. Samples of this type are also referred to as *directed* or *purposive*. When selected by persons with an expert knowledge of the universe being sampled, these samples may well be superior to a somewhat larger random sample. However, since each item in the universe does not have an equal opportunity of being selected, judgment samples cannot be evaluated by reliability tests which are based on the laws of probability.

Since populations being sampled are almost always heterogeneous, judgment samples are usually stratified. In marketing research and public opinion polling, interviewers often are directed to select quotas of specified size from certain strata which have been judged to be representative of the population. Price indexes such as the *Consumers'*

Price Index and the *Wholesale Price Index* are based on samples of prices of selected items which are considered representative of the vast universe of prices.

Judgment samples are of course subject to criticism because of the ease with which bias may be introduced, intentionally or unintentionally, and because tests of sample reliability may not be applied. Nevertheless, in the many situations where probability samples are not practicable, judgment samples often provide data which are helpful to businessmen in formulating their plans.

MULTIPLE SAMPLING

Multiple sampling has developed along two different lines. It first developed as a cost-saving technique. A first sample of a population is used to determine certain broad characteristics of the population. This information is used in designing a more efficient subsequent sample to obtain the specific detailed information of interest in the study. The first sample is done as inexpensively as possible, so that, even with that expense, the increased efficiency in the design of the second sample results in a lower total cost for the total sample operation. This method is commonly called *double sampling*.

The second type of multiple sampling is a process of collecting repeated small samples from a population until the evidence collected indicates that a particular answer is justified. The development of this method was completed early in World War II for testing explosives. Since such tests involve the destruction of the explosive, it was highly desirable to develop a testing method which required a sample of minimum size. This method has been gaining increased acceptance as a technique for controlling the quality of material in purchasing and manufacturing. In recent years, attention has been directed toward application of this method to administrative control problems and to the selection of accounting record items in auditing.

This latest development has been given the name of *sequential sampling*, because it involves drawing a sequence of small samples, sometimes of one item each. A very small sample (or one item) is chosen by random selection from the population, tested, and determined to be satisfactory or defective. The results are recorded and compared with a table such as Table 1. The first column lists the number of items in a sample at each point where a change in acceptance or rejection action is required. The next three columns indicate the number of defective items which, when related to sample size, determines (1) acceptance, (2) rejection, or (3) continued testing of the lot from which the sample has been drawn.

The process of selecting, testing, and recording the sample or item is continued only up to the point where the proportion of either defective or satisfactory items reaches a predetermined significant level. For example, the entire lot is rejected if the first two items tested fail to meet desired specifications. Similarly, the entire lot is rejected if three items out of the first seven tested are failures, or four of the

TABLE 1. A sequential sample plan schedule indicating when to accept the lot, reject the lot, or continue testing the lot

Number of items tested	NUMBER OF DEFECTIVE ITEMS REQUIRING DECISION TO: Accept lot	Reject lot	Continue testing lot
2	.	2	0–1
7	.	3	0–2
19	.	4	0–3
27	0	4	1–3
30	.	5	1–4
31	1	5	2–4
40	.	6	2–5
42	2	6	3–5
54	3	6	4–5
63	4	6	5
65	5	6	. . .

first 19, and so on. If no failures occur in the first 27 items tested, sampling is discontinued and the lot is accepted. If one failure has been recorded, testing must continue until a total of 31 items have been tested and 30 items accepted. In this illustration the sample size must be at least two items and may be as large as 65. Table 1 is purely illustrative; acceptance and rejection limits for each sampling problem are determined by a mathematical process designed to provide a desired degree of confidence that the proportion of defective items will not exceed the allowed maximum in accepted lots. It will be observed that sequential sampling uses only the minimum size of sample required. If simple random sampling were to be employed in the above illustration, the minimum acceptable size of sample would be 65.

The sampling operation

When required data can be obtained only by sampling, a businessman would be wise to engage the services of a professional statistician. However, a general knowledge of sampling procedure will prove invaluable to the businessman in working with a professional statistician and in evaluating sampling results. This knowledge will also be useful to the businessman in evaluating the results of surveys made by other organizations. Such surveys are frequently employed to influence businessmen's decisions; decisions based on inadequate or inappropriate samples may prove to be costly.

The sampling operation consists of four phases. In the first phase the predetermined conditions and requirements are established. In phase two, the type and size of sample and the actual method for collecting the data are determined on the basis of the predetermined conditions and requirements. Phase three consists of the collection of the data and their preparation for analysis. In the last phase, the data are analyzed and the results reported.

THE PREDETERMINED CONDITIONS AND REQUIREMENTS

A successful sampling operation must be both well-planned and well-executed. Making a survey involves considerably more than addressing questions to a number of persons. First of all, the objective of the survey must be clearly stated and understood by all persons involved. It is essential that the business executives and the researchers have a meeting of minds as to the purpose of the survey. Only then can a sampling plan be designed which will obtain the information required for sound decisions and policy formulation. This requirement, of course, also applies to statistical investigations based on data contained in internal records or published sources.

A clear statement of purpose requires a careful definition of terms. Seemingly simple terms are found to have a variety of meanings. Personal income, for example, may be gross, taxable, or take-home income; for certain studies, family take-home income may be more significant than per capita data. Studies of wage rates may prove useless if both standard and overtime rates are not properly considered. Sales, costs, profits, employment, residences, and farms are only a few illustrations of other terms which have a variety of interpretations. The reader is urged to review the careful, though lengthy, definitions of terms in census volumes.

In addition to a "meeting of the minds" concerning what is being studied, there must be agreement concerning how reliable the results must be. Sampling projects are sometimes only a waste of money because the results are not reliable enough to fit the purpose for which they have been collected. The budget requirements for a survey are very important in this connection. Major budget items are consulting fees, salaries, supplies and postage, field expenses, and publication costs for the report of survey findings. The amounts of funds available are a limit to the scope and the mechanics of the sampling operation. If the results desired cannot be obtained for the funds available, the project will have to be redesigned or abandoned.

Once the purpose and nature of the investigation have been determined, a search should be undertaken for similar studies which have been completed in the past. Much can be learned and frequently pitfalls can be avoided by reviewing the methods and results of such studies. On occasion, a recent study may be found which appears valid and which provides answers to most or all phases of the problem and, hence, obviates the need for further investigation in whole or in part. Also, it is necessary to assemble all information possible concerning the population being sampled. The amount of variability within the population, the location of the population, and knowledge of population characteristics related to the factor being studied are important in planning the type of sample used and the method of data collection.

THE SAMPLE AND THE SAMPLING INSTRUMENT

Size of sample. The major determinants of sample size are population variability in relation to the precision required in the results, the amount of time and resources available for carrying out the sampling operation, and the cost of collecting sample information. The relation of sample size and population was discussed in an earlier section.[2]

[2] *Size of Sample and Size of Population,* pages 23 ff.

The relation of sampling costs and availability of time and resources to sample size will become clear as the following sections are studied. The sampling operation must be planned to obtain the greatest possible return per dollar of cost.

Type of sample. Three factors determine the type of sample to be used: (1) the size and distribution of the population, (2) the resources available, and (3) the extent of prior knowledge concerning population characteristics. If the population is widely distributed geographically and also large, a simple random sample will be very expensive. It is also difficult to use simple random samples when no list of population members is available. However, even area sampling requires maps indicating the location of individual population members or groups of such members. For large, widely dispersed populations, area sampling is less costly than simple random samples because contact is with several sample members in each area from which the sampling takes place. In simple random sampling, the sample will tend to be widely dispersed over the entire area covered by the population. The use of stratified sampling requires some knowledge of population characteristics which may be used as a basis for delineating the various strata.

The sampling instrument. In order to collect data, a means must be employed to measure the pertinent sample characteristics (age, sex, length, opinion, acceptability, etc.); that means is the *sampling instrument.* The amount of funds available will often control the type of sampling instrument used. In sample surveys, the mail questionnaire, which is used extensively, is usually the least costly but may also be the least reliable. Response to mail questionnaires is often limited; follow-up letters are usually a must. Even so, a return of 20 to 30 per cent is considered good. A serious limitation is the fact that respondents to a mail questionnaire may not be representative of the population being sampled; the bias thus introduced may invalidate the results. Best results are usually obtained when (1) the subject is of interest to the respondent, (2) the questionnaire is brief, and (3) a self-addressed, stamped envelope is enclosed with the questionnaire.

A more desirable method of conducting the survey is to interview personally the persons selected in the sample. This method involves employment and training of field interviewers or enumerators and is much more costly than the mail questionnaire method. Improved survey results frequently more than justify this additional expense, particularly when respondents to a mail questionnaire would not be likely to constitute a representative sample of the group being surveyed. However, use of the personal interview method usually restricts a business firm to a survey of a relatively small geographic area, whereas mail questionnaires can be given wide distribution at little extra cost. A third alternative, and somewhat of a compromise, is the telephone survey, which has been used widely to measure audience reaction to radio and television programs. Business executives should seek professional advice before selecting the method of data collection; although mail questionnaires may be entirely adequate for some investigations, executives should avoid being "penny wise and pound foolish." Some organizations which use mail questionnaires for local surveys reward respondents with a market basket of groceries. Respondents are required to return personally the completed questionnaire, which is checked for accuracy and completeness before the groceries are awarded. Care must be exercised to prevent such rewards from introducing bias into the results by encouraging a higher rate of response among the less well-to-do.

Much painstaking work is involved in designing a good questionnaire or interview schedule. Each question should be clearly and simply stated; questions which at first glance appear straightforward to the planner may be subject to a great many interpretations by persons to be interviewed. A question must be uniformly interpreted if the answers are to have any value. Questions on mail questionnaires need to be briefer and more explicit than those on schedules which are to be used in personal interviews.

All questions on a schedule should be pertinent to the problem being investigated. Planners are frequently subject to pressure to include pet questions which may have little or no bearing on the main purpose of the survey. It should be remembered that each additional question raises the resistance of prospective respondents.

There is no point in asking persons questions which reasonably they could not be expected to answer. Where practicable, "yes" and "no" or multiple choice questions should be used; this makes it possible for the respondent to complete the questionnaire merely by placing check marks in appropriate blank spaces. When questions are to be answered in terms of quantities, the units of measurement and the periods of time involved should be indicated. Leading questions almost always insure a biased answer and should never be used. Questions which are likely to arouse a person's emotions should be avoided, unless, of course, the object of the survey is to measure emotional reactions toward an issue.

Questions concerning financial status and income should not be included unless such data are of great importance to the investigation. In such instances, these questions should be placed at the end of the questionnaire and stated optionally; the person being interviewed should be tactfully informed that his name will not be placed on the questionnaire and that all information will be held confidential. A further inducement to secure response to income questions is to ask the respondent merely to indicate the appropriate range of income. The final steps in preparing a questionnaire are test checking and final revision. Presurvey tests of questionnaires almost invariably reveal questions which either are not understood or are misunderstood. Appropriate rewriting of such questions substantially increases the reliability and value of the subsequent survey results.

Figure 1 illustrates two pages of a four-page mail questionnaire which was used by the market research division of R. L. Polk and Company, New York. Several points are worthy of note. First, cartoons have been used effectively to stimulate interest; respondents who are thus placed in a favorable frame of mind will be more inclined to complete the questionnaire promptly. A cover letter to this questionnaire informed the recipient that only about seven minutes would be required to answer the questions. Questions have been stated clearly in an easy conversational style. Questions can be answered by merely checking appropriate spaces; however, brief additional comments are invited on each question. Finally, questions of a personal nature have been deferred to the end of the schedule.

Selecting the sample. All samples, regardless of size or type, should be selected in such a manner that the results will reveal a reasonably accurate picture of the population being investigated. In a controlled illustration, such as with dice or coins, the true characteristics of the population are known. In business research, methods developed in controlled situations are employed in studying populations whose characteristics are unknown. Market research in the construction industry is undertaken to discover the market potential for new housing in particular areas at particular times. Manufacturers of automobiles, household appliances, television sets, cigarettes, toothpaste, chewing gum, and countless other items engage in continuous market research. Movie producers test their new productions in theaters where movie

ENGINE PERFORMANCE:

4. Now, from a standpoint of good motor performance for both city and country driving, including smoothness, quietness, and acceleration, would you say that your engine was:

CHECK ONE

Excellent? .... ☐
Better than most? .... ☐
About average? .... ☐
Not so good as most? .... ☐
Bad? .... ☐

a. If you have any words of praise—or gripes—on this score, won't you write them for us here?

WHAT YOU **LIKE**.............................. WHAT YOU **DON'T LIKE**........................

MECHANICAL PERFORMANCE:

5. Now, from a standpoint of the other mechanical parts like the brakes, the clutch, the windshield wipers, the headlights, etc., would you say that with your car you'd had:

CHECK ONE

No trouble at all? .... ☐
A little trouble? .... ☐
A lot of trouble? .... ☐

a. If you have any complaints whatsoever about the mechanical operation—or if you have some favorable comments, won't you detail them for us here:

WHAT YOU **LIKE**.............................. WHAT YOU **DON'T LIKE**........................

ITS EASE OF HANDLING:

6. Taking into consideration all the factors that make for easy driving (factors like steering, gear shifting, parking, etc.), would you say that your car was:

CHECK ONE

Easy to handle? .... ☐
About average? .... ☐
Tiring to drive? .... ☐

a. Any comments about the way your car "handles"?

WHAT YOU **LIKE**.............................. WHAT YOU **DON'T LIKE**........................

THE HEATING AND VENTILATING SYSTEM:

7. Now what would you say about the heating and ventilating system in your car? Is it:

CHECK ONE

Excellent? .... ☐
Satisfactory? .... ☐
Poor? .... ☐

a. Anything at all that bothers you about it? Or anything that seems especially good? If so, here's the place to tell us about it.

WHAT YOU **LIKE**.............................. WHAT YOU **DON'T LIKE**........................

Fig. 1. Part of a questionnaire designed to sample satisfaction of car buyers. (Courtesy Geyer Advertising Agency)

NOW, THEN:

12. If you've given us any criticisms, anywhere in this interview, won't you tell us here which ONE gripe you consider the most important—which one you'd most like to see improved?

....

....

13. Now let's switch to the rosy side of the picture. Is there any one feature of your new car that has particularly pleased you? Yes ☐ No ☐

If yes:

a. Which one is it?...

14. When you bought your car, was it your first choice, or was it the best of those you could get?

CHECK WHICH

- It was my 1st choice.......................... ☐
- It was the best of those I could get............. ☑

15. What about the car you owned before you bought this new one?

Did you......

CHECK ONE

- Trade it in on the new one?................... ☐
- Sell it?.................................... ☐
- Keep it?.................................... ☐
- Didn't own a car............................. ☐

a. If you traded it in, or sold it, what make was it?....HONDA............

ABOUT PRICE:

16. Sure—like everything else—your new car cost a lot more than it would have a few years back. But think for a minute about COMPARATIVE values. Considering what you would have paid for other makes, how do you feel about the price you paid for your 1949 model?

Compared with other makes:

CHECK WHICH

- I received excellent value..................... ☐
- I received good value......................... ☐
- I received fair value.......................... ☐
- I received poor value......................... ☐
- I was stung.................................. ☐

NOW PUT ON YOUR THINKING CAP:

Let's pretend you had to do it all over again, and that all makes of cars were freely available to you (AND keep in mind that several makes have announced their 1949 models since you got your present car)......

17. What make would be your first choice?....MUSTANG.....HARDTOP

18. What two other makes would you investigate?.MUSTANG.......CONV.....

.MUSTANG...2+2.....

FINALLY: What make and model of car have you been talking about all through this?

..MUSTANG.. (MAKE) .....HARDTOP (MODEL)

Do you own another car? Yes ☑ No ☐

If yes: What make and model is it?

.....V.W...... (MAKE) ......COACH..... (MODEL)

It would help us immensely if you'd be kind enough to indicate by a check mark in which of the classifications below your annual family income happens to be.

CHECK WHICH

- Less than \$ 2,000......... ☐
- Between \$ 2,000—\$ 3,000. ☐
- Between \$ 3,000—\$ 5,000. ☐
- Between \$ 5,000—\$10,000. ☐
- Over \$10,000 a year... ☐ ✓

This questionnaire was filled out 100,000 ✓

- by a man ☐
- by a woman ☐

who is approximately....years old.

Thanks very much for your help!

goers, by electrical devices, can record their likes and dislikes to any portion of the film. Sampling is utilized by management to determine operating characteristics of production processes, clerical operations, and other activities in order to establish standards for control of operations. The value of all such research is dependent upon the representativeness of the samples selected.

The best method of insuring randomness is to select the sample by use of a table of random numbers.[3] Such tables usually consist of many groups of five-digit numbers arranged in five rows, as illustrated by these four groups:

06494	14856	59842	17374
61773	42108	02753	59202
12202	05347	14141	83012
20717	61996	61472	09504
47619	39890	17028	98524

Random numbers can be employed in any systematic manner, since each digit appearing in the table has been selected at random. Numbers may be used as they appear in rows or in columns, singly or in combinations of two or more digits. For example, in an area survey of a city or a section of a city which had no more than 9,999 blocks, either the first four or the last four digits of the random number group would need to be considered. If the first four digits were to be used, the first lot selected would bear the number 649. If numbers were to be selected in sequence from the top to bottom in each column, the second lot selected would bear the number 6,177. Selection would continue until the desired sample size had been obtained. Since most business papers are now prenumbered in serial order, it is simple to use a random number table to determine which papers should be selected for auditing purposes or for other administrative studies.

Sometimes sample items are selected according to a *systematic* plan.

[3] Random sampling numbers may be found in the following publications: Arkin, H. and R. R. Colton, *Tables for Statisticians*, College Outline Series, New York, Barnes & Noble, 1950; Fisher, R. A. and F. Yates, *Statistical Tables for Biological, Agricultural, and Medical Research*, London, Oliver and Boyd, 1938; Interstate Commerce Commission, Bureau of Transport Economics and Statistics, *Table of 105,000 Random Decimal Digits*, Washington, D. C., May 1949; Kendall, M. G. and B. Babington Smith, *Tables of Random Sampling Numbers*, *Tracts for Computers*, No. XXIV, London, Cambridge University Press, 1939; The Rand Corporation, *A Million Random Digits with a Hundred Thousand Normal Deviates*, Santa Monica, California, 1955; Tippett, L. H. C., *Random Sampling Numbers*, *Tracts for Computers*, No. XV. London, Cambridge University Press, 1927.

For example, every 10th, 50th, or 100th name in a telephone directory may be selected to suitably approximate random selections. The first name is selected at random, but thereafter the systematic pattern is followed. Use of a telephone directory or other listing is appropriate only if the names listed therein are representative of the universe which is to be sampled and there is no periodicity of population characteristics (alternating clusters of high and low income groups, ethnic groups, etc.) which would introduce bias into the results of the particular study.

Some sampling problems do not lend themselves to use of random numbers. Where strata of the population which are significant for a particular investigation are known, it is possible to instruct interviewers to interview a specified number of persons in each stratum. This method, sometimes referred to as *quota sampling*, is used in combination with other methods in the Gallup Polls and in some surveys by market research firms. It is extremely important, of course, that interviewers be well trained and highly reliable.

COLLECTING AND EDITING THE DATA

Collecting the Data. After the sampling instrument has been prepared and the sample has been selected, the actual collection of data must be conducted as expeditiously as possible. If data are to be obtained by personal interview, interviewers who have been trained must be given specific assignments. Close follow-up and liaison must be maintained with interviewers during the course of the survey.

If questionnaires are distributed by mail, returned questionnaires must be checked in and follow-up letters must be sent to nonrespondents. If possible, it is desirable to personally interview a sample of the final nonrespondents in order to determine whether or not their responses would differ considerably from the replies to the mail questionnaires. If a significant difference is indicated, sample results can be adjusted accordingly.

It is important that the collection operation adhere to a timetable. The longer the period required to collect the data, the less homogeneous the data are likely to be. Business data are not static; prices, costs, quality of product, profits, consumer preferences, personal opinion, and many other factors change with the passage of time. Consequently, the validity of results often diminishes as the time required to collect the data increases.

Editing and tabulating the returns. All returned questionnaires and data schedules must be edited. Obviously incorrect answers must either be corrected or voided. Sometimes it is possible to make corrections by reference to other data on the schedule; if this is not possible, follow-up with the respondent may be necessary.

If data are to be recorded in punched cards for electric or hand sorting and tabulation, coding is often required. Codes are merely numbers; use of number codes makes possible the recording of a tremendous amount of data on a single punched card; in addition it greatly facilitates sorting operations.

If the sample has been small and the quantity of data obtained is not large, manual tabulation of the data is often the most economical and efficient method. Large work sheets or tally sheets can easily be designed for recording the data in the proper classifications and cross classifications. These tally sheets should be designed to classify the data in the form desired for the tables and charts which are to reflect the results of the survey. In fact, the wise planner will have integrated preparation of the questionnaire, tabulation sheets, and sketch forms for the final tables and charts.

If a large quantity of data has been obtained, machine sorting and tabulation is usually the most practical. Firms which do not rent or own such equipment can engage service firms to perform these operations. However, instructions specifying the desired classifications and cross classifications of data must be prepared.

Analyzing the data and reporting the results

Data collected either by survey or from published or unpublished records ordinarily must be reduced to meaningful summary figures. Page after page of tabulated data is relatively meaningless. However, expressions of these data in ratios, averages, index numbers, trends, and measures of variation are highly significant and can be interpreted and analyzed intelligently. Methods for computing and using these measures will be described in Chapters 4 through 8 and Chapter 11. Tables and charts which can be employed both in the analysis and in the illustration of final results are discussed in Chapters 9 and 10.

Care should be exercised in analysis of the data and reporting the results to insure that data are applied only in answering those questions to which they clearly relate. It is deceptively easy to find statistics to support almost any point of view if questions of accuracy and validity of the data are ignored.

Questions and Exercises

1. What are some of the purposes for which business management may collect data by sampling processes? Why might management prefer samples to censuses? Explain fully.

2. Take ten samples consisting of ten coin tosses each. Record your results in a tally form as illustrated.

COIN SAMPLE TALLY FORM

	Results by sample number										Total sample results
Coin face	1	2	3	4	5	6	7	8	9	10	
Head											
Tail											

(a) How do you account for the differences among sample results?
(b) Combine samples 1 and 2. Does this result more closely approximate the mathematical probability of results than the results of either single sample? Now increase the size of this sample by successive additions of the remaining samples, checking your results after each addition.
(c) Does the sum of all sample results (100 tosses) more closely approximate the mathematical probability (50:50) than the results of the small individual samples? Should it? Explain.

3. Define each of the following types of samples: (a) random, (b) stratified, (c) area, (d) sequential, (e) judgment. What are the conditions appropriate to the use of each type?

4. What increase in a random sample of 2,500 items would be required to reduce sampling errors by one-half? by two-thirds?

5. If one were interested in determining the average take-home pay of workers in Big-Town, U.S.A., what would be the population? What definitions would be necessary?

6. Select a manufacturing corporation listed on the New York Stock Exchange. Consult the various appropriate sources (see Chapter 2) and determine in how many ways the production, sales, and income

figures are reported for the corporation. What implications does such knowledge have for sampling studies?

7. What are the characteristics of a good questionnaire or interview schedule?

8. The Puff-Up Company produces cardboard air pumps designed for use in inflating children's air-filled toys. The pumps are subjected to a final sample inspection to determine that each can be expected to emit air at a pressure of at least 10 lb per sqaure inch. Pumps not capable of developing a pressure of 10 lb psi are considered defective and returned for further processing. The figures below are pressure readings for a lot of 100 pumps. (In the real situation, readings for all pumps in a lot would not be available, but readings would be taken as the sample was selected.)

(1) Number the 100 readings from 01 to 00, with 00 standing for 100; any systematic pattern of numbering may be used.

(2) Prepare a tally sheet on which you can show the selected reading, an indication of whether or not that pump is considered acceptable, and the total number of defective pumps found to that time.

(3) Refer to a table of random digits designated by the instructor and use it to select one of the readings. Clearly describe your selection process.

(4) Randomly select an additional reading, make the quality determination and accumulate the results.

(5) Refer to Table 1, page 30 and determine whether the entire lot should be accepted or rejected or testing should continue.

(6) Continue steps (4) and (5) until a point of acceptance or rejection for the entire lot is attained.

15	12	17	20	14	19	13	10	19	9
10	21	18	16	17	18	8	15	14	18
13	14	11	7	12	21	13	9	15	20
16	8	20	14	19	14	16	12	17	11
17	19	12	15	13	11	17	16	13	19
12	17	18	11	15	14	10	16	18	13
15	14	13	14	18	9	17	12	14	21
14	8	15	12	13	18	16	15	13	15
16	11	22	10	15	11	9	13	16	17
15	16	17	7	16	20	10	14	22	9

4 *Statistical techniques: frequency distributions, averages, and dispersion*

Large masses of data are virtually incomprehensible when merely presented in raw form. For example, it is doubtful if a person could determine personal income characteristics by scanning a random listing of hundreds, thousands, or millions of individual incomes. Important characteristics of any large mass do not become apparent until individual items have been grouped into a relatively few classifications. This summarization of mass data is, of course, a prerequisite to preparation of tables and charts.

Frequency distributions

Arrangements of homogeneous data by value intervals or *classes* are referred to as *frequency distributions*; these distributions show the frequency with which data occur in each *class.* Table 2 is a frequency distribution of a random sample of 280 savings account balances drawn from the active accounts of a savings and loan association early in 1958. The first column shows the several account sizes, the second

TABLE 2. Frequency distribution of random sample of 280 savings account balances

Amount of savings account balance in dollars	Number of accounts with balances in class given	Per cent of accounts with balances in class given
Less than 100	78	27.8
100 and under 300	31	11.1
300 and under 600	29	10.4
600 and under 900	8	2.8
900 and under 1,400	29	10.4
1,400 and under 2,000	15	5.4
2,000 and under 3,000	20	7.1
3,000 and under 4,000	15	5.4
4,000 and under 6,000	20	7.1
6,000 and under 8,000	14	5.0
8,000 and under 10,000	5	1.8
10,000 and over	16	5.7
Totals:	280	100.0

Source: Adapted from a random sample of 280 account balances drawn from the active savings account balances of a savings and loan association, 1958.

column shows the number of accounts by size groups, and the third column indicates the per cent of accounts at each size level. Data in Table 2 also could have been presented in two separate tables, one for actual number and one for percentages.

TERMINOLOGY

Data which have been collected and edited, but not summarized, are referred to as *raw data.* A listing of data by order of magnitude is referred to as an *array.* The following tabulation shows a rearrangement of data into an array. An array is useful if the number of individual items is relatively small. Clusters of items which have the same value are at once apparent. An array may help in the selection of classes into which the data can be grouped. However, if the mass of data is large, use of the array is by-passed and data are sorted directly into frequency distributions, preferably by electrical sorting equipment.

List of Data	*Array of Data*
21	16
22	17
17	18
20	19
21	20
27	21
16	21
24	21
22	22
23	22
19	22
22	23
25	24
21	25
18	27

Classes are the subdivisions within a frequency distribution. Table 2 has 12 classes. *Class limits* are the "boundaries" of a class, the uppermost and lowermost values which may be placed in a class. A *class interval* refers to the range of the values included in a class. A *class midpoint* is the value which lies midway between an upper and lower limit of a class. A *class frequency* is the number of items which fall into that class. For example, in Table 2, the class frequency in the $10,000 and over income level is 16.

CONSTRUCTION OF A FREQUENCY DISTRIBUTION

Raw data may be grouped or classified by use of either a *tally* form or an *entry* form. Table 3 is a tally form used to classify a sample of production workers in the XYZ Steel Foundry according to levels of average hourly earnings. Payroll records provided the raw data; a mark, or tally, was made in the appropriate class for each worker.

Table 4 illustrates use of an entry form. The only basic difference between Tables 3 and 4 is that in Table 4 the average hourly earnings, rather than tally marks, have been entered in appropriate classes. Use of the entry form is more time consuming, but it provides the researcher with knowledge of the distribution of data in each class. Distributions within individual classes are important in deciding if the chosen class limits are desirable. If changes appear desirable they are facilitated by the listing of data on an entry form.

TABLE 3. Tally form for straight-time average hourly earnings of production workers in the XYZ Steel Foundry, September, 1960

Average hourly earnings (in cents)	Number of employees
125 and under 150	~~1111~~ 1111 (9)
150 and under 175	~~1111~~ ~~1111~~ ~~1111~~ (15)
175 and under 200	~~1111~~ ~~1111~~ ~~1111~~ ~~1111~~ ~~1111~~ ~~1111~~ 1111 (34)
200 and under 225	~~1111~~ ~~1111~~ ~~1111~~ ~~1111~~ ~~1111~~ 1 (26)
225 and under 250	~~1111~~ ~~1111~~ 1 (11)
250 and under 275	~~1111~~ 1111 (9)
275 and under 300	~~1111~~ 111 (8)
300 and under 325	~~1111~~ (5)
325 and under 350	111 (3)

Source: Hypothetical

TABLE 4. Entry form for straight-time average hourly earnings of production workers in the XYZ Steel Foundry, September, 1960

125 & under 150	150 & under 175	175 & under 200	200 & under 225	225 & under 250	250 & under 275	275 & under 300	300 & under 325	325 & under 350
125.0	170.0	185.0	200.0	242.5	262.5	282.5	307.5	330.5
137.5	153.0	178.0	224.0	237.5	272.5	297.5	312.5	342.0
146.0	152.5	196.0	212.5	233.0	272.5	277.5	305.0	345.0
145.0	162.5	180.0	217.5	242.0	250.0	275.0	324.5	(3)
132.0	162.0	192.5	208.0	249.5	257.5	285.0	315.0	
145.0	155.0	197.5	202.5	238.0	262.5	290.0	(5)	
137.5	161.0	182.0	201.0	227.5	270.0	276.5		
etc.	etc.	etc.	etc.	etc.	etc.	etc.		
(9)	(15)	(34)	(26)	(11)	(9)	(8)		

Source: Hypothetical

Table 5 is a frequency distribution which could have been derived from either Table 3 or 4. It should be pointed out again that electric sorting and tabulating equipment is a tremendous time-saver when dealing with large masses of data. Raw data may be punched into cards which can then be sorted with great speed; if desired, individual items can be printed by classes on a report which also can include the total number of items in each class and in the entire frequency distribution.

TABLE 5. Frequency distribution for straight-time average hourly earnings of production workers in the XYZ Steel Foundry, September, 1960

Average hourly earnings (in cents)	Number of employees
125 and under 150	9
150 and under 175	15
175 and under 200	34
200 and under 225	26
225 and under 250	11
250 and under 275	9
275 and under 300	8
300 and under 325	5
325 and under 350	3

Source: See Table 3 or 4.

A major problem encountered in the construction of frequency distributions is the selection of appropriate classes. If the distribution is divided into a very few large classes, the characteristics of the mass of data will be concealed. Similarly, if the distribution is divided into a great many small classes, the concentration of data around certain values will not be readily apparent. These points are illustrated in the following tabulations of frequency distributions.

It is not possible to provide a hard and fast rule by which the appropriate number of classes can be determined; sound judgment and a certain amount of trial and error must be relied upon. The number of classes used is seldom fewer than five or more than twenty-five; in general, the number of classes required increases as the number of frequencies becomes larger and as the interval between the values of the highest and lowest items becomes greater.

Class limits also must be selected with care. Obviously, classes must be mutually exclusive; class limits must be selected so that each item may be placed in one, and only one, class. Limits of 125 to 135 and

135 to 145 would be inappropriate; an item with a value of 135 could be placed in either class and the distribution would be meaningless.

TOO MANY CLASSES

Class Limits	Number of Frequencies
125–134.9	3
135–144.9	2
145–154.9	7
155–164.9	5
165–174.9	7
175–184.9	12
185–194.9	15
195–204.9	14
205–214.9	7
215–224.9	12
225–234.9	7
235–244.9	4
245–254.9	6
255–264.9	4
etc.	

TOO FEW CLASSES

Class Limits	Number of Frequencies
120–179.9	31
180–239.9	61
240–299.9	20
300–359.9	8
Total:	120

Data are either exact counts or measurements, the latter always being approximations. Of course, estimates are often made both of data which may be counted and of data which may be measured. Generally speaking, data which are subject to count are whole numbers—integers—such as persons, machines, and stores. Such data are called *discrete*, or *discontinuous*. On the other hand, measurements are principally fractional values which occur at minute intervals, and hence are *continuous*. No doubt the reader can think of some series which could be classified either as continuous or discontinuous. Monetary values expressed in dollars and cents may be a case in point. A good rule to follow is to treat as continuous any series which is not clearly discontinuous. The nature of a series of data has a bearing upon the selection of class limits. If the data being classified are integers—that is, whole numbers—and the data have not been rounded to whole numbers, the class limits can be stated in whole numbers. If the data are continuous, the class limits should either be expressed in decimals (as in the preceding tabulations) or expressed as ranging between one whole number *and under* another whole number (as 125 and under 150 in Table 5).

Class mid-points are important factors to be considered while class limits are being selected. Mid-points are important because in later computations they are treated as being representative of all the values in their respective classes. Consequently, class limits should be selected in such a fashion that values in the class either tend to be distributed evenly through each class interval or tend to cluster around the mid-point. Judgment is again required, because frequently it is impossible to select class limits so that the mid-points of all classes are equally good representatives of values in their respective classes. In order to simplify future computations, class mid-points should be whole numbers rather than fractional values whenever possible.

Mention should also be made of the problems involved in use of *unequal* class intervals and *open-end classes.* Examples of both are found in Table 2. The first and last classes are open-end—less than $100 and $10,000 and over. Since only one class limit is known in each case it is impossible to determine the mid-points and hence impossible to make further computations which require determinate mid-points. Further, classes with known limits in Table 2 are of unequal intervals. Classes have intervals of 100, 200, 300, 600, 1,000, and 2,000 in addition to the two classes with indeterminate intervals. Unequal class intervals also complicate further computations. However, in many instances open-end classes and unequal class intervals cannot be avoided. Consider the unwieldly number of classes which would be required to accommodate all account balances in classes with intervals of only $100; many of the higher classes would have no frequencies, but extremely high classes would be required to record balances of tens of thousands of dollars. Although only limited computations can be made from frequency distributions with unequal class intervals and open-end classes, distributions such as Table 2 perform a useful function in illustrating the general shape of a distribution and the concentration of data in the various classes.

summary

Frequency distributions are constructed for the purpose of condensing and summarizing large masses of data, thereby revealing important characteristics which would not be evident in a mere listing of a large number of items. Construction of a frequency distribution is often the first step toward a more complete analysis of data. Care should be exercised to select class limits which are mutually exclusive and within which the data tend to distribute themselves evenly or tend to concentrate at the class mid-point. For ease in computation, mid-points should be whole numbers and all classes should have an equal interval.

Averages

Statistics is sometimes referred to as the "science of averages." Averages can be useful and informative, but they can also be misleading. A man with one bowlegged son and one knock-kneed son maintained that "on the average" his sons had the straightest legs in the county. Averages should not be used unless they are representative of the data from which they were computed. Average monthly sales of $40,000 for a given year does not accurately describe monthly sales of a firm which sells $315,000 in one month and $15,000 during each of the other eleven months.

Averages are referred to as *measures of central tendency* because they are designed to measure the central values around which data tend to cluster. Computation of a single type of average is frequently inadequate to describe the manner in which data tend to concentrate. Consequently several types of averages have been developed. The three types which are most useful in business statistics are (1) *the arithmetic mean*, (2) *the median*, and (3) *the mode*. The arithmetic mean is what most readers recognize as the ordinary arithmetic average. The median is simply the value of the middle value in an array of data. The mode is the value possessed by the greatest number of items in the mass. Consider the following arrays:

	Array No. 1		*Array No. 2*
	4		4
	5		5
	5		6
	5		7
	6		7
	6		7
	8		8
	11		9
	13		10
Total	63	Total	63

The arithmetic mean of Array No. 1, computed by dividing the total (63) by the number of items (9), is 7. The median, the middle value, is 6. The mode, the value which occurs most frequently, is 5. In contrast the arithmetic mean, median, and mode for Array No. 2 are the same value, 7.

Computation of the above averages from a frequency distribution is more complex than computation from a list or an array. Methods of computation and characteristics of each type of average are described in the sections which follow.

ARITHMETIC MEAN

This measure of central tendency, hereafter referred to as the *mean*, is a value which is influenced by each value in the distribution. For example, if the value 8 in the above arrays were changed to 17, the

TABLE 6. Computation of a student's grade point average

(1) Grade (Classes)	(2) Grade-points (Midpoints)	(3) Course hours (Frequencies)	(4) Col. 2 × Col. 3 (Weighted values)
A	4	5	20
B	3	5	15
C	2	3	6
D	1	2	2
Totals:		15	43

$$\text{grade-point average} = \frac{43}{15} = \mathbf{2.87}$$

means of each distribution would be changed from 7 to 8; however, the values of the medians and modes would have remained unchanged.

Method of computation. Computation of the mean from a frequency distribution is a bit more involved than computation from an array. However, most students have already been introduced to the method through the computation of school grade-point averages. This method is reviewed in Table 6 where it is assumed that a student has received A, B, C, and D, respectively, in four courses. The grades in column 1 may be considered as classes in a frequency distribution; similarly, the grade-point values in column 2 may be regarded as class midpoints. Column 3 contains the course hours for each of the four courses in which our hypothetical student was enrolled. These course hours are, in effect, frequencies which must be applied as weights against the grade points in column 2; the resulting products are shown in column 4. The final step in computation of the grade-point average requires the division of the sum of column 4 (43) by the sum of column 3 (15); the result is a grade-point average of 2.87. Note the importance of weighting the grade points by the number of course hours; if the grade points had been totaled (10) and divided by the number of courses (4), the grade point average would have been computed incorrectly as 2.5.

TABLE 7. Computation of mean hourly earnings of production workers in the XYZ Steel Foundry: Long method

(1) Classes	(2) Midpoints m	(3) Frequencies f	(4) Weighted mid-points fm
125 and under 150	137.5	9	1,237.5
150 and under 175	162.5	15	2,437.5
175 and under 200	187.5	34	6,375.0
200 and under 225	212.5	26	5,525.0
225 and under 250	237.5	11	2,612.5
250 and under 275	262.5	9	2,362.5
275 and under 300	287.5	8	2,300.0
300 and under 325	312.5	5	1,562.5
325 and under 350	337.5	3	1,012.5
	Totals:	120	25,425.0

$$\text{mean} = \frac{25{,}425.0}{120} = 211.88 \quad \text{or} \quad \mathbf{211.9}$$

Now let us consider the hypothetical frequency distribution developed earlier and reproduced in Table 7. Column 1 contains the class intervals; column 2, the class mid-points; column 3, the class frequencies; and column 4, the products of the respective class frequencies and class mid-points.

The mean is computed by dividing the sum of column 4 (25,425.0) by the sum of column 3 (120); the result is a mean of 211.9. The importance of selecting class limits so that class mid-points are truly representative of the items in the respective classes is now apparent. If class values tend to concentrate near the upper class limits, the computed mean will be too low; if they concentrate near the lower class limits, the computed mean will be too high.

Symbols. The above computations involved only simple arithmetic and were accomplished without the use of "mysterious mathematical symbols." However, the mystery which enshrouds symbols can be effectively dispelled by demonstrating that symbols are merely a form of shorthand. In longhand, the formula for computing the mean would be as follows:

$$\text{mean} = \frac{\text{sum of the products of class frequencies and their respective class mid-points}}{\text{sum of the number of items in the frequency distribution}}$$

Symbols for the above items are

$\bar{X}$ = mean[1]

m = a class mid-point

f = frequency with which an item occurs (items represented by class mid-points)

Σ = a sum, such as a total of a column

N = number of items

Substituting these symbols in the longhand formula, we have

$$\bar{X} = \frac{\Sigma fm}{N} \quad \text{or} \quad \bar{X} = \frac{25{,}425.0}{120} = 211.88 \quad \text{or} \quad \mathbf{211.9}$$

Short method of computation. Although the computations in Table 7 were relatively simple, it is possible to introduce a further simplification which is a great timesaver. The key to this simplification is a significant characteristic of the mean: the sum (algebraic) of the deviations of values of individual items from the value of their mean is always zero. This may be demonstrated as follows:

Array of Items	*Deviation of Items from Mean*
3	−3
4	−2
6	0
8	+2
9	+3
Total = 30	Total = 0

$$\text{mean} = \frac{\Sigma X}{N} = \frac{30}{5} = \mathbf{6}$$

[1] Another symbol frequently used to designate the mean is M.

Knowledge of this characteristic enables us to compute a mean by the following steps:

1. Arbitrarily choose or assume a value for the mean.
2. Compute the deviations of the items from the assumed mean.
3. Compute the mean of the deviations as a correction factor for adjusting the assumed mean. (Be sure to preserve the sign of this mean.)
4. Correct the assumed mean (step 1) by adding (algebraically) to it the mean of the deviations computed in step 3.

To illustrate this technique let us assume the mean of the following array to be 4. Then,

Array of Items	*Deviation of Items from Assumed Mean* (d')
3	−1
4	0
6	+2
8	+4
9	+5
	Total = +10

$$\text{Assumed mean} = 4$$

$$\text{mean} = \text{assumed mean} + \frac{10}{5}$$

$$\bar{X} = 4 + 2 = \mathbf{6}$$

If we use $\bar{X}'$ to indicate the assumed mean, the formula for this process becomes

$$\bar{X} = \bar{X}' + \frac{\Sigma\, d'}{N}$$

Now let us apply this technique to the frequency distribution, where class mid-points are used to represent values in the respective classes. The following steps are observed:

1. Select any class mid-point as the assumed mean; however, the arithmetic is simplified if the mid-point selected is in the class with the greatest number of frequencies.
2. Express each class mid-point as a deviation from the assumed mean and divide by the class interval. (Note that the resulting deviations are in terms of class intervals rather than in terms of the units in which the data are expressed.)

3. Multiply the deviations by their respective class frequencies.
4. Take an algebraic sum of the weighted deviations computed in step 3; divide this sum by N to obtain the mean of the weighted deviations.
5. Convert the mean deviation (step 4) to terms of units by multiplying it by the number of units in the class interval. This amount becomes the correction factor.

TABLE 8. Computation of the mean hourly earnings of steel foundry workers from the frequency distribution: short method

(1) Classes	(2) Mid-points m	(3) Frequencies f	(4) Deviations in class interval units d'	(5) Weighted deviations fd'
125 and under 150	137.5	9	−2	−18
150 and under 175	162.5	15	−1	−15
175 and under 200	187.5	34	0	0
200 and under 225	212.5	26	1	26
225 and under 250	237.5	11	2	22
250 and under 275	262.5	9	3	27
275 and under 300	287.5	8	4	32
300 and under 325	312.5	5	5	25
325 and under 350	337.5	3	6	18
	Totals:	120		117

$$\bar{X} = \bar{X}' + \frac{\Sigma fd'}{N}(i), \qquad \bar{X} = 187.5 + \frac{117}{120}(25)$$

$$\bar{X} = 187.5 + 24.58 = 211.88 \quad \text{or} \quad \mathbf{211.9}$$

6. Correct the assumed mean (step 1) by adding (algebraically) to it the correction factor (step 5).

This procedure is illustrated in Table 8. Symbols required are

$\bar{X}'$ = assumed mean

d' = deviation of class mid-points from the estimated mean in class interval units $= \dfrac{m - \bar{X}'}{i}$

i = class interval

Compare Table 7 with Table 8. The amounts in column 5, Table 8 are much smaller and easier to work with than are the amounts in column 4, Table 7.[2] Herein lies the advantages of the short method. It should be emphasized that the short method can be fully utilized only if two conditions are met: (1) all class intervals are equal and (2) a class mid-point is chosen as the assumed mean.

Characteristics of the mean. The reader should be familiar with the following characteristics of the mean:

1. The mean is influenced by the value of each and every item in a series of data. When a series of data has been classified in a frequency distribution, the mean is influenced by the values of all class mid-points weighted by their respective class frequencies.
2. The sum (algebraic) of the deviations of values from their mean is always zero. This characteristic makes possible the short method of computation.
3. The sum of the squared deviations of values from their mean is always less than the sum of the squared deviations of values measured from any point other than the mean. This characteristic has significance in further computations which are explained in a later section of this chapter.

MEDIAN

In a series of data which include some very high or very low values, the value of the mean will not be representative of the values which occur most frequently. This is often true of income and price data, where a relatively few very high values cause the mean to be higher than the most "common" values. In such instances, the median, or middle value, of the series may be a more representative figure to use in describing the mass of data.

Method of computation. When a series has relatively few values, the median can be located simply by arranging the items in an array and then counting down to the middle value. If the series has an even number of items, the average or mean of the two middle values is designated as the median. This is shown in the following computation.

[2] Note that if the assumed mean also had been the actual mean, the sum of column 5 would have been zero.

Array of Items
23
24
26
27
29
32
33
46

$$\text{Median} = \frac{27 + 29}{2} = \mathbf{28}$$

The median is a *positional* measure. It is determined by the *position* rather than the *value* of items in a series. Changing any or all of the first three values in the above series to any other numbers with values of 27 or less, and/or changing any or all of the last three values to any other numbers with values of 29 or more, would not affect the value of the median, which would remain 28. In contrast, changing the value of a single item would cause the value of the mean to be changed.

Computation of the median from data which have been classified in a frequency distribution is also quite simple. Consider the distribution of wages portrayed in Table 9. First, it may be determined from inspection of column 3 that the mid-point of the frequencies ($N/2 = \frac{120}{2} = 60$) occurs somewhere between the class limits of the fourth class, 200 and under 225. That is, the sum of the frequencies in the first three classes is 58 ($9 + 15 + 34$); hence the median must be located in the fourth class, which contains 26 frequencies. Since the mid-point of the frequencies (60) is 2 more than 58, it may be assumed that the median is $\frac{2}{26}$ of the class interval (25) beyond the lower class limit of 200; or $200 + \frac{2}{26} \times 25 = \mathbf{201.9}$.

What we have done is indicated in the following long-hand formula:

$$\text{median} = \begin{pmatrix}\text{lower limit}\\ \text{of median}\\ \text{class}\end{pmatrix} + \frac{\begin{pmatrix}\text{frequencies in the}\\ \text{median class below}\\ \text{the median value}\end{pmatrix}}{\begin{pmatrix}\text{total frequencies in}\\ \text{the medium class}\end{pmatrix}} \times \begin{pmatrix}\text{the value of}\\ \text{the median}\\ \text{class interval}\end{pmatrix}$$

or, in *shorthand*, where

Md = median
L_M = lower limit of median class
N = total number of frequencies
Σf_c = cumulative sum of frequencies below the median class
f_M = frequencies in the median class

then, $$Md = L_M + \frac{\frac{N}{2} - \Sigma f_c}{f_M}(i)$$

It should be noted that the median also could be computed by subtracting from the upper class limit rather than adding to the lower

TABLE 9. Computation of median hourly earnings of steel foundry workers from the frequency distribution

(1) Classes	(2) Frequencies f	(3) Cumulative frequencies below lower limit of class Σf_c
125 and under 150	9	0
150 and under 175	15	9
175 and under 200	34	24
200 and under 225	26	58
225 and under 250	11	84
250 and under 275	9	95
275 and under 300	8	104
300 and under 325	5	112
325 and under 350	3	117
Totals:	120	

$$Md = L_M + \frac{\frac{N}{2} - \Sigma f_c}{f_M}(i)$$

$$= 200 + \frac{\frac{120}{2} - 58}{26}(25)$$

$$= 200 + \tfrac{2}{26}(25) = 200 + 1.92 = 201.92 \quad \text{or} \quad \mathbf{201.9}$$

class limit as in the above illustration. To illustrate, 225 minus $\frac{24}{26} \times 25$ equals 201.9.

Characteristics of the median. The reader should be familiar with the following characteristics of the median:

1. The median, as the middle value in a series or distribution of data, is a positional measure which is influenced by the position (determined by size) rather than by the value of each individual item. This is in contrast to the mean which is affected by the

values of individual items. Consequently, we can say that the median is less affected than the mean by extreme values in a distribution.

2. Medians can be computed from frequency distributions which have open ends or unequal class intervals, since only the position and not the values of items must be known.
3. The sum of the deviations (signs ignored) of values from their median is less than the sum of the deviations of values from any other point. However, the reader should recall that the sum of the *squared* deviations is less when measured from the mean. These characteristics may be illustrated as follows:

Array of Items	DEVIATIONS (Signs ignored)		DEVIATIONS SQUARED	
	From Mean	*From Median*	*From Mean*	*From Median*
2	3	4	9	16
4	1	2	1	4
6	1	0	1	0
6	1	0	1	0
7	2	1	4	1
—	–	–	—	—
25	8	7	16	21

Mean = **5**, Median = **6**

The reader is urged to construct similar illustrations to further demonstrate these characteristics, each of which has significance in computations which are described in a later section of this chapter.[3]

MODE

The mode is the value possessed by the greatest number of items in the series or distribution. In a series of income data, the mode is that income which occurs most frequently; it is affected neither by the value nor the position of other incomes in the series. Since income series are usually characterized by many low and medium incomes and a few very high incomes, the mode in most cases would be a lower value than the median, which in turn would be lower than the mean. For many purposes the modal income, the modal scale, modal expenditure, modal production, modal time, or other modal value may be more significant than the mean or median values.

[3] It will be noted that if signs of deviations are recognized, the algebraic sum of the deviations from the mean in the above illustration is 0, whereas the algebraic sum of the deviations from the median is −5.

Method of computation. From a series of ungrouped data the mode is located simply by determining the value which occurs most frequently. When data have been grouped in a frequency distribution, the class which contains the most frequencies is said to be the modal class. Since class limits should be selected so that frequencies concentrate around the class mid-point, the value of the mid-point of the modal class may be regarded as the modal value.[4] Hence the modal value in the distribution in Table 9 would be 187.5, the mid-point of the modal class, 175 and under 200. For most purposes in business statistics it is unnecessary to employ further refinements in computation of the mode. This is true because use of mathematical techniques does not necessarily lead to a more representative measure of the mode which—for a frequency distribution—is an estimate at best.

However, brief mention will be made of a formula which may be used to compute the mode from a frequency distribution. It is reasoned that the modal value lies nearest the class limit which is adjacent to the class which (second to the modal class) has the greatest number of frequencies. Hence, in the frequency distribution in Table 9, it would be reasoned that the mode would be closer to 200 than to 175. The difference between the frequencies (34) in the modal class and the frequencies (15) in the preceding class is 19, and the difference in frequencies between the modal class and the succeeding class is 8; the total of these differences is 27. It is then reasoned that the mode is the value which lies $\frac{19}{27}$ of the distance of the class interval (25) above the lower limit of the modal class 175; this value is 192.6. If we use the following symbols,

L_{mo} = lower limit of modal class
d_1 = difference between the frequencies in the modal class and the preceding class
d_2 = difference between the frequencies in the modal class and the succeeding class
i = size of the modal class interval

then we may say that:

$$\text{mode} = L_{mo} + \frac{d_1}{d_1 + d_2} \times i$$

[4] A frequency distribution is said to be *bimodal* if the frequencies tend to concentrate in and around two nonadjacent classes. Computation of a single mode would be inappropriate for such a distribution.

For the data in Table 9:

$$\text{mode} = 175 + \frac{19}{19 + 8}(25) = 175 + 17.58 = 192.58 \quad \text{or} \quad \mathbf{192.6}$$

Characteristics of the mode. The reader should be familiar with the following characteristics of the mode:

1. The mode is the value which occurs most frequently in a series or a distribution. Like the median, it is a *positional* measure of central tendency. It is affected neither by the value of other items (as is the mean) nor by the position of other items (as is the median). It is simply the value (or "position") which is most commonplace—which occurs most often.
2. Modal values can be estimated from frequency distributions which have open ends or unequal class intervals.
3. Modal values from small samples or samples taken from distributions with more than one point of concentration tend to be unreliable.
4. The mode can be affected more by the arbitrary selection of class intervals and class limits in developing a frequency distribution than either the mean or the median.

RELATIONSHIP OF THE MEAN, MEDIAN, AND MODE

In a perfectly symmetrical frequency distribution, the values of the mean, median, and mode will be exactly the same. If the distribution is tapered (skewed) toward high values, the mean will have the highest value, followed in order by the median and mode. This sequence is

CHART 1. Relative position of the mean, median, and mode in symmetrical and tapered distributions

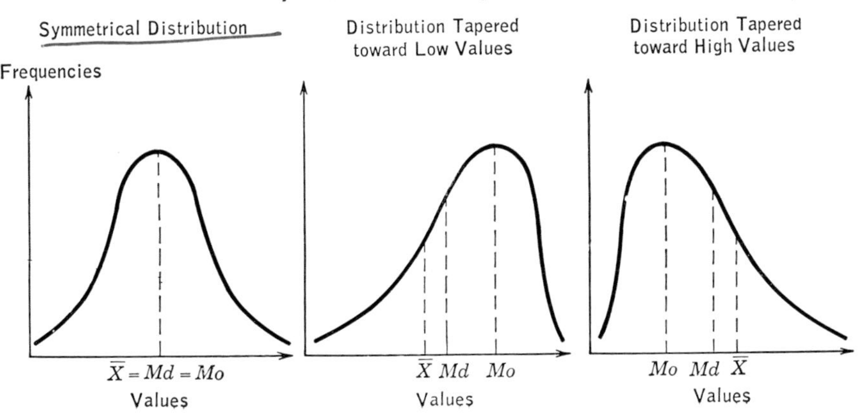

reversed if the distribution is tapered toward low values. The direction of the taper can be determined by knowledge of any two measures of central tendency. These relationships are graphically illustrated in Chart 1. These relationships should be considered whenever a measure of central tendency is being selected to represent a distribution.

Variation

The mean, median, and mode variously describe the points around which data tend to cluster; hence, they are commonly referred to as measures of central tendency. However, computation of these averages alone provides an inadequate description of a mass of data. Also required are measures of variation, that is, dispersion, deviation, spread, or scatter of the data around the measures of central tendency. The need for such measures is easily demonstrated by the simple illustration which follows:

Group I	*Group II*
23	2
24	6
24	15
25	22
25	25
25	25
25	25
26	30
26	40
27	60
250	250

In each of the groups above, the mean, median, and mode are 25. But data in Group I are obviously more concentrated than data in Group II. The interval from the lowest to the highest values in the first group is only 4, in contrast to an interval of 58 between the lowest and highest values in the second group.

Just as there were several measures of central tendency, so there are several measures of variation, each providing certain specific information concerning the dispersion or scatter of values in a series or distribution. Those measures of variation which are of most importance in business administration are described below.

RANGE

The most easily understood measure of variation is the *range* between the lowest and highest value in a group of data. In the above illustration the range for Group I was 4 and for Group II was 58. When data have been classified into a frequency distribution, the range is the interval between the lower limit of the lowest class and the upper limit of the highest class. Although this measure is simple to compute and easy to understand, it is a rather unsatisfactory measure of variation in many instances. This is true because extreme values may be very rare and consequently not representative of the range within which most of the values may be found. Consider the following illustration:

Group I	*Group II*
4	4
8	5
8	6
9	7
9	8
9	10
9	11
10	12
10	13
14	14
—	—
90	90

The mean for each group is 9 and the range for each group is 10. However, the data in Group I are much more concentrated—and hence have less variation—than the data in Group II. This greater concentration in Group I becomes more evident when the extreme values, 4 and 14, are not considered; the range for Group I then becomes 2 as compared with a comparable range of 8 for Group II. Elimination of extreme values often is desirable when computing simple ranges, particularly when dealing with small samples.

INTERQUARTILE RANGE

A common practice is to disregard the lowest quarter and the highest quarter of the data. The range of the remaining values, the range within which the middle 50 per cent of the values are located, is referred to as the *interquartile range*.

The first step in the computation of the interquartile range for a frequency distribution is the computation of *quartiles*, that is, the *points* which divide a distribution into quarters. One measure is required to separate the lower 25 per cent of the values from the upper 75 per cent, and another measure is needed to separate the upper 25 per cent of the values from the lower 75 per cent. These measures are known, respectively, as the first quartile (Q_1) and the third quartile (Q_3). The median, which separates the lower 50 per cent of the values from the upper 50 per cent, is also the second quartile (Q_2).

The first and third quartiles may be computed by using slight modifications of the formula for the median which we recall was

$$Md(\text{or } Q_2) = L_M + \frac{\dfrac{N}{2} - \Sigma f_c}{f_M}(i)$$

The only change required is in the fraction $N/2$, where N is the total number of frequencies in the distribution. Since the purpose of $N/2$ was merely to divide the distribution into two equal groups of values, $N/4$ will separate the lower quarter from the upper three quarters of values, and $3N/4$ will separate the upper quarter from the lower three quarters of values. Hence formulas for Q_1 and Q_3 are as follows:

$$Q_1 = L_1 + \frac{\dfrac{N}{4} - \Sigma f_c}{f_1}(i)$$

$$Q_3 = L_3 + \frac{\dfrac{3N}{4} - \Sigma f_c}{f_3}(i)$$

where values of L and f are associated with the classes which contain the values of Q_1 and Q_3 and where Σf_c is the cumulative sum of frequencies below the specific quartile class.

To compute Q_1 for the distribution in Table 9, page 58, we first compute $N/4$, which is $120/4 = 30$. The largest cumulative sum less than 30 is the sum of the frequencies in the first two classes (24). Consequently, the value of Q_1 (below which lie 30 frequencies) must be in the third class (175 and under 200). We may now substitute values in the formula for Q_1.

$$Q_1 = L_1 + \frac{\dfrac{N}{4} - \Sigma f_c}{f_1}(i) = 175 + \frac{\frac{120}{4} - 24}{34}(25)$$

$$= 175 + \frac{30 - 24}{34}(25) = 175 + \tfrac{6}{34}(25) = 179.41 \quad \text{or} \quad \mathbf{179.4}$$

Similarly Q_3 is computed as follows:

$$Q_3 = L_3 + \frac{\frac{3N}{4} - \Sigma f_c}{f_3}(i) = 225 + \frac{\frac{3(120)}{4} - 84}{11}(25)$$

$$= 225 + \frac{90 - 84}{11}(25) = 225 + \tfrac{6}{11}(25) = 238.64 \quad \text{or} \quad \mathbf{238.6}$$

The *interquartile range* is the range between Q_1 and Q_3, or $(Q_3 - Q_1)$. The interquartile range for the above illustration is 238.6 − 179.4 = 59.2. This interval, which includes 50 per cent of the frequencies, is much smaller than the range for the entire distribution which is 350 − 125 = **225**.

Another measure of variation which statisticians compute from Q_1 and Q_3 is the *quartile deviation*, also referred to as the *semi-interquartile range*. The simple formula for this measure is

$$Q \quad \text{or} \quad QD = \frac{Q_3 - Q_1}{2}$$

For the above exercise

$$QD = \frac{238.6 - 179.4}{2} = \mathbf{29.6}$$

In a symmetrical distribution the range of the median plus and minus QD would include 50 per cent of the items, and the extremities of the range would, of course, be the same values as Q_1 and Q_3. In the above illustration the range of the median $\pm$ QD is 201.9 $\pm$ 29.6, or 172.3 to 231.5.

Occasionally it may be desirable to divide a distribution into more than four segments; for example, a distribution may be divided into deciles. The formula[5] needed for the lower decile is

$$D_1 = L_1 + \frac{\frac{N}{10} - \Sigma f_c}{f_1} \times i$$

The *interdecile range* includes 80 per cent of the values, in contrast to the interquartile range which contains but 50 per cent of the values.

Two weaknesses of all range measures which are dependent on the

[5] Formulas for any positional divider may be obtained simply by changing the divisor of N in the basic formula for the median.

values of position items (quartiles, deciles, etc.) are (1) that the values within the range may not be evenly distributed and (2) that no information is provided about values outside the range. These weaknesses are partially overcome by the measures of average deviation and standard deviation which are discussed in the following sections.

AVERAGE DEVIATION

This measure of variation is computed by taking an average of the deviations of individual items in a series from either the mean or median of the series. Technically, it is preferable to measure deviations of items from their median, since the sum of deviations (signs ignored) around the median is a minimum. However, it is quite common practice to measure deviations from the mean; obviously, the two procedures yield identical results when the values of the mean and median are identical.

The method of computation is simple. Consider a series of five items with values of 2, 4, 6, 6, and 7. Deviations from the median, 6, are computed as follows:

Array of Items	*Deviations (signs ignored)*
2	4
4	2
6	0
6	0
7	1
	—
	7

The average deviation from the median equals $\frac{7}{5}$ or 1.4. Had deviations been measured from the mean, the average deviation would have been $\frac{8}{5}$ or 1.6.

When data have been grouped in a frequency distribution, deviations from the several class mid-points and the median (or mean) are computed and weighted by the respective class frequencies. The sum of these products is divided by the sum of frequencies to obtain the average deviation. This procedure is illustrated in Table 10.

New symbols are AD for average deviation and $|d|$ for deviations, signs ignored. It will be noted that all deviations from the median (201.9) in column 4 are regarded as being positive. The average deviation is 37.6; that is, items in the frequency distribution in Table 10 differ or vary from their median by an average of 37.6.

An important characteristic of the average deviation is that approximately 57.5 per cent of the items in a distribution lie within the range of the $Md \pm AD$. This characteristic holds for distributions which have the major concentration of data near the center of the range; it does not necessarily hold for distributions which have major con-

TABLE 10. Computation from a frequency distribution of the average deviation of hourly earnings of steel foundry workers from their median average hourly earnings

(1) Classes	(2) m	(3) f	(4) $\lvert d \rvert$	(5) $f\lvert d \rvert$
125 and under 150	137.5	9	64.4	579.6
150 and under 175	162.5	15	39.4	591.0
175 and under 200	187.5	34	14.4	489.6
200 and under 225	212.5	26	10.6	275.6
225 and under 250	237.5	11	35.6	391.6
250 and under 275	262.5	9	60.6	545.4
275 and under 300	287.5	8	85.6	684.8
300 and under 325	312.5	5	110.6	553.0
325 and under 350	337.5	3	135.6	406.8
	Totals:	120		4,517.4

$$Md = 201.9$$

$$AD = \frac{\Sigma f|d|}{N} = \frac{4{,}517.4}{120} = 37.64 \text{ or } \mathbf{37.6}$$

centrations at extremes of the range. In Table 10 the range $Md \pm AD$ is 164.3 to 239.5. If frequencies in the second (150 and under 175) and fifth (225 and under 250) classes are evenly distributed, it would appear that approximately 73 frequencies lie within this range; it may be observed that 73 is very nearly 61 per cent of 120, the total frequencies.

The average deviation is more descriptive of the variation among items in a mass than is either the range or the interquartile range. The value of each item in a mass exerts an influence on the value of the average deviation. However, for some purposes in business administration the average deviation is not as satisfactory as the standard deviation, a more complex measure which is described in the following section. The standard deviation is somewhat more stable as a descriptive constant and it is also vastly more important than the average deviation in further statistical computations.

STANDARD DEVIATION

Whereas the average deviation may be computed around either the median or the mean, the standard deviation is always computed around the mean. A further distinction between these two measures of variation is that the standard deviation is computed by squaring the deviations of individual items from their mean. It will be recalled that the sum of squared deviations from the mean is less than the sum of squared deviations measured from any other point in a distribution.

The method of computation consists of the following basic steps:

1. Compute the deviations of items from their mean.
2. Square the deviations computed in step 1.
3. Compute the sum of the squared deviations.
4. Compute the mean of the squared deviations.
5. Compute the square root of the mean of the squared deviations.

Step 5 is required to obtain a measure which is expressed in the same units as the original data. Squared variations of income, production, or sales data would be relatively meaningless.

The above method is illustrated in the following tabulation where the standard deviation is computed around the mean of 5.

Array of Items	*Deviations*	*Deviations Squared*
2	−3	9
4	−1	1
6	+1	1
6	+1	1
7	+2	4
		16

The mean of the squared deviations is $\frac{16}{5}$, or 3.2. The square root of 3.2 is 1.79, or 1.8. It is this figure which is the standard deviation. This computation can be expressed algebraically as follows:

$$s = \sqrt{\frac{\Sigma\, d^2}{N}}$$

where

s = standard deviation[6]

Σd^2 = sum of squared deviations

N = number of items or frequencies in the series

Square roots may be determined (1) by reference to prepared tables of squares and square roots, (2) by use of a slide rule, (3) by use of machine calculators, or (4) by a simple long-hand method. Tables of square roots and a description of the longhand method for computation of square roots are included in the Appendix, pp. 310–328.

Method of computation for grouped data. Computation of the standard deviation for data in a frequency distribution is accomplished most easily by a continuation of the short method for computation of the mean. That is, rather than measure deviation from the actual mean, it is simpler to measure deviation in class intervals from an assumed mean and then subsequently make correction for the difference between the assumed mean and the true mean. This may be done by adding a sixth column to Table 8, page 55, which illustrated the short method for computation of a mean. This sixth column would contain the squared deviations for each class weighted by the respective frequencies in each class. This can be seen in Table 11 where column 6 is merely the product of columns 4 and 5.

Since the sum of the squared deviations from an assumed mean is greater than the sum of squared deviations from the actual mean, it follows that the average of the squared deviations from an assumed mean $[\Sigma f(d')^2/N]$ is too large. This average may be corrected by using the same correction factor $(\Sigma fd'/N)$ as was used to adjust the assumed mean in computing the actual mean. However, two important points must be observed in this adjustment. First, since the deviations have been squared, the correction factor as a whole must also be squared. Second, since $\Sigma f(d')^2/N$ is always too large, the correction factor $(\Sigma fd'/N)^2$ must always be subtracted. After this correction has been made the square root must be computed. The final step is to multiply the square root by the amount of the class interval; this is necessary because deviations were measured in terms of class intervals rather than in original units of data.[7] The method for computing the

[6] Other symbols sometimes used to denote the standard deviation are *SD* and σ. Some writers use s or *SD* to indicate the standard deviation of a sample, and σ to refer to the standard deviation of a population or universe.

[7] Use of an assumed mean and measurement of deviations in terms of class intervals greatly simplifies the arithmetic computations; this was explained in an earlier section in the computation of the mean.

standard deviation as described in this paragraph may be expressed in the following formula:

$$s = i\sqrt{\frac{\Sigma f(d')^2}{N} - \left(\frac{\Sigma fd'}{N}\right)^2}$$

Computation of the standard deviation from a frequency distribution by the short method is illustrated in Table 11.

TABLE 11. Computation from a frequency distribution of the standard deviation of average hourly earnings of steel foundry workers: short method

(1) Classes	(2) m	(3) f	(4) d'	(5) fd'	(6) $f(d')^2$
125 and under 150	137.5	9	−2	−18	36
150 and under 175	162.5	15	−1	−15	15
175 and under 200	187.5	34	0	0	0
200 and under 225	212.5	26	1	26	26
225 and under 250	237.5	11	2	22	44
250 and under 275	262.5	9	3	27	81
275 and under 300	287.5	8	4	32	128
300 and under 325	312.5	5	5	25	125
325 and under 350	337.5	3	6	18	108
	Totals:	120		117	563

$$s = i\sqrt{\frac{\Sigma f(d')^2}{N} - \left(\frac{\Sigma fd'}{N}\right)^2} = 25\sqrt{\frac{563}{120} - \left(\frac{117}{120}\right)^2}$$

$$= 25\sqrt{4.692 - \frac{13{,}689}{14{,}400}} = 25\sqrt{4.692 - .951}$$

$$= 25\sqrt{3.741} = 25(1.933) = 48.325 \quad \text{or} \quad \mathbf{48.3}$$

Interpretation of the standard deviation. The standard deviation is most useful and reliable when computed from data of a symmetrical, bell-shaped distribution.[8] In such distributions, the range of the mean plus and minus the standard deviation ($\bar{X} \pm s$) includes 68.27 per cent of all items in the distribution; the range of $\bar{X} \pm 2s$ includes 95.45 per cent of all items; the range of $\bar{X} \pm 3s$ includes 99.73 per cent of all items. For the distribution in Table 11, the range of $\bar{X} \pm s$ is

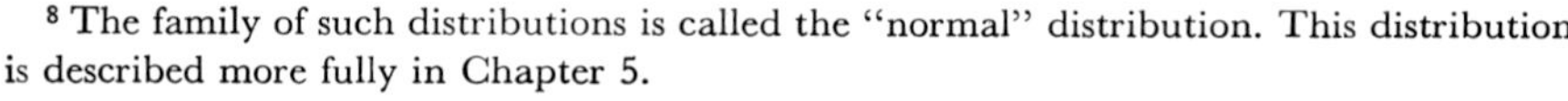

[8] The family of such distributions is called the "normal" distribution. This distribution is described more fully in Chapter 5.

163.6 to 260.2—within this range there are about 81.5 items, or almost 68 per cent of the total items in the distribution; the range of $\bar{X} \pm 2s$ is 115.3 to 308.5—within this range are about 115 items or almost 96 per cent of the total items; in the range $\bar{X} \pm 3s$ all the items are included. Had the distribution been "normal," 68.27 per cent of the items would have been within the range of $\bar{X} \pm s$, 95.45 per cent within the range of $\bar{X} \pm 2s$, and 99.73 per cent within the range of $\bar{X} \pm 3s$. The results above indicate that this distribution is very similar to a normal distribution in this regard.

Relative measures of variation

COEFFICIENT OF VARIATION

The preceding measures of variation have been absolute, that is, they have been expressed in the same units as the original data. If original data were expressed in dollars and cents, the absolute measures of variation would also be expressed in dollars and cents. Although these measures are valuable as tools for describing variation in a mass of data, they are frequently inadequate for making comparisons of variation in several masses. Obviously a comparison of a standard deviation of hourly earnings in one industry and a standard deviation of weekly, monthly, or annual earnings in another industry, would be meaningless. Furthermore, two standard deviations of hourly earnings are wholly comparable only if the means of the two series of earnings data are the same. For example, if the mean hourly earnings in industries A and B were $2.00, and the standard deviations were 0.20 for A and 0.15 for B, then it could be said that the variation of hourly earnings is greatest in industry A. However, it would be impossible to determine which industries had the greatest *relative* variation solely on the basis of the two standard deviations, 0.20 for A and 0.15 for B. If the mean wages in industries A and B were $2.00 and $1.50 respectively, the *relative* variation of hourly wages in the two industries would be the same. However, if the mean wages were $2.00 and $1.00 respectively, the *relative* variation of hourly earnings would be greatest in industry B.

The *coefficient of variation* has been designed to measure *relative* variation. This is accomplished by expressing the standard deviation as a percentage of the mean.

Hence, coefficient of variation $= V = \frac{s}{\bar{X}} \times 100$

This formula may be applied to the above three situations as follows:

1. Industry A: $\bar{X} = \$1.50$; $s = 0.20$
   Industry B: $\bar{X} = \$1.50$; $s = 0.15$

$$V \text{ of A} = \frac{0.20}{1.50} \times 100 = 13.3$$

$$V \text{ of B} = \frac{0.15}{1.50} \times 100 = 10$$

2. Industry A: $\bar{X} = \$2.00$; $s = 0.20$
   Industry B: $\bar{X} = \$1.50$; $s = 0.15$

$$V \text{ of A} = \frac{0.20}{2.00} \times 100 = 10$$

$$V \text{ of B} = \frac{0.15}{1.50} \times 100 = 10$$

3. Industry A: $\bar{X} = \$2.00$; $s = 0.20$
   Industry B: $\bar{X} = \$1.00$; $s = 0.15$

$$V \text{ of A} = \frac{0.20}{2.00} \times 100 = 10$$

$$V \text{ of B} = \frac{0.15}{1.00} \times 100 = 15$$

Relative variation of hourly wages was greatest in industry A in example 1 and in industry B in example 3; the same relative variation occurred in A and B in example 2.

COEFFICIENT OF SKEWNESS

Occasionally it is desirable to compare the degree of taper or *skewness* in two or more series of data. Skewed or tapered distributions were illustrated in Chart 1, page 61. It will be recalled that values of the mean, median, and mode are identical in symmetrical distributions. In tapered or skewed distributions the interval between the mean and the median is approximately one-third of the interval between the mean and the mode. It is this relationship which provides a means of measuring the degree of skewness.

The difficulty of using absolute measures as a basis for comparison was discussed in the preceding section on the coefficient of variation. Fortunately this difficulty may be overcome by computing a *relative* measure. A measure of relative skewness may be computed by dividing the interval between the mean and the mode by the standard deviation. Since the mode is frequently rather indeterminate, the interval of 3(mean − median) is divided by the standard deviation. This computation is symbolized in the following formula:

$$\text{Skewness} = \text{Sk} = \frac{3(\bar{X} - Md)}{s}$$

Values of $\bar{X}$, Md, and s for the illustrative frequency distribution in Table 11, page 70, were as follows:

$$\bar{X} = 211.9, \qquad Md = 201.9, \qquad s = 48.3$$

The degree of skewness may be computed by substituting these values in the above formula.

$$\text{Sk} = \frac{3(211.9 - 201.9)}{48.3} = \frac{+30.0}{48.3} = +0.62$$

Distributions which are tapered toward high values, such as our illustrative distribution, are said to be *positively* skewed. Conversely, distributions which are tapered toward low values are said to be *negatively* skewed. It may be noted that the value of the median (and mode) would be greater than the value of the mean in negatively skewed distributions; consequently a minus sign would prefix the computed measure of skewness.

The coefficient of skewness is also useful in determining whether or not it is reasonable to describe a distribution by its mean and standard deviation. It will be recalled that these two measures are most useful as descriptions of symmetrical, bell-shaped distributions. The coefficient of skewness provides a means of determining when a distribution is not "normal." Whenever the value of this coefficient falls outside the range of -3 to $+3$, the distribution is considered to be badly skewed and it is not reasonable to use the mean and standard deviation to describe it. In the distribution of Table 11, Sk $= +0.62$ indicating that the distribution is positively skewed, but not enough to make it unreasonable to describe it by its mean and standard deviation.

Standards

Modern-day management relies heavily upon the use of standards in controlling complex business activities. An alert management establishes standards of performance for each responsible individual in the organization and checks the actual performance against these standards. This technique is known as "management by exception"; when exceptions to the standards occur, management is alerted to take immediate corrective action.

In the broad sense, a firm's budget is a standard. The budget, of course, is based upon many other standards. Among these standards are standards for sales performance, production administration, and almost all activities of personnel. Standard costs are determined for material, labor, and overhead expenses.

Standards may be of several types. Some are *ideal* standards based upon optimum operating conditions. *Normal* standards are based upon supposedly normal operating conditions. Some standards are based on *expected actual* conditions for the approaching operating period. *Basic* standards reflect conditions at the time the standards are set. Basic standards serve as a fixed base from which to measure future changes in factors; these standards are, in effect, a form of index number, a topic which is treated in Chapter 6.

Many standards are averages which have been modified by judgment based on a knowledge of operations and business conditions. Time studies, which are used in production planning and wage determination, consist in part of recording repeated observations of the amount of time required for each operation. An average of these observations is then computed to serve as the "standard" time. This average may be the mean; it also may be the median or mode, depending upon the circumstances of the particular case. Similarly, the standard of performance for salesmen may be the mean, median, or modal sales for salesmen during the preceding period; or the standard may be any one of these measures adjusted for anticipated changes in business conditions or anticipated benefits from increased advertising or improved sales training. Performance of typists and clerks may be measured against a standard number of letters or documents to be prepared or processed.

Business management requires a thorough understanding of the nature and characteristics of basic averages in order to intelligently construct and interpret the multitude of standards which may be employed in an effort to attain maximum efficiency, productivity, and profits.

The six measures of variation or scatter described briefly in this chapter are also important in determining and utilizing standards. The first four of these measures—(1) range, (2) interquartile range, (3) average deviation, and (4) standard deviation—are *absolute* in nature, *i.e.*, they are expressed in the same units as the original data. The method of computation is increasingly difficult for each successive measure. However, for many purposes the increased complexity of computation is more than offset by the improved descriptive attributes possessed by these measures. The standard deviation, particularly, has mathematical properties which are important in advanced statistical analysis. These measures of variation are useful in setting up ranges of allowable variation around any averages which have been set as standards. For example, it cannot be assumed that all clerks type at the same speed nor with the same degree of accuracy. Some variation is normal, only excessive variation need be a matter for concern. Similarly, variation from any standard is of concern only when it is excessive.

Two other measures of *relative* variation—(1) coefficient of variation, and (2) coefficient of skewness—were also computed. These measures are expressed in *pure* numbers which have lost the identity of the units or terms in which the original data were expressed. These measures provide a means of comparing the degree of variation in two or more distributions where comparisons based on absolute measures are not possible because (1) the series to be compared are expressed in different units, or (2) the series have mean values which are substantially different. The coefficient of skewness is also useful in determining whether or not it is reasonable to describe a distribution with its mean and standard deviation.

Questions and Exercises

1. Define the following terms:
- (a) Array
- (b) Frequency distribution

(c) Class limits
(d) Class intervals
(e) Class mid-point
(f) Class frequencies
(g) Discrete data
(h) Open-end classes

2. For what purposes are frequency distributions constructed?

3. What considerations are involved in the construction of a frequency distribution?

4. Explain how measures of central tendency and measures of variation complement each other in describing a mass of data.

5. (a) For each of the following frequency distributions, compute the mean, median, mode, quartiles, average deviation, standard deviation, coefficient of variation, and coefficient of skewness.

(1)

Class Intervals	*Frequencies*
35 and under 45	4
45 and under 55	7
55 and under 65	10
65 and under 75	5
75 and under 85	4

(2)

Class Intervals	*Frequencies*
10 and under 30	4
30 and under 50	8
50 and under 70	10
70 and under 90	8
90 and under 110	6
110 and under 130	4

(3)

Class Intervals	*Frequencies*
25 to 75	4
100 to 150	7
175 to 225	9
250 to 300	6
325 to 375	4

(b) What are the true limits of the modal class in distribution 3?

6. (a) Compute the mean, median, and mode for each of the three frequency distributions in the following table:

Percentage distribution of production workers in pulp, paper, and paperboard mills by average (straight-time hourly earnings,* selected regions, April 1952)

Average hourly earnings*	United States	South Region	Pacific Region
95 and under 105	1.1	0.7	. . .
105 and under 115	3.2	4.9	. . .
115 and under 125	6.9	6.9	. . .
125 and under 135	18.3	27.9	0.4
135 and under 145	19.2	13.2	1.6
145 and under 155	12.9	9.6	0.3
155 and under 165	8.6	7.0	0.6
165 and under 175	10.0	7.0	36.4
175 and under 185	6.5	3.3	18.9
185 and under 195	4.0	3.2	12.7
195 and under 205	2.1	2.3	6.2
205 and under 215	4.4	9.9	14.1
215 and under 225	1.1	1.8	3.4
225 and under 235	0.8	0.9	2.5
235 and under 245	0.9	0.3	1.5
245 and under 255	. . .	1.1	1.4
Total:	100.0	100.0	100.0

* Excludes premium pay for overtime and night work.
Source: Adapted from *Monthly Labor Review*, December 1952, p. 626.

(b) What conclusions are suggested by the results of your computations in (a)?
(c) What are some of the factors which limit the conclusions which may be drawn from the above data?
(d) Compute the range, interquartile range, average deviation, standard deviation, coefficient of variation and coefficient of skewness for each of the three frequency distributions.
(e) What conclusions are suggested by the results of your computations for these distributions (i.e., which areas pay the highest wages, have the least variability in wages, etc.)?
(f) What are some of the factors which limit the conclusions which may be drawn from the above data?

7. State the distinguishing characteristics of the (1) mean, (2) median, and (3) mode.

8. Discuss the relationship of the mean, median, and mode. Illustrate your answer by drawing appropriate charts.

9. State the distinguishing characteristics of the range, interquartile range, average deviation, standard deviation, coefficient of variation, and coefficient of skewness. Indicate the uses and interpretations appropriate to each.

5 *Probability and statistical inference*

Most of the time when a researcher is faced with a question concerning some population, he has a choice. He can either make a complete survey of the population or settle for an estimate based on a sample. If he chooses to survey the entire population, there is no need for any generalization. However, if he surveys only a part of the population (uses a sample), he *infers* that the statistics (means, proportions, etc.) which describe the sample also describe the entire population. He is then faced with the question as to how well these sample statistics describe the population.

Statistical inferences are, in reality, inductive arguments based on probability considerations. Following a brief discussion of deductive and inductive reasoning in the next section, an introduction to elementary probability is presented as a basis for understanding the concept of a sampling distribution—a frequency distribution reflecting the expected (or probable) distribution of values from repeated random samples. The concept of sampling distributions is basic to the development of the concepts and techniques of statistical inference in the second half of the chapter.

A glossary of technical terms and symbols introduced in this chapter is presented on pages 109–111 as an aid to the reader's comprehension of the materials.

Deductive and inductive reasoning

The nature of deductive reasoning is often explained with an example such as:

All U. S. Citizens are men.
All New Yorkers are U. S. Citizens.
Therefore all New Yorkers are men.

The conclusion is a *necessary* consequence of the premises in such a *deductive* argument. In the process of arriving at a *deductive* conclusion we do not use any information that is not contained in the premises. In areas such as chemistry, biology, etc., these premises are called *laws* or *known behavior characteristics*. For instance,

All sodium salts are water-soluble substances.
All soaps are sodium salts.
Therefore all soaps are water-soluble substances.

In those areas which deal with the actions and reactions of humans, there are few "laws" and the form of reasoning in seeking truth must change. The argument involves a presentation of evidence as the basis of an induction or generalization. To restate the initial syllogism:

We know over 300 New Yorkers.
All New Yorkers whom we know are men.
Therefore all New Yorkers are men.

This kind of reasoning is typical of what is called an *inductive* argument. This is the kind of generalization involved when we make a gallon of soup, sip a little from a spoon and proclaim the whole gallon to be excellent soup. Similar arguments are being made when the voting intentions of a small part of the eligible voters are determined and an election predicted, or a few items produced on an assembly line are tested and all items produced are declared satisfactory.

To contrast deductive and inductive reasoning, the former entails constructing an argument that is of the proper form, that is, one that is internally valid; *inductive* arguments cannot be checked for internal validity because they involve a generalization which is *not* a *necessary* consequence of the premises. One can only ask if the inductive argument is "reasonable." If only one sip of soup were used as a test of the excellence of all batches of soup ever made by one person, the "reasonableness" of the resulting generalization would be extremely doubtful. Conversely, if the tester had tested the soup of the soup maker at least 100 times, the resulting generalization would be more willingly accepted. (Of course, it must be assumed that our tester is a good judge of soup.)

Inductive generalizations are forced upon us every day; decisions are often based on partial information. Probability and statistics deal with the theories, methods, and criteria which make it possible to evaluate the "reasonableness" of inductive generalizations. The sections below are intended to develop an insight into these areas.

Probability

If a well-balanced coin were tossed once, a head would be just as likely to result as a tail. However, this does not mean that if the coin were tossed ten times it would come up heads five times and tails five times. Rather, it means that if the coin were tossed a large number of times the result *in the long run* would be close to an even split between heads and tails. This relative frequency of an outcome over the long run is defined as the *probability* of that outcome. Actually, the population in which this probability would be exactly realized consists of an indefinite repetition of coin tosses.

When the rules of the game are properly specified, it is possible to predict the probability of a given outcome. For instance, let us assume we are going to play a game with a pair of standard dice and the outcome of the game is dependent on the total number of spots which show up on the two dice at the end of each roll. Assuming that the roll of the dice is not controlled, what is the probability of a particular outcome? First, what are the possible outcomes? A die has six faces differentiated by one to six spots each. With two dice, then, the smallest number of total spots is two (one on each die), the largest number of spots is 12 (six on each die), and the remaining possibilities are the sums of all possible pairs of results shown in Table 12

If the die is evenly weighted and the roll is uncontrolled, the probability of any particular face coming up is equal to the probability of any other face coming up. Since there are six faces, the probability for each face is one-sixth. The probability that some one of the six faces will come up on a particular roll (the probability of a result) is one; i.e., a certainty. However, the occurrence of one of them precludes the possibility of any other; these six results are mutually exclusive. This illustrates a rule in probability mathematics which states that *the probability of the occurrence of any one of a group of mutually exclusive events is the sum of their individual probabilities.*

We have found that the probability of any particular result (say one) on the roll of one die is one-sixth ($\frac{1}{6}$). What then is the probability

TABLE 12. Possible pairs of results when rolling two dice

Given number of spots on die No. 1	Possible number of spots on die No. 2 for given result on die No. 1					
1	1	2	3	4	5	6
2	1	2	3	4	5	6
3	1	2	3	4	5	6
4	1	2	3	4	5	6
5	1	2	3	4	5	6
6	1	2	3	4	5	6

that two dice when rolled will come up with a total of two spots (one on each die)? There is one chance in six of getting a one on the first die and also one chance in six of getting a one on the second die. However, any of the six faces is equally likely as a result on die No. 2 on the same roll. Since each die has six faces, there are 36 (6×6) possible combinations, only one of which has a total of two spots. Therefore, the probability of pairing one spot on die No. 1 with one spot on die No. 2 is one in thirty-six, that is, $\frac{1}{6} \times \frac{1}{6} = \frac{1}{36}$. The above illustrates a rule of probability which states that *if two events are independent, the probability that both will occur is the product of their individual probabilities.*

The probabilities of a pair of two's as the result on our two dice would be ascertained in exactly the same way. But what about four spots as a result? What is its probability? It could occur in three ways:

Die No. 1	*Die No. 2*	*Total on two dice*	*Probability of occurrence*
2	2	4	1/36
1	3	4	1/36
3	1	4	1/36

By reasoning analagous to that for paired values it can be demonstrated that the probability of each of the three possibilities is $\frac{1}{36}$. The three combinations are mutually exclusive, so their total probability will be the sum of their individual probabilities. Therefore the probability of *any* one of them (of a total equal to four) is $\frac{3}{36}$ or $\frac{1}{12}$.

> *Note:* The correctness of the probabilities obtained can be verified by a reference to Table 12. The student should work out for himself the probability of rolling a six, a seven, and an eight. Also, what is the probability that the total on any roll will be no greater than five? no less than five?

Sampling distributions

When the subject of sampling was introduced earlier, major attention was directed to random methods of selecting items for samples. This emphasis was given to random sampling because two advantages result from the use of random samples: (1) the *sampling distribution* of a sample statistic can usually be foretold and (2) the probability that statements based on sample indications are true for the population can be determined.

When many random samples *of the same size* are taken independently from a given population, arithmetic means and other statistics computed from data in each sample will themselves form frequency distributions. Such frequency distributions are called the *sampling distributions* of the sample statistics. For example, random selection is assumed to operate in the rolls of dice described above. Table 13 is the sampling distribution of the total spots on two standard dice resulting from such rolls. The first column lists all possible totals on two dice and the second column indicates the relative frequency of occurrence of each of these results in an indefinite repetition of the rolls.

There are infinitely many sampling distributions, each of which differs from the others in one or more respects such as central tendency, symmetry, and dispersion. One important difference is related

TABLE 13. Sampling distribution of total spots on two standard dice

Total on two dice	Frequency of expected occurrence
2	1/36
3	2/36
4	3/36
5	4/36
6	5/36
7	6/36
8	5/36
9	4/36
10	3/36
11	2/36
12	1/36

to the continuity of the distribution.[1] The distribution in Table 13 is discrete, that is, the number of possible values is limited. This is clearly indicated in Chart 2 where the height of each bar indicates the relative frequency of occurrence of that value in the distribution. Note that the heights of the bars sum to a total of one (1).

CHART 2. Distribution of totals when rolling two dice

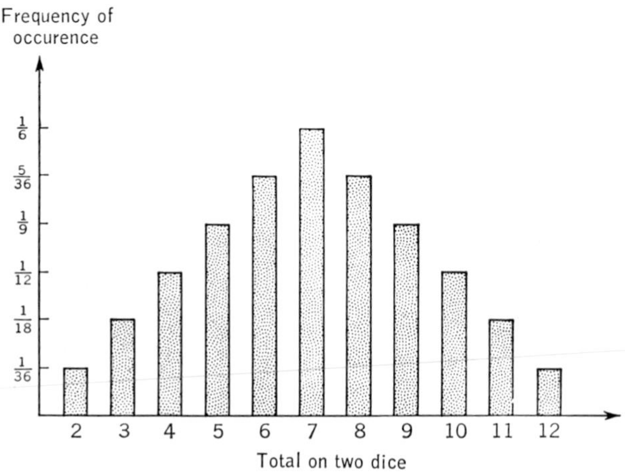

Source: Table 13.

[1] The difference between discrete and continuous distributions was explained in Chapter 4, page 48.

THE NORMAL DISTRIBUTION

One type, or family, of continuous sampling distribution which is particularly useful is called the *normal probability distribution*, or more briefly, the normal distribution. Note, though, that *there is no one normal distribution*; rather, the "normal distribution" is a *type* or *family* of distributions which have certain characteristics in common.

Chart 3 indicates that normal distributions are bell-shaped; they

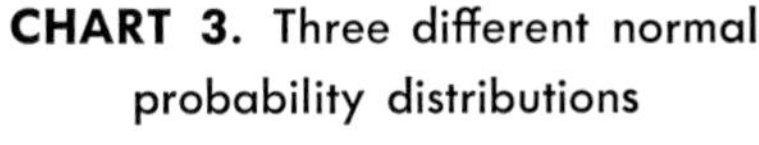

CHART 3. Three different normal probability distributions

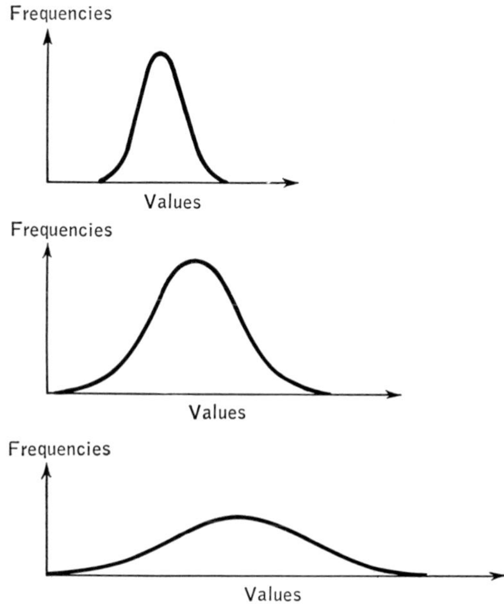

are symmetrical and have a single peak in the center of the distribution. They vary, however, in the location of the average (center of the distribution) and in the extent of variability. For instance, one normal distribution may have a mean of \$300 and a standard deviation of \$20; another may have a mean of \$100 and a standard deviation of \$2. Many phenomena seem to follow a pattern of variation such that their respective populations may be described by a normal distribution. For instance, the height of persons, the thickness of iron bars, the tensile strength of steel cables, the intelligence test scores of persons, and many other phenomena have been found to follow one of the normal probability distributions. More briefly, we say that all of these phenomena have been demonstrated to be *normally distributed.*

When working with a continuous sampling distribution, the probability of the occurrence of any particular value in the distribution (which would be represented by a point on the horizontal axis) is indicated by the height of the curve at that point as measured along the vertical axis.[2] This again would be a *relative* value. The probability of occurrence of any range of values (represented by a range along the horizontal axis) would be indicated by the relative proportion of the total area under the curve which is located directly above that range. The total area under the curve equals one (1) as in any continuous probability distribution.

To determine a desired probability we might laboriously calculate the appropriate area under the probability distribution—in this instance, a normal probability distribution. A table of areas for normal probability distributions enables one to avoid these calculations. Since all normal probability distributions belong to the same family of distributions and have certain properties in common, one table of areas can be used for any normal distribution. Such a table is reproduced as Table II in Appendix B together with directions for its use. Table II gives the area between the mean and any other specified value for all normal distributions. Normal distributions are symmetrical, that is, the shape of the distribution on either side of the peak is identical. Therefore, Table II gives only the areas to the right of the mean because the areas to the left of the mean correspond to those to the right.

The following generalizations apply to any normal probability distribution:

1. The area under the normal distribution between the mean ± 1 standard deviation is 0.6827 out of a total area of 1.
2. The area under the normal distribution between the mean ± 2 standard deviations is 0.9545 out of a total area of 1.
3. The area under the normal distribution between the mean ± 3 standard deviations is 0.9973 out of a total area of 1.

These areas are illustrated in Chart 4 on page 87. One cannot memorize the entire table of areas under the normal probability distri-

[2] A discussion of the computation and use of the ordinates (heights) of the normal distribution can be found in F. E. Croxton and D. J. Cowden, *Applied General Statistics*, Second Edition, Prentice-Hall, Inc., Englewood Cliffs, N. J., 1955, pages 594 ff.

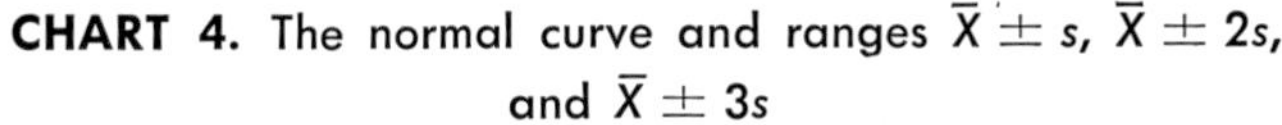

CHART 4. The normal curve and ranges $\bar{X} \pm s$, $\bar{X} \pm 2s$, and $\bar{X} \pm 3s$

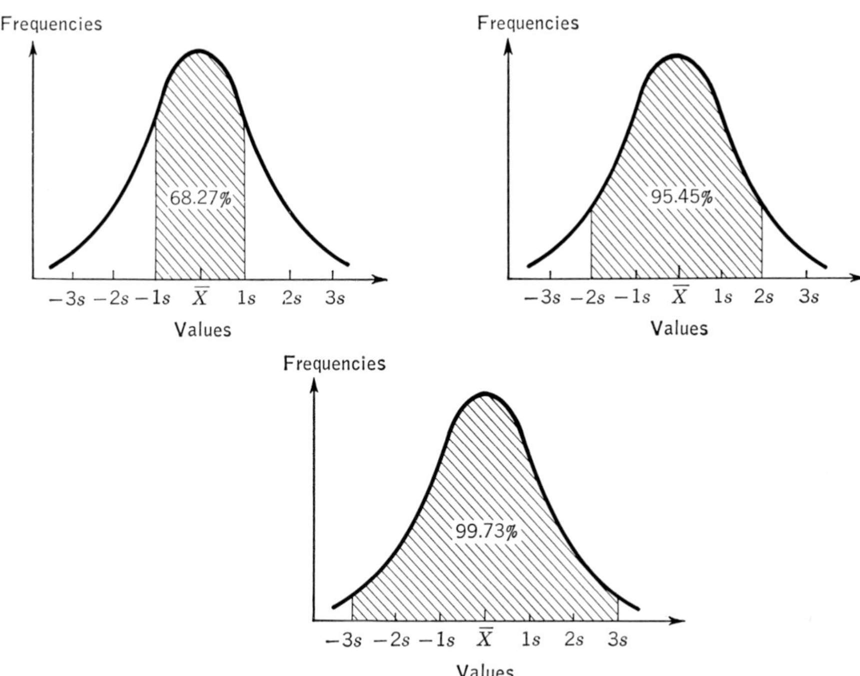

bution, but the above three relationships are often adequate for quick analysis.

The normal probability distribution is particularly important as it is often used in developing estimates and in making decisions based upon statistical considerations. These uses of the normal distribution are explained in later sections of this chapter.

THE BINOMIAL DISTRIBUTION

It is possible to express other probability distributions in generalized forms. One such relation is that involved where the event in question is dichotomous, that is, has only two possible outcomes. Examples would include coin flipping, asking yes–no type questions, polling voters as to whether they intend to vote Democratic or Republican in a presidential election, and sampling for proportion defective in statistical quality control.

The binomial expansion. If two unbiased coins are tossed simultaneously, there are four possible outcomes:

Outcome No.	*Coin A*	*Coin B*	*Probability*
1	Head (H)	Head (H)	1/4
2	Head (H)	Tail (T)	1/4
3	Tail (T)	Head (H)	1/4
4	Tail (T)	Tail (T)	1/4

Since the coins are unbiased, the probability of either face coming up is $\frac{1}{2}$. Because the result on one coin is independent of the result on the other coin, the probability of any combination (with order specified) is $\frac{1}{2} \times \frac{1}{2} = \frac{1}{4}$. If we designate p as the probability of a head, then $p = \frac{1}{2}$. Likewise, if we designate q as the probability of a tail, then $q = \frac{1}{2}$. Each result has a probability of $\frac{1}{4}$ (pp, pq, qp, qq). The second and third outcomes each represents a combination of one head (H) and one tail (T). The probability of such a mixed result (order ignored) is the sum of the individual probabilities; $\frac{1}{4} + \frac{1}{4} = \frac{1}{2}$, or $2pq$.

The generalization of this process of estimating the probabilities of various combinations of independent dichotomous events with known probabilities is accomplished through the *binomial expansion.* The probabilities of the various combinations are given by the successive terms of the expansion. For the simple case of two coins, we have:

$$(p + q)^2 = p^2 + 2pq + q^2$$

Where p^2 is the probability of two heads (or *successes* to use the more general term), $2pq$ is the probability of a mixed result, and q^2 is the probability of two *failures*. For our coin example, the probabilities of the several outcomes are found to be:

$$(\tfrac{1}{2} + \tfrac{1}{2})^2 = \tfrac{1}{4} + \tfrac{1}{2} + \tfrac{1}{4}$$

This same technique can be used with any number of coins. For instance, three coins have the following possible results:

Possible outcome					*Probability*
Number	*Outcome*	*Coin A*	*Coin B*	*Coin C*	*of the outcome*
1	(3 H)	H	H	H	1/8
2	(2 H, 1 T)	H	H	T	1/8
3	(2 H, 1 T)	H	T	H	1/8
4	(2 H, 1 T)	T	H	H	1/8
5	(1 H, 2 T)	H	T	T	1/8
6	(1 H, 2 T)	T	T	H	1/8
7	(1 H, 2 T)	T	H	T	1/8
8	(3 T)	T	T	T	1/8

The probabilities of the several combinations can be seen to be:

Outcome	*Probability*
3 H	1/8
2 H, 1 T	3/8
2 T, 1 H	3/8
3 T	1/8

By the binomial expansion:

$$(p + q)^3 = p^3 + 3p^2q + 3pq^2 + q^3$$

With $p = q = \frac{1}{2}$,

$$(\tfrac{1}{2} + \tfrac{1}{2})^3 = \tfrac{1}{8} + \tfrac{3}{8} + \tfrac{3}{8} + \tfrac{1}{8}$$

These are the probabilities given in the direct count.[3]

If we wish to know the *probable frequencies* of the various outcomes rather than their probabilities, we can use the expression:

$$N(p + q)^n$$

where N represents the number of trials and n the number of inde-

[3] When n becomes larger, it becomes difficult to expand the binomial directly and other methods are employed. When an unbiased coin is flipped n times (one coin three times is equivalent to three coins one time), the total number of different sequences is 2^n and each is considered equally likely. The number of ways of combining n things of which r are heads and $n - r$ are tails (without regard to order) is

$$C_r^n = \frac{n!}{r!(n-r)!}$$

the probability of exactly r heads in n tosses becomes

$$\left(\frac{n!}{r!(n-r)!}\right) \div 2^n$$

The symbols have the following meanings:

$n! =$ factorial $n = n(n-1)(n-2)\ldots(n-n+2)(1)$; the product of the integers from 1 through n.

$r! =$ factorial $r = r(r-1)(r-2)\ldots(r-r+2)(1)$; the product of the integers from 1 through r.

Using this approach, the total number of outcomes $= 2^n = 2^3 = 8$, the number of ways of obtaining 2 heads (r heads) is

$$C_2^3 = \frac{3!}{2!(3-2)!} = \frac{3 \cdot 2 \cdot 1}{2 \cdot 1 \cdot 1} = 3$$

and the probability of 2 heads in three flips $= (C_2^3/2^n) = \frac{3}{8}$. The same result is also possible using the formula below:

$$\text{Probability} = C_r^n p^r q^{n-r} = \frac{n!}{r!(n-r)!} p^r q^{n-r}$$

$$= \frac{3!}{2!(3-2)!}\left(\frac{1}{2}\right)^2\left(\frac{1}{2}\right)^1 = 3\left(\frac{1}{2}\right)^3 = \frac{3}{8}$$

pendent events in each trial. Thus, if two coins are flipped 1,000 times, the probable frequencies are found to be:

$$1000(p + q)^2 = 1000p^2 + 1000(2pq) + 1000q^2$$

Since $p = q = \frac{1}{2}$ this gives:

$$1000(\tfrac{1}{4}) + 1000(\tfrac{1}{2}) + 1000(\tfrac{1}{4}) = 250 + 500 + 250$$

which indicates the probable frequency of 2 heads (2 successes), 1 head (1 success), and no heads (no successes) or, alternatively, the probable frequency of no tails, 1 tail, and 2 tails.

The binomial distribution. The results we might expect from experiments similar to those above are part of the family or type of distributions called binomial distributions. The binomial distribution has certain characteristics:

1. It is a discrete distribution; there are only two results possible.
2. Its form depends on the values of P and n (Q is equal to $1 - P$ and is therefore determined by P), where P is the probability of a *success* and n is the number of independent events in each trial.
3. The distribution will be symmetrical if P is equal to Q and asymetrical if P and Q are unequal. However, in the latter case, as n increases, the degree of skewness decreases sharply. When P and Q are approximately equal and n is very large, the discrete nature of the distribution is less apparent and it becomes practically indistinguishable from the normal curve. In fact, the normal distribution is utilized in analyzing sample results from binomial populations in such cases. When P or Q approaches zero (is very small) and n is very large, the resulting smoothed representation of the binomial is essentially indistinguishable from the Poisson distribution. (The Poisson is discussed in the next section of this chapter.)
4. The mean of a binomial distribution is nP (the average number of successes). The standard deviation of a binomial distribution measured around nP in number of occurrences is:

$$\sigma_{np} = \sqrt{nPQ}$$

5. The binomial can also be used in working with the proportion of successes; its mean is then P (the average proportion of suc-

cesses). The standard deviation measured around P in proportion of occurrences is:

$$\sigma_p = \sqrt{PQ/n} = \sqrt{P(1 - P)/n}$$

The binomial probability distribution is widely used in interpreting sample results stated in terms of proportions. For example, in acceptance sampling the decision to accept or reject a lot of materials, a tray of accounts, or batch of letters, etc., is based upon the proportion defective; consumer preference for a brand or style of a product is estimated as a proportion of the total population.

It would be a laborious process to compute all the terms of the binomial when n is large and it is fortunate that with n equal to 30 or more and P between 0.20 and 0.80, satisfactory approximations can be made with the table of areas under the normal curve. In those cases where P is less than 0.10 or larger than 0.90 with n equal to 30 or more, the binomial probabilities are satisfactorily approximated by Poisson probabilities. Thus, only when n is less than 30 or P is between 0.10 and 0.20 or between 0.80 and 0.90 is it necessary to use the binomial itself. Once again, tables are available which make it easy to use this probability distribution in statistical analysis.[4]

THE POISSON DISTRIBUTION

Another probability distribution which has been found applicable to a number of sampling problems is the Poisson probability distribution. This type of distribution applies when there is a large number of independent events for each of which there is only a small probability that a particular outcome will result. It is widely used in quality control work where the proportion defective in any lot tested is expected to be very small.

The Poisson distribution has the interesting characteristic that its standard deviation is equal to the square root of its mean. Table 14 reveals the skewed nature of this distribution; note that the smaller the mean, the greater the degree of skewness. Tables are available where the Poisson probabilities have already been computed for a large number of mean values.[5]

[4] See for instance Tables I and II, pp. 247–254 in Burington, R. S. and D. C. May, *Handbook of Probability and Statistics with Tables*, Handbook Publishers, 1953.

[5] Burington and May, *op. cit.*, Tables VII and VIII, pp. 259–266.

TABLE 14. Selected Poisson probability distributions

Number of occurrences	Probability of occurrence when: Mean = 0.1	Mean = 1.0	Mean = 5.0
0	0.9048	0.3679	0.0067
1	.0905	.3679	.0337
2	.0045	.1839	.0842
3	.0002	.0613	.1404
4	.0000	.0153	.1755
5	.0000	.0031	.1755
6	....	.0005	.1462
7	....	.0001	.1044
8	....	.0000	.0653
9	....	....	.0363
10	....	....	.0181
11	....	....	.0082
12	....	....	.0034
13	....	....	.0013
14	....	....	.0005
15	....	....	.0002

THE SAMPLING DISTRIBUTION OF THE ARITHMETIC MEAN

When random selection is used in selecting a very large number of samples of a given size, n, and a mean, $\bar{X}$, is computed for each of these random samples, the distribution of these means will conform to a pattern described by the normal distribution. Regardless of the form of the population, whether normal or otherwise, it can be assumed that the mean of the distribution of sample means ($\bar{\bar{X}}$) equals the mean of the population ($\bar{X}_P$). It is also safe to assume that the distribution of averages of samples from an unknown population will be close to normal. Even if the sample size is as small as $n = 4$ and the universe is far from normal, the distribution of the averages of samples will be very close to normal.

The dispersion of the frequency distribution of sample means depends upon the dispersion of the individual items in the population and also on the sample size, n. The larger the size of the sample, the less the dispersion of the sample means. The standard deviation of the frequency distribution of sample means ($\sigma_{\bar{X}}$), which is called the *standard error of the mean* in order to distinguish it from other standard deviations, will be equal to the standard deviation of the population (σ) divided by the square root of the sample size;

$$\sigma_{\overline{X}} = \frac{\sigma}{\sqrt{n}}$$

The variation in a distribution of sample means is reduced directly as the square root of the sample size is increased. To reduce variability one-half the sample must be four (4) times as great as before.

In actual practice, the standard deviation, mean, and other population statistics are unknown. The purpose of sampling is to estimate these and other characteristics of the population. Usually it is practical neither to draw a great many samples nor to draw samples whose size approximates that of the population. However, we do wish to know how closely a sample mean is likely to approximate the population mean. Fortunately, the standard error of the mean can be estimated by substituting the standard deviation of *one* sample (s) for the standard deviation of the population (σ) in the above formula. When this is done, $n - 1$ should be substituted for n to correct for the *degree of freedom lost* by using the sample estimate.[6] Thus,

$$\sigma_{\overline{X}} = \frac{s}{\sqrt{n-1}}$$

Theoretically, the correction of sample size should always be made; however, it has no significant influence on the results if n is over 30.

THE SAMPLING DISTRIBUTION OF SAMPLE PROPORTIONS

This can be a case of dichotomy—yes or no, Republican or Democrat, acceptable or defective—and would therefore be interpreted using the binomial distribution. Note that even three or more classes can be summarized into two classes for purposes of analysis as "yes" and "not yes." However, as was indicated when discussing the binomial distribution (page 91), the sample proportion is most often

[6] In every statistical problem in which *degrees of freedom* are involved it is necessary to determine the number of freely-determined variables. This may be done by reducing the total number of variables by the number of independent restrictions upon them. Thus, if you are told to write down three numbers with no restrictions, you have *complete* freedom of choice as to what numbers to use. If you are told to write down three numbers whose sum is 17, you are no longer completely free to choose *any* three numbers. Two numbers can be chosen freely, but the restriction on the sum then determines the third number; one degree of freedom has been lost. In the problem above, we gave up one degree of freedom in estimating the standard deviation (s) by computing it around the sample mean. Note that s is in reality $\sqrt{\Sigma (X - \overline{X})^2/n}$.

interpreted using either the normal distribution or the Poisson distribution. Only when sample size is less than 30 is it practical to use the binomial. In other cases the two limiting distributions are satisfactory. The standard error of a proportion (the measure of sampling variability for a proportion) is computed as $\sigma_p = \sqrt{PQ/n}$ in applying either the binomial or the normal distribution. For the Poisson, the standard error is equal to the square root of nP.

Statistical inference

The processes by which conclusions concerning a population are drawn from sample results is called *inference*. There are two basic classes of inference: (1) estimates of population values (parameters) on the basis of sample values (sample statistics) and (2) testing hypotheses, i.e., testing the truthfulness of statements about a population on the basis of sample values.

In estimation problems, the interest centers on making estimates of population values (parameters) on the basis of samples values (sample statistics). Thus, if we have a random sample of 1,000 grades of statistics students, this information can be used to estimate the mean grade for all possible statistics students. *Statistical inference* would indicate the sampling variability of that estimate, i.e., how close it is likely to be to the population mean.

In testing statistical hypotheses, the interest centers either on determining whether the sample could have come from a population with stated characteristics, or on evaluating two samples to determine if they could have come from the same population. For example, perhaps it has been asserted that the mean grade of statistics students is 75. Should this be accepted as the true population value if the mean grade of a random sample of statistics students is 70? The second type of hypothesis testing would arise if we had two samples of statistics students drawn from two different universities and the average grades in the two samples were different. Even though the average grades are different, can we conclude that there is a real difference in the average grades of statistics students at the two schools? We know that random samples drawn from the same population will usually show somewhat different results. If a statistical hypothesis is properly formulated, the statistical significance of observed differences such as those illustrated above can be determined.

STATISTICAL ESTIMATION

This is a problem of basing estimates of population values (parameters) on data from a single sample with specification of the range of error attributable to random sampling variability (random error of sampling). Estimates are made of an unknown population parameter on the basis of one or more known sample statistics.

Estimating means—large random samples. The standard error of the mean is the standard deviation of a distribution of random sample averages. Since the distribution of means tends to be closer and closer to normal as sample size gets larger, even though the population itself is not normal, the standard error of the mean may be interpreted using the characteristics of the normal curve in developing interval estimates of means.

The proportion of all possible sample means lying within given intervals of the standard error of the mean ($\sigma_{\bar{X}}$) around the true population mean, $\bar{X}_p$, can be determined. This is possible because the sampling distribution is known to be normal. The percentage of the total area included within a given interval around its mean represents the percentage of all possible sample means falling within that stated interval around the true mean of the universe. From these proportions of area under the normal curve we can determine the probability that our *one* actual sample mean lies within any stated interval (in standard error of the mean units) measured from the true mean of the population. For example, 68.27 per cent of all sample means of random samples of a given size lie within one standard error of the mean from the true mean of the universe ($\bar{X}_p \pm \sigma_{\bar{X}}$). The probability that our *one* sample mean lies within that interval is therefore 0.6827. Similarly, there is a 0.9545 probability that our *one* sample mean lies in the interval $\bar{X}_p \pm 2\sigma_{\bar{X}}$.

If it is true that the *one* sample mean has a 0.9545 probability of being within two standard errors of the population mean, then it is also true that the interval $\bar{X} \pm 2\sigma_{\bar{X}}$ has a 0.9545 probability of including the population mean. This latter interval is called a *confidence interval*, an interval within which we have a stated degree of confidence of finding the population value. It is expected that out of a large number of instances in which a sample is drawn and its mean computed, the sample mean will fall within two standard errors of the population parameter 95.45 per cent of the time. Whenever this occurs, our statement that the interval within two standard errors of the mean from the sample mean, $\bar{X} \pm 2\sigma_{\bar{X}}$, includes the population mean is correct. However, almost 5 per cent of the time the sample mean will fall outside the interval $\bar{X}_p \pm 2\sigma_{\bar{X}}$. Whenever this occurs, the statement that $\bar{X} \pm 2\sigma_{\bar{X}}$ includes the population mean will be an incorrect statement. In the long run such statements will be correct 95 out of 100 times.

In Chapter 4, we described the distribution of straight-time hourly earnings of a random sample of 120 production workers from the XYZ Foundry; the sample mean was found to be 211.9; the sample standard deviation was 48.3. The standard error of the mean would be:

$$\sigma_{\bar{X}} = \frac{s}{\sqrt{n-1}} = \frac{48.3}{\sqrt{120-1}} = \frac{48.3}{10.9} = \mathbf{4.43}$$

This information can be used to set up a confidence interval estimate of the average straight-time hourly earnings of all XYZ production workers. Suppose we would like to set up an interval such that there are no more than two chances in 100 that the interval *does not* include the population parameter; that is, we want to set up an interval estimate which has a 0.98 probability of including the population mean. Referring to Table II in Appendix B, we find that the interval of 2.33 standard errors on each side of the mean includes 0.98 of the area under a normal curve. The 98 per cent confidence interval in this case would be:

$$\begin{aligned} \bar{X} \pm 2.33\sigma_{\bar{X}} &= 211.9 \pm 2.33(4.43) \\ &= 211.9 \pm 10.3 \\ &= \mathbf{201.6} \text{ to } \mathbf{222.2} \end{aligned}$$

There is 0.98 probability that the given interval includes the average straight-time hourly earnings of all production workers at the XYZ Foundry.

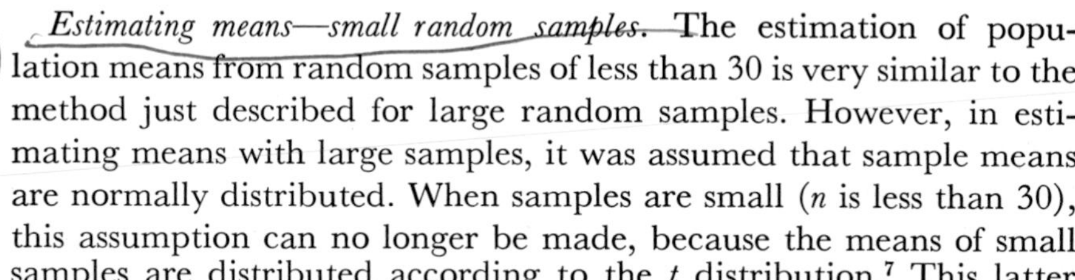

Estimating means—small random samples. The estimation of population means from random samples of less than 30 is very similar to the method just described for large random samples. However, in estimating means with large samples, it was assumed that sample means are normally distributed. When samples are small (n is less than 30), this assumption can no longer be made, because the means of small samples are distributed according to the t distribution.[7] This latter

[7] Just as the normal curve depends upon its mean and its standard deviation and the binomial distribution depends upon p, n, and N (respectively the probability of a success-

distribution must be used in determining the number of standard error units corresponding to the desired confidence level. The t distribution is given in Table III, Appendix B, together with instructions for its use.

In order to make statements concerning the t distribution similar to those made in discussing the normal distribution, it is necessary to refer to a series of tables similar to Table II for the normal distribution. Table III presents information concerning the t distribution in a highly condensed form. The figures in the body of the table indicate the value of t, $t = (\bar{X} - \bar{X}_p)/\sigma_{\bar{X}}$, corresponding to specified levels of significance. For example, suppose we wish to estimate the mean of the population with 99 per cent confidence when sample size (n) is 15, the sample mean ($\bar{X}$) is 70 and the standard error of the mean ($\sigma_{\bar{X}}$) is 2.5. The degrees of freedom in this case are 14 ($n - 1$); this determines where we enter Table III. Since we wish to establish a 99 per cent confidence interval, we check the last column (probability of 0.01 that $\bar{X}_p$ will fall outside the interval). Table III indicates that 2.98 standard error units must be included in the range on either side of the sample mean ($\bar{X}$).

$$\bar{X} \pm 2.98\sigma_{\bar{X}} = 70 \pm 2.98(2.50) = 70 \pm 7.45$$
$$= \mathbf{62.55 - 77.45}$$

There is 0.99 probability that the given interval includes the population mean.

It should be noted that the best single valued estimate of the mean of the population is that it is equal to the mean found in the sample, whether the sample is large or small. This is because the sampling distribution of the mean reaches its maximum frequency at the mean of the population; from which it follows that the most probable single value for the mean of the sample is that it be equal to the mean of the population. Note, however, that there is an exceedingly slight probability that the mean of the sample is *precisely equal* to the mean of the population and not until we set up intervals around the mean of the sample do we come to have any appreciable confidence that we are making correct statements about the location of the mean of the pop-

ful outcome, the number of independent events per trial, and the number of trials) the t distribution depends upon a *parameter* called *degrees of freedom* (n). There is a different t distribution corresponding to each degree of freedom. Table 2, Appendix C shows the value of t for a given area in both tails of the curve for various degrees of freedom. It should be noted that as n increases, the t distribution approaches the normal distribution. It is used in interpreting normally distributed statistics from samples of 30 or less.

ulation. This test of the reliability of the mean of the sample is aimed at determining the degree of confidence we may rationally hold with respect to the population mean being included within certain intervals set up around the mean of the sample.

Estimating proportions. The confidence interval for the population proportion (the probability of a "success" occurring when there are only two possible outcomes, "success" and "failure") can be constructed in the same way as for the population mean. For large random samples (n over 30) where P is not less than 0.20 and does not exceed 0.80, the normal distribution is utilized in determining the number of standard error units in the confidence interval. In other cases, the standard error of a proportion (the standard deviation of the sampling distribution of the sample proportion) must be interpreted using either the binomial distribution (n less than 30 and P greater than 0.10) or the Poisson distribution (P less than 0.10).

The standard error of the proportion is computed from:

$$\sigma_p = \sqrt{\frac{P(1 - P)}{n}}$$

where P is the population proportion, and σ_p the estimated standard error. If the sample proportion, p, is substituted for the population proportion, P, then the formula for the standard error of the proportion is:

$$\sigma_p = \sqrt{\frac{p(1 - p)}{n - 1}}$$

The confidence interval for the population proportion is:

$$p \pm Z\sigma_p$$

where Z is the number of standard error units in the desired confidence interval. Z is determined from areas under the normal curve when the sample is large and P neither too large nor too small. In other cases the binomial distribution or the Poisson distribution are used to determine Z.

Suppose the manufacturer of No-Soap Laundry Powder surveys a random sample of 1600 families and determines that 360 or 22.5 per cent of these families prefer No-Soap over all other laundry powders. What can the manufacturer conclude about the preferences of *all* families for No-Soap? Since the sample is large and p is greater than 0.20, the standard error of a proportion (σ_p) can be used with a table of areas under the normal curve (Table II, Appendix B) to set up confidence intervals.

$$\sigma_p = \sqrt{\frac{pq}{n-1}}$$

Since n is very large, the degrees of freedom correction may be ignored; hence,

$$\sigma_p = \sqrt{\frac{pq}{n}} = \sqrt{\frac{(0.225)(0.775)}{1600}} = \sqrt{\frac{0.1642}{1600}}$$

$$= \sqrt{0.0001} = 0.01$$

Suppose the manufacturer is interested in knowing the limits of preference for his product with 90 per cent confidence. Table II, Appendix B indicates that 90 per cent of the items in a normal distribution would fall within 1.645 standard deviations from the mean. Then the confidence interval would be:

$$p \pm 1.645(\sigma_p) = 0.225 \pm 1.645(0.01)$$

$$= 0.225 \pm 0.016$$

$$= \mathbf{0.209} \text{ to } \mathbf{0.241}$$

That is, there is a probability of 0.90 that the proportion of all families preferring No-Soap is somewhere between 0.209 and 0.241 or 21 to 24 per cent.

Estimating other parameters. The general method used in estimating means and proportions is applicable to the estimation of other population parameters from sample statistics. It can be summarized in the following three steps:

1. Compute the *sampling error* of the sample statistic upon which the estimate is to be based. This is an *estimated* sampling error because sample statistics are substituted for population parameters in the computation. This is usually called the standard error of the sample statistic.[8]
2. Determine the proper confidence coefficient: the arbitrarily cho-

[8] The general method is subject to some revision when the sample size is large in relation to the population size. Whenever the sample comprises ten per cent or more of the total population, the finite population correction should be used. For the standard error, this adjustment is:

$$\text{corrected } \sigma_{\overline{X}} = (\text{estimated } \sigma_{\overline{X}}) \sqrt{\frac{N-n}{N-1}}$$

where N is the population size and n is the sample size.

sen probability which indicates the relative frequency with which the method may be expected to produce a range that includes the population parameter. This determines the number of standard error units to be included in the range on either side of the sample statistic. This number is symbolized as Z.

3. Compute the confidence interval: the sample statistic plus and minus the proper number of estimated standard errors.

Note: The probability statement evaluates the *method* of making the estimate, not the probability of the computed range including the population parameter in the *particular* case.

The standard errors of other statistics can be quickly estimated. The sampling distributions of medians and standard deviations are related to the standard error of the mean. The standard error of the median can be approximated as:

$$\sigma_{Md} = \frac{5}{4}\frac{s}{\sqrt{n-1}}, \quad \text{or} \quad 1.25\sigma_{\overline{X}}$$

The standard error of the standard deviation is estimated as:

$$\sigma_s = \frac{s}{\sqrt{2(n-1)}} = \frac{1}{\sqrt{2}}\sigma_{\overline{X}} = 0.7070\sigma_{\overline{X}}$$

These latter relations are useful in analysis based on large random samples where it is reasonable to assume the sampling distributions are normal.

TESTING STATISTICAL HYPOTHESES

A *statistical hypothesis* is a statement about a population. It is sometimes based on assumptions about that population. Again, it may be based on empirical evidence. A third possibility is that it is based on both assumptions and empirical evidence. A statistical hypothesis is always stated in such a fashion that a *statistical test* will provide the basis for *accepting* or *rejecting* the hypothesis. The statistical test consists in giving sample data an opportunity to discredit the hypothesis. Statistical tests never completely prove nor disprove any hypothesis but only indicate the degree of credibility associated with accepting the hypothesis.

Tests of hypotheses are evaluations of the probability of occurrence of the observed result if the hypothesis is true. If it is found that the observed conditions are very unlikely to occur if the hypothesis is true, the hypothesis is rejected. If, on the other hand, it is found that the observed conditions could very easily have occurred under such conditions as the hypothesis may specify, the hypothesis is accepted.

Tests of hypotheses are applied in two general cases. In the first case, tests are concerned with observed differences between an observed sample statistic and a population parameter (either known or hypothetical). The second general case to which statistical tests are applied relates to differences between sample results.

The null hypothesis. A statistical hypothesis is a reformulation of the observed facts into a form that can be subjected to statistical testing. The usual type of hypothesis employed in statistical tests is termed the *null* (i.e., negative) *hypothesis*. In this approach the original problem is put into the form of a hypothesis which states that the *observed* or *apparent* differences (between the sample statistic and the population parameter or between the statistics from different samples) are due solely to the variations attributable to random sampling (random errors of sampling).

The process of stating a null hypothesis can be illustrated by the problem of determining whether the employees of Exwhysee Corporation are in favor of an incentive wage plan being considered for adoption by the management. The results of a random sample of 225 employees indicate that 124, or 55 per cent, favor the proposed plan. The null hypothesis would state that the sample percentage of 55 per cent does not represent a significant preference for the incentive plan. This statement provides the criterion of significance, namely: that the employees are in reality equally divided on the issue with one-half (50 per cent) in favor of the plan and one-half (50 per cent) opposed to the plan. The test of significance then proceeds to determine the likelihood that a sample of the given size (225) will deviate from the assumed population percentage (50 per cent) by as much as five per cent.

In other cases, the conditions of the problem may determine the criterion of significance. Thus, we might assume that the Exwhysee Corporation is considering the incentive wage plan a second time. At the time the plan was first considered, out of a random sample of 225 employees only 110 votes (49 per cent) were cast for the plan. Have the employees changed their attitude? That is, is the difference between the two sample results of 49 per cent and 55 per cent significant? The null hypothesis, in this instance, would be that the observed difference of 6 per cent is attributable to random sampling fluctuations and is therefore not significant.

Significance tests. The general approach to both of these significance-test problems is essentially the same. In order to determine the significance of any difference, we must determine to what extent that difference is attributable to random sampling fluctuations. As explained in the earlier sections of this chapter, the measure of sampling fluctuations in any statistic is the estimated standard error of that statistic. Thus it is known that the mean value of random samples will differ from the population mean value as a result of random sampling variations by more than 1 standard error of the mean approximately 32 times out of 100,[9] by more than 2 standard errors of the mean approximately 45 times out of 1,000, by more than 3 standard errors of the mean only 27 times out of 10,000, etc.; and the same thing is true if we substitute the standard deviation, the median, a percentage, or any other statistic for the mean, provided that statistic is normally distributed.

A sample statistic deviating from the population value by 1 standard error or less would occasion no surprise because of the high expected frequency of such an occurrence (in 68 samples out of every 100), and the difference would immediately be charged to sampling variation. If, however a sample statistic were found to deviate from the supposed population value by as much as 4 standard errors, its membership in this population would be seriously questioned, for the extreme rarity of such an occurrence (6 out of 100,000) renders it very unlikely that the sample could have been drawn from this population. Although there is always the possibility that this might be one of the six instances out of 100,000 in which a randomly drawn sample from this population could have such an atypical statistic, the probability of such an event is so small (0.00006) that the other alternative must be selected as by far the most likely. This slim probability indicates why a statistical hypothesis cannot be definitely confirmed or denied.

Since the standard error of any statistic measures the expected sampling fluctuations in that statistic, the significance of a sample difference can readily be evaluated by first calculating the difference between the sample value and the other (population or sample) value in standard error units. This is done by dividing the difference be-

[9] Since, from Table II, Appendix B, roughly 68 per cent of the area of the normal curve lies within the range of the mean plus and minus 1 standard deviation, it follows that 32 per cent of the area will lie outside this range. The other statements are derived in similar fashion.

tween the two values by the standard error of the difference between the two statistics, as estimated from the sample. The symbol Z is again used to designate the value which results.

The probability of such a difference (of a Z value as large or larger than that obtained) is then determined from an appropriate distribution table. If this probability is high, it indicates that the difference might easily be due to random sampling and the difference would be taken to be nonsignificant. If the probability is low, this indicates that the probability of their belonging to the same population is questionable. The lower the probability, the more likely it is that the difference is significant.

Suppose that management and the production workers' union at XYZ Steel Foundry are negotiating a wage contract. The union is dissatisfied with the mean straight-time hourly rate of \$2.12, arguing that take-home pay for the production worker is insufficient. Management counters with the argument that overtime raises weekly pay from the apparent straight-time weekly average of \$84.80 (\$2.12 × 40) to an average total weekly pay of \$100.00. The union finds that for the random sample of 120 workers, the average total weekly pay is only \$93.35 and challenges management's estimate of \$100.00. It is decided to test the significance of the difference with a significance of 5 per cent (0.05). From Table II, Appendix B, it can be seen that a significance coefficient of 0.05 (which corresponds to a confidence coefficient of 0.95) corresponds to a Z value of 1.96. If the difference between the supposed population mean claimed by management (\$100.00) and the sample mean (\$93.35) is larger than 1.96 standard errors of the mean, the difference will be considered significant and the management figure for the population value will be refuted. Summarizing:

$$\bar{X}_p = \$100.00$$

$$\bar{X} = \$93.35$$

$$\sigma_{\bar{X}} = \$4.43 \text{ (from page 96)}$$

$$\text{Critical value of } Z = 1.96, \text{ where}$$

$$Z = \frac{\bar{X} - \bar{X}_p}{\sigma_{\bar{X}}}$$

$$= \frac{93.35 - 100.00}{4.43} = \frac{6.65}{4.43} = \mathbf{1.50}$$

The Z value of 1.50 is below 1.96 and indicates the difference is to be accepted as being due to chance. Note, however, that this test does not indicate that \$100.00 is the *true* average total weekly pay but only that the sample of 120 with a mean of \$93.35 could easily have been drawn from a population with a mean of \$100.00.

The exact point at which a probability becomes significant—the significance level—is not capable of a unique answer, but must be left to judgment. A probability level of 0.05, *i.e.*, a confidence coefficient of 0.95, is often used as the dividing line. In other words, if a difference as great as the one in question could have occurred as a result of random sampling fluctuations no more than 5 times out of 100, it is concluded that the difference is too large to be attributable to sampling variation and is therefore significant. If the difference could have occurred more frequently than 5 out of every 100 times, say, 5 times out of 50 or 10 times out of 50, it is very likely that the difference was due to chance fluctuations and hence is not significant. A significance level of 0.01 (confidence coefficient of 0.99), is used at other times under the assumption that only if the observed difference could have occurred less than 1 time out of 100 purely by chance, can it be concluded that factors other than sampling variability could have caused this difference.

Once a confidence coefficient is selected in a particular problem, the probability of rejecting the hypothesis when it is true is fixed. This follows from the definition of the confidence coefficient. Thus, an 0.95 confidence coefficient means that in 95 cases out of 100 the mean of a large sample will fall within 1.96 standard errors of the true mean when the sample is taken from this population, *i.e.*, when the null hypothesis is true. However, it is also true that with an 0.95 confidence coefficient, there is an 0.05 probability that the sample mean will fall outside the confidence region (the region of acceptance) even when the sample is a member of this population. Technically, this probability of rejecting the hypothesis when it is true is known as a *Type I error*.

There is also the danger that we may accept the hypothesis when it is actually false—this is known as a *Type II error*. That is, although our sample is not a member of the particular population, the computed value of Z (the number of standard error units in the difference) indicates that the sample value happens to fall in the confidence region and we erroneously conclude that the sample was drawn from this population. The probability of making a Type II error varies directly with the size of the selected confidence region and inversely to the size of the sample. The wider the confidence region, the more likely is it to include samples from other populations. For example, suppose that a sample mean is 60, with a standard error of 8. An 0.68 confidence coefficient would cover the interval from 52 to 68, indicating that this sample might have been drawn from a population whose mean is anywhere between 52 and 68. For an 0.95 confidence coefficient, the population mean could lie anywhere between 44 and 76 ($60 \pm 1.96 \times 8$). Since the latter range is greater, it clearly is more likely to admit other populations. If sample size were greater, the standard error would be less ($\sigma_{\bar{X}} = \sigma/\sqrt{n}$) and all confidence intervals smaller and thus less likely to admit other populations.

The relative importance of the two types of errors influences the selection of the confidence coefficient (significance coefficient). If it is more important to avoid rejecting a true hypothesis, a relatively high confidence coefficient (low significance coefficient), say 0.99, will be used. If it is more important to avoid accepting a false hypothesis, a low confidence coefficient (high significance coefficient), say 0.90, will be used.

A significance test may be characterized as a ratio of the difference to be tested to a measure of the random sampling influence that might be present in this difference, this measure being the standard error of the difference between the statistics.

$$Z = \frac{\text{sample statistic} - \text{other (sample or population) statistic}}{\text{estimated standard error of the difference}}$$

If the value of Z is such that the probability of its occurrence, as indicated by the appropriate distribution table, is less than the probability level selected, the difference is assumed to be significant and the null hypothesis is rejected; if however, the computed probability is greater than the selected probability level, the difference is assumed to be due to chance and the null hypothesis is accepted.

Although this principle is equally applicable to both of the significance-test problems mentioned above, the actual procedure varies slightly with each type of problem. If the significance of the difference between the sample value and some hypothetical or actual population value is being tested, the standard error of the population statistic—when it is not known—is estimated from the sample data. If the significance of the difference between values based on two samples is being tested, a weighted average of the computed standard errors of each of the two separate samples is estimated to be the true population standard error *of the difference*. Of course, if the necessary population data are known, the problem is considerably simplified (and the accuracy of the test is similarly greatly increased).

The two sections below summarize the techniques used in testing statistical hypotheses.

Evaluating the difference between a sample statistic and a population value. This process involves the following:

1. State the hypothesis to be tested. The observed difference between the sample statistic and the population value (actual or hypothetical) is no greater than the maximum difference we are willing to attribute as due to the chance forces of sampling (random error).
2. Determine the level of significance. This is a more or less arbitrarily selected probability or risk of Type I error (rejecting a true hypothesis). This also defines the critical value for Z, for Z is determined by the level of significance and the appropriate sampling distribution. For large samples (N larger than 30) the normal distribution is most often used. The t distribution is most often used for samples of 30 or less.
3. Compute the appropriate standard error. When population parameters (P or σ) are known, this is the *true* standard error. When sample statistics (p or s) are substituted for population parameters, this is the *estimated* standard error. In any case, there is a given sample size (n) used in the computations and the derived sampling error statistic refers only to samples of that given size.
4. Compute the value of Z and determine if it is larger than the critical value of Z established in (2):

$$Z = \frac{\text{sample statistic minus parameter}}{\text{computed standard error}}$$

Evaluating the difference between two sample statistics. This process differs from the previous process only in that observed difference is between two sample statistics rather than between a sample statistic and a population parameter. It involves the following:

1. State the hypothesis to be tested. The observed difference between the two sample statistics is no greater than the maximum difference we are willing to accept as due to the chance forces of sampling. Note that there are, however, *two* possible questions. First, one might ask if the two samples come from the same population? Second, one might ask if the two samples come from

different populations which have corresponding parameters, *i.e.*, are there two like populations?

2. Determine the level of significance and the critical value for T. See step 2 in the previous section.
3. Compute the appropriate standard error. The basic formula is that for the standard error of a difference:

$$\text{est. } \sigma_{1-2} = \sqrt{\text{est. } \sigma_1^2 + \text{est. } \sigma_2^2}$$

where est. σ_{1-2} is the estimated standard error of the difference, est. σ_1 is the estimated standard error of the statistic from the first sample, and est. σ_2 is the estimated standard error of the statistic from the second sample. There is a distinction between situations where the two samples are equal in size ($n_1 = n_2$) and situations where the samples are unequal in size ($n_1 \neq n_2$) or samples are small. In the latter case, the variance of the two samples is pooled and the standard error of the difference of means is:

$$\sigma_{\bar{X}_1 - \bar{X}_2} = \sqrt{\frac{[(n_1 - 1)s_1^2 + (n_2 - 1)s_2^2](n_1 + n_2)}{(n_1 + n_2 - 2)(n_1 n_2)}}$$

4. Compute the value of t, but recognize the complete form for this test is:

$$t = \frac{\text{statistic}_1 \text{ minus statistic}_2 \text{ minus zero}}{\text{computed standard error of the difference}}$$

The t distribution must be used for this test unless the true value of the population standard deviations (1, 2) are known. The t table is entered with $n_1 + n_2 - 2$ degrees of freedom. Alternatively, if the samples are not small, the normal deviate (Z) may be used.

summary

The process of making statements about populations on the basis of samples drawn from those populations is called *inference*. If the samples are drawn by probability selection techniques, the probability that the inference is correct can be determined. Inference statements are of three types: interval estimates of population values, tests of the significance of the observed difference between sample values and corresponding population values, and tests of the significance of observed differences between sample values.

Sampling error and estimates of sample size

The size of the standard error is, of course, related to sample size. This fact can be utilized in arriving at estimates of the minimum size of sample required to give a particular level of sampling variability. Consider the case of sampling for a mean. Since $\sigma_{\bar{X}} = \sigma/\sqrt{n}$, it is also true that $n = \sigma^2/\sigma_{\bar{X}}^2$.

All that is required to make use of this relation is a specification of the reliability desired and an estimate of population variability. For instance, the manager of a men's clothing store located near a large university might wish to know the average expenditure for clothing during the regular school term by male college students. He might specify a desire to know this value within \$40 with 95 per cent certainty. We know that 95 per cent certainty is possible within a range of two standard errors around the mean and interpret this to mean that he expects a standard error of approximately \$20. If prior knowledge, judgment, and a few inquiries among male college students indicate a conservative estimate of the population standard deviation would be \$200, how large a sample is required? Substituting into the formula for n:

$$n = \frac{(200)^2}{(20)^2} = \frac{40,000}{400} = 100$$

indicating an unbiased random sample of 100 students, would be adequate to attain the required reliability.

The same technique can be utilized in determining the minimum size sample to furnish a proportion of specified reliability. Suppose we are interested in predicting the result of the next presidential election. Let P stand for the proportion of Republican preferences and $1-P$ (or Q) stand for the proportion of Democratic preferences. Suppose the required reliability is that $\sigma_p = 0.01$ (one per cent); since $\sigma_p = \sqrt{PQ/n}$; $n = PQ/\sigma_p^2$. In this case, with $\sigma_p = 0.01$ and the hardest probable result to predict being a 50–50 split;

$$n = \frac{(0.50)(0.50)}{(0.01)^2} = \frac{0.2500}{0.0001} = 2500$$

This demonstrates why the public opinion pollsters successfully use samples as small as 3,000 interviews as a basis for predicting election results.

SUMMARY

Statistical inferences are inductive arguments evaluated on the basis of probabilities. The probability of any outcome is the relative frequency of its occurrence over a very large number of events for which it is a possible outcome. Sample statistics from random samples follow known probability distributions (sampling distributions). This fact is utilized in statistical inference problems. There are three basic inference problems: (1) setting up interval estimates of population parameters (confidence intervals) around sample statistics; (2) testing the significance of the difference between a sample statistic and a real or assumed population parameter; (3) testing the significance of the difference between statistics from different samples. A confidence interval is an interval within which there is a stated probability of finding the population parameter. The confidence coefficient determines the number of standard errors of the sample statistic to be included in the interval on either side of the statistic. The significance of a difference is indicated by the probability that such a difference could have occurred purely because of random sampling errors.

In testing statistical hypotheses, two errors are possible. Type I error is encountered when a difference due to chance errors is judged to be significant. Type II error occurs whenever a difference which is truly significant is not recognized as such. Because of these two possible errors, no statistical hypothesis is ever completely proven or disproven, but is only indicated to be relatively likely to be true or false.

Glossary of terms and symbols

TERMS

Confidence Coefficient: The complement to the significance coefficient (α); the probability that a confidence interval includes the population parameter.

Confidence Interval: An interval within which one has a stated degree of confidence of finding the population parameter.

Degrees of Freedom: The number of elements which can be drawn into a distribution without restriction as to the value of the elements.

Null Hypothesis: A hypothesis stating that any observed differences are not significant but are due only to random errors of sampling.

Parameter: The true value of a statistic (mean, proportion, standard deviation, etc.) in the population.

Probability: The relative frequency of occurrence of a given outcome over a very large number of occurrences of the event for which it is a possible outcome.

Sample Statistic: The value of a statistic (mean, median, standard deviation, etc.) computed from a sample.

Sampling Distribution: A frequency distribution which indicates the expected (probable) distribution of a statistic (mean, proportion, etc.) computed from an infinite number of randomly selected samples of a given size.

Significance Coefficient (α): The probability of rejecting the null hypothesis that the difference between the statistics is due to chance when such is the case.

Statistical Hypothesis: A reformulation of the observed facts in a problem into a form which can be subjected to a statistical test.

Statistical Test: A process which gives the sample data an opportunity to discredit a statistical hypothesis; an evaluation of the probability of occurrence of the observed result if the hypothesis is true.

Type I Error: The arbitrarily selected risk of making a wrong decision by indicating that a difference between statistics is significant when in reality it is due only to random errors of sampling.

Type II Error: The risk of accepting a difference between statistics as being the result of random errors of sampling when in reality it is due to the operation of a definable non-random cause.

SYMBOLS

C_r^n the number of ways of combining n things of which r are heads and $n-r$ are tails;

$$\frac{n!}{r!(n-r)!}$$

N the size of the population.

n the size of the sample.

$n!$ $n(n-1)(n-2)\ldots(1)$; the product of the integers from 1 through n.

P the proportion of "successes" in the population.

p the proportion of "successes" in the sample.

Q the proportion of "failures" in the population; $(1 - P)$.

q the proportion of "failures" in the sample; $(1 - p)$.

s the standard deviation computed from a sample.

$\overline{X}$ the mean computed from a sample.

$\overline{\overline{X}}$ the mean of a group of sample means.

$\overline{X}_p$ the mean of the population.

σ the standard deviation of the population.

σ_p the standard error of a proportion; $\sqrt{\frac{PQ}{n}}$ or $\sqrt{\frac{pq}{n-1}}$.

σ_{np} the standard deviation of the number of occurrences (frequencies) in a binomial distribution; $\sqrt{nPQ}$.

$\sigma_{\overline{X}}$ the standard error of the mean; $\frac{\sigma}{\sqrt{n}}$ or $\frac{s}{\sqrt{n-1}}$.

Questions and Exercises

1. Why would a sample consisting of one item be inadequate for the purpose of statistical induction?
2. What is a "sampling distribution?"
3. What is a confidence interval?
4. What is the probability of drawing each of the following by random selection from an ordinary deck of 52 playing cards? (Assume replacement after each draw.) Indicate how you arrive at each answer.
   (a) One red ace?
   (b) One red card followed by one black card?
   (c) One red card other than an ace followed by one red ace?
   (d) One spade followed by one club?
   (e) The ace of spades followed by one heart?
   (f) Either the ace of spades or the ace of clubs?
   (g) Either one red ace or one black ace?
5. If the mean wage of a random sample of production workers in a large food cannery is \$85 and the standard error of the mean is \$1.80, what confidence can you place in the statement that the mean wage of all production workers in the food cannery lies between \$82.30 and \$87.70? Explain fully.

6. A sample survey of average total yearly expenditures included 225 students at State University. The mean total expenditure per student per school year for the sample was \$2,750, with a standard deviation of \$600. How likely is it that students spend an average of \$3,000 per year as claimed by one irate parent? What is the likelihood that students spend an average of at least \$2,650 per year? at least \$2,800 per year? Explain fully. Illustrate your answers with rough sketches.

7. A survey including 225 students was also taken at State College. The results indicated an average expenditure of \$2,600 per school year, with a standard deviation of \$585. Does this difference of \$150 in mean total expenditure indicate students at State University spend more per year than students at State College? Explain fully.

8. A buyer for the Small-Way Department Store is considering a new supplier of shirts for sale at Small-Way. He is testing a sample of 50 shirts from the new supplier.
(a) What two types of error is it possible for the shirt buyer to make? Explain each fully.
(b) How may each of these types of error be reduced?

9. Suppose that reliable information is available which indicates that the average total yearly expenditure for clothing by single male students at State University ranges between \$50 and \$750 for the middle 95 per cent of the students. What size of simple random sample would be necessary to obtain an estimate of the average total yearly expenditure by single male students at State University with a probability of 0.95 of being within \$50 of the true average?

10. What is the smallest random sample a public opinion poll will have to take in order to be able to assert with a probability of 0.95 that their estimate of the proportion of persons favoring a hotly contested bond issue will not be off more than 3.92 per cent?

11. A random sample of 100 delinquent charge accounts at the Sell-All Department Store has an arithmetic average size of \$94.50 with a standard deviation of \$42.00.
(a) Management has asked that you estimate the average size of the delinquent accounts with no more than 2 chances in 100 of being wrong. What is your estimate?
(b) What is the probability that the average size of account might be as high as \$105?

12. In an experiment conducted to determine the average lifetime of No-Lite electric light bulbs, a random sample of 26 bulbs burned an average (mean) of 869 hours with a standard deviation of 55 hours.
(a) If we estimate the average lifetime of all bulbs as 869 hours, with

what confidence can we assert that our error is less than 13 hours?
(b) A second sample of 26 No-Lite bulbs is tested one year later and the mean life of the second sample is found to be 903 hours with a standard deviation of 65 hours. What is the probability that the average burning life of No-Lite bulbs has changed?

13. Management of the Dustee Corporation are considering a style change for their Dustee Cleaner. Since the adoption of the new cleaner will necessitate a complete retooling of the assembly department, management decides not to switch to the new style unless it is preferred by two-thirds of their potential customers. Test results from a random sample of 49 housewives indicate that 30 definitely prefer the new style. What would be your recommendation to management? Explain fully on the assumption that management is not well-versed in statistical inference techniques.

14. Would your answer to exercise 13 change if the number of housewives preferring the new style were:
(a) 32? Explain.
(b) 28? Explain.

6 *Analysis of general business conditions*

As pointed out in Chapter 1, businessmen cannot avoid making forecasts, they can only neglect to make as intelligent forecasts as possible. Formally or informally—knowingly or unknowingly—businessmen are making forecasts when they purchase inventories, when they determine sale prices on their merchandise, when they purchase or sell plant and equipment, when they engage or discharge personnel, in fact, whenever they make a business decision. The decision to continue operations in the future at the same level as in the past reflects a forecast that sales will remain relatively stable. Since forecasts are inescapable, it is but common sense that forecasts should be based on a careful evaluation of pertinent data.

Admittedly, formal forecasts are more important in management planning for some firms than for others. Owners and managers of small firms may be so familiar with all operational aspects of their firms, and so astute in their appraisal of business conditions, that formal forecasts and budgets are not essential. However, a great many small firms could improve their internal operations and could capture a larger share of the market if they would initiate sound programs of budgetary control geared to intelligent forecasts.

Formal forecasting is more important for firms which must cope with sharp seasonal and cyclical fluctuations than it is for firms whose sales remain relatively stable from month to month and year to year. Organized forecasting becomes increasingly important for all firms as they expand in size, enter new and varied market areas, and merchandise a greater variety of products.

Forecasts are required for planning sales and production in the immediate future and for planning capital investment over a period of several years. All of a company's budgets—sales, production, inventory, expense, cash, and capital expenditure budgets—should be geared to sales forecasts. Sales forecasts, in turn, should be based upon forecasts of industry conditions and upon forecasts of general business conditions.

In chronological sequence, a firm should first make a forecast of general business conditions, giving consideration to economic and political conditions on both the national and international level. In the light of this general business forecast, a firm should then make a forecast of future business conditions within the industry of which it is a part. After these forecasts have been prepared, a firm is in a position to proceed with its sales forecast, which is the cornerstone of a sound program of administrative planning and control.

Relation of individual firm to industry and to general economy

An individual firm is more likely to prosper when the industry of which it is a part is prospering and when general business conditions also are prosperous. However, flourishing general business conditions are in no way a guarantee that favorable conditions exist for specific industries or for specific firms.

The spectacular rise of the television industry and the concurrent decline of the movie theater industry during prosperous times is a case in point. Although industry conditions were good for television and poor for theaters, some firms in the television industry were experiencing difficult times while some theaters in the movie industry were enjoying profitable operations.

There is no simple explanation for this business phenomenon. Location, of course, is one of the more important factors. Theaters in areas not yet adequately served by television have fared better than theaters which must compete with television. Drive-in theaters, generally, have been more profitable than conventional theaters. Other factors contributing to this situation are the clientele in the various areas, the grade and type of films which have been shown, the promotion and advertising programs, and the over-all efficiency of administration. Firms in the television industry which have had unprofitable operations may have suffered from lack of capital, lack of adequate facilities, incompetent management, excessive competition, or other factors. Conversely, the success of a thriving firm in a declining industry can usually be attributed to superior management, fortuitous location, or a combination of factors which offset or retard the forces which are causing the industry to deteriorate.

It becomes apparent, therefore, that forecasting involves analysis of the general business outlook, the industry outlook, and the outlook for the individual firm. This chapter is principally concerned with means of forecasting business conditions for the general economy and the industry. Chapters 7 and 8 are devoted more specifically to sales forecasting for the individual firm.

In forecasting, as elsewhere in managerial statistics, there is no substitute for judgment and knowledge. In recent years an increasing amount of knowledge has been made available by the regular publication of numerous business indexes and indicators.[1]

Useful indicators of business conditions

Numerous indicators of business conditions are regularly published in the *Survey of Current Business*, the *Federal Reserve Bulletin*, the *Monthly Labor Review*, financial papers, trade journals, business magazines, and daily papers. Most comprehensive of these indicators is the Gross National Product (GNP) estimated by the Department of Commerce.[2] The GNP measures the monetary value of the entire national output of goods and services. During periods when the value of the dollar

[1] An excellent description of individual business indicators is presented in Arthur H. Cole, *Measures of Business Change*, Richard D. Irwin, Inc., 1952.

[2] A description of the Gross National Product may be found in the *National Income* supplement to the *Survey of Current Business* and in numerous other publications.

fluctuates markedly, the GNP may be misleading. To overcome this weakness the Department of Commerce also has computed the GNP in terms of 1939 dollars and in terms of 1954 dollars. To illustrate, in 1958 the GNP in current inflated dollars was $441.7 billion, whereas in constant 1954 dollars it was only $399.0 billion. Changes which occur in GNP expressed in constant dollars reflect changes in the physical quantities of goods and services produced rather than changes in their value, as reflected by the GNP expressed in current dollars.

The Federal Reserve Board *Index of Industrial Production* measures physical production of durable manufacturers, nondurable manufacturers, minerals, and utilities. Since activities in the first three of these industries fluctuate more widely than general business activity, the F. R. B. *Index of Industrial Production* fluctuates more widely than the GNP.

Among major indexes of prices are the *Wholesale Price Index* and the *Consumer Price Index* compiled by the Bureau of Labor Statistics. The latter index, popularly though erroneously referred to as the cost-of-living index, has been widely used in union wage contracts as a basis for changes in wage rates.

Business Week magazine publishes a weekly index of business activity which is a composite of several indicators of physical volume of business. Weekly movements of each of the component indicators are also published, thereby enabling businessmen to observe changes in those series which hold most significance for specific industries.

The Associated Press releases weekly statistics on the following business indicators:

Steel production (per cent of capacity)
Freight carloadings (cars)
Miscellaneous freight (cars)
Auto production (units)
Soft coal production (tons)
Crude oil production (barrels)
Engineering awards (dollars)
Paper production (per cent of capacity)
Paperboard production (per cent of capacity)
Stock sales (shares)
Bond sales (par value)
Business failures (number)
Wholesale prices (Bureau of Labor Statistics index)
Electric power production (kilowatt hours)

Bank clearings (dollars)
Demand deposits (dollars)
Business loans (dollars)
Excess reserves (dollars)
Treasury gold stock (dollars)
Brokers' loans (dollars)
Money in circulation (dollars)

University bureaus of business research publish business indicators for the states and regions which they serve. This is also done by some large banks and other private organizations.

Index numbers

As indicated above, businessmen have a wealth of business indicators available to them. It should be observed that some indicators are merely listings of physical quantities, dollar amounts, per cent of capacity, and other units. However, the most comprehensive of the individual series are combined in various ways and expressed as *index numbers*. A later section of this chapter illustrates methods of utilizing these indicators in making forecasts. First, however, it is desirable that readers obtain a general understanding of the nature of index numbers and their construction.

NATURE OF INDEX NUMBERS

Index numbers are constructed to reflect changes which occur from time to time in the same place or to reflect variations which exist among different places at the same time. Index numbers are numbers which are expressed as relatives—that is, percentages—of a selected base number. For example, an index of the supply of money with a base of 1946 = 100 is illustrated in Table 15. The index for each year other than 1946 was computed merely by expressing the supply of money for that year as a percentage of the supply of money in 1946. Reference to the index facilitates comprehension of the increase which has occurred in the money supply—an increase which has been a major inflationary force.

Ordinarily, indexes measuring changes in the business economy are more than percentage relatives of a single series of data as appear in Table 15; rather, they are indexes (percentage relatives) of averages or totals of many series of data. The F. R. B. *Index of Industrial Production* comprises about 100 series. The B. L. S. *Wholesale Price Index* and *Consumer Price Index* are made up of approximately 2,000 and 300 series, respectively. Obviously, some of these series will be going up while other series are declining or remaining stable. An average of these series conceals the movements of individual series but reveals the trend for the group. Expression of these averages as percentage relatives, or indexes, facilitates comprehension of the changes which have occurred from time to time.

TABLE 15. U. S. money supply, 1946–1958

Year	Money supply* (billions)	Index of money supply (1946 = 100)
1946	$110.0	100.0
1947	113.6	103.3
1948	111.6	101.5
1949	111.2	101.1
1950	118.2	107.0
1951	117.1	106.5
1952	129.0	117.3
1953	130.5	118.6
1954	134.4	122.2
1955	138.2	125.6
1956	139.7	127.0
1957	138.6	126.0
1958	143.1	131.1
1959	144.9	131.7

* Demand deposits and currency outside banks.
Source: *Federal Reserve Bulletins.*

KINDS OF INDEXES

Price indexes. These indexes are constructed to measure changes which have occurred in prices of selected commodities or groups of commodities. Although prices may be weighted by quantities in order to give recognition to the relative importance of the commodities, the indexes are computed in such a way that changes in the index reflect changes in prices rather than changes in quantities. The Department of Commerce *Index of Retail Prices* (last published for February, 1959) and the Bureau of Labor Statistics *Wholesale Price Index* and *Consumer Price Index* are illustrations of this type.

Quantity indexes. As the name implies, indexes which measure changes in quantities produced, sold, shipped, or consumed are referred to as quantity indexes. The F. R. B. *Index of Industrial Production* is a quantity index.

Value indexes. Value is the product of price and quantity; a low price and a large quantity could represent the same value as a high price and a small quantity. Hence a value index which remains stable for a period of time may reflect: (1) stable prices and stable quantities, (2) increasing prices and decreasing quantities, or (3) decreasing prices and increasing quantities. Since movements of prices and quantities are somewhat concealed, value indexes are not as useful for many purposes as are separate indexes of prices and quantities. This is not to deny the real importance of such series as the *Gross National Product*, which is a value indicator. The F. R. B. *Index of Department Store Sales* is another important value indicator.

Business activity indexes. These indexes are frequently constructed by combining independent indicators or indexes of prices, production, trade, employment, finance, and other series. Selection of series to be included in such indexes, and assignment of weighting factors, is largely a matter of judgment. Although these indexes are easy to criticize, they nevertheless serve a useful purpose in reflecting the approximate trend of general business activity. The index of business activity published in *Business Week* magazine is an example of this type of index. Several university bureaus of business research publish indexes of business activity for states or regions.

Other indexes. Indexes or other indicators are available for almost all types of business activity. Specialized indexes have been developed for most major industries. For example, in the transportation industry indicators are published for: (1) railroad freight, (2) scheduled air carrier operations, (3) ton-miles of railway freight, (4) freight carloadings, (5) steam locomotives undergoing or awaiting repairs, and other phases of operations. Among indicators in the retail industry are: (1) retail sales, (2) department store sales, (3) department store stocks, (4) ratio of stocks to sales of department stores, and (5) men's clothing (ratio of stocks to sales). Financial indicators include numerous measures of changes in (1) bond prices, (2) bond yields, (3) stock prices, (4) stock yields, (5) bank debits, (6) bank clearings, (7) loans, (8) reserves, (9) money supply, and (10) rate of money turnover. Similar listings could be made for commodity prices, employment and earnings, construction activity, and many phases of industrial and agricultural production.

Methods of computing index numbers

Both the number and the per cent of businessmen who have occasion to construct index numbers are exceedingly small. But the number and the per cent of businessmen who have occasion to follow the movements of published indexes and indicators are quite substantial. Analysis of these indicators becomes increasingly important as businessmen advance from rung to rung on the executive ladder. Knowledge of the rudiments of index number construction greatly facilitates intelligent appraisal of business indexes. It is particularly important that businessmen be aware of the weaknesses and limitations inherent in the various methods of index number construction.

Index numbers may be computed by a variety of methods, some of which are complex and time consuming. Discussion in this text will be restricted to four methods: (1) the simple aggregative, (2) the simple average of relatives, (3) the weighted aggregative method, and (4) the weighted average of relatives method. Each of these methods has deficiencies; however, the last two methods are reasonably satisfactory and are widely used. Methods for computing the simple aggregative and the simple average of relatives indexes are described principally to inform the reader of their serious limitations which are largely overcome by the weighted aggregative and the weighted average of relatives methods.

PRELIMINARY CONSIDERATIONS

Selection of a base. Since index numbers are constructed to reflect changes which occur from time to time, selection of a base for purposes of comparison is a matter of prime importance. Two general rules should be observed. First, the base period should be a relatively recent period. This is true because business and economic conditions experience significant changes with the passing of time; new commodities are introduced and some old commodities decline in importance or wholly disappear from the business scene. Consequently, conditions in periods too far into the past are not comparable with the current and recent periods. This situation requires that index numbers be periodically revised and brought up to date.

The second rule to be observed in selection of a base is to select a year, or period, when business conditions were neither unusually good nor unusually poor. For example, if a year of very low prices is selected, price indexes for subsequent years will appear unrealistically high. Conversely, if a year, or period, of very high prices is chosen as a base, price indexes for subsequent periods will appear unduly depressed.

Selection of data. Series of data to be included in an index must be selected with care. The selection of such data is a sampling problem. For example, price series to be used in construction of a consumer price index should be representative of the great mass of consumer prices.

Selection of data should also be consistent with the purpose for which the index is to be used. Inclusion of wholesale prices obviously would be inappropriate in the construction of a consumer price index.

As always, accuracy and validity of the data should be verified. Data in the same series should be comparable from period to period. Frequently the nature and characteristics of a commodity undergo substantial changes although the name remains the same. Sometimes changes occur in the units in which quantities are expressed and prices are quoted. Examination and selection of data to be included in an index is a more complicated task than actual computation of the index.

Symbols. Formulas and symbols are a form of shorthand adopted for the sake of convenience. It is customary to use p and q to denote prices and quantities, respectively. Subscripts are used to differentiate among prices and quantities of different periods as follows:

p_0 = price in base period,
q_0 = quantity in base period,
p_1 = price in first period following the base period,
q_1 = quantity in first period following the base period,
p_2 = price in second period following the base period,
q_2 = quantity in second period following the base period, etc.

Prices and quantities in the period for which the index is being computed are indicated by p_n and q_n in index number formulas. In the sections which follow, formulas are introduced only after arithmetic computation of each type of index has been fully illustrated. The illustrations are primarily illustrations of price indexes. It should be noted that the same techniques and considerations apply in constructing quantity indexes.

SIMPLE AGGREGATIVE METHOD

This method consists merely of totaling (aggregating) prices of commodities by periods and expressing each of these totals as a per cent of the total in the period which has been selected as a base. Table 16 illustrates this method. To simplify computations, the number of commodities and the number of years have been limited. The year

TABLE 16. Computation of simple aggregative index of lumber wholesale prices, 1946 = 100

Lumber	Dollars per 1,000 board feet					
	1946	1950	1952	1954	1956	1958
Douglas fir[a]	40.72	76.99	84.91	79.22	86.38	77.89
Western pine[b]	39.49	71.27	81.82	71.08	77.96	68.70
Southern pine[c]	48.09	74.36	80.45	73.91	82.21	76.08
Totals:	128.30	229.19	247.18	224.21	246.55	222.67
Index:	100.0	178.6	192.7	174.8	192.2	173.6

[a] Dimension construction, 2 in. × 4 in., random lengths.
[b] Boards, No. 3 common, 1 in. × 8 in.
[c] Boards, No. 2 common and better, 1 in. × 6 in., random lengths.
Source: Adapted from *Business Statistics, 1959,* U. S. Department of Commerce.

1946 was selected as a point of reference as the first post-World War II year; the other years were selected from more current periods. Wholesale prices of the specified cuts of Douglas fir, Western pine, and Southern pine were selected as being representative of prices of all cuts of the respective kinds of lumber.

The first step in this method is to total prices for each year. The second step is to select a base; the base year in Table 16 is 1946. By definition, the index value in the base year or period is always 100. Index values in other years are computed by expressing their respective totals as percentages of the total in the base year. For example, the index value of 178.6 in 1950 was computed by expressing $229.19 (price total in 1950) as a per cent of $128.30 (price total in base year,

1946); the index value of 173.6 in 1958 was computed by expressing \$222.67 as a per cent of \$128.30. A formula for these computations may be expressed as follows:

$$\text{simple aggregative index for period } n = \frac{\Sigma\, p_n}{\Sigma\, p_0}(100)$$

A wholesale lumber price index of 173.6 in 1958 indicates that prices in that year were 73.6 per cent higher than prices in 1946. Expression of price totals as percentages facilitates comprehension of changes which occur over time. Most persons are unable to readily discern relative changes between absolute numbers; that is, most persons are unable at a glance to recognize that a change from 128.30 (1946) to 222.67 (1958) amounts to an increase of 73.6 per cent.

Years other than 1946 could have been selected as a base year for the computations in Table 16. Had 1952 been used as the base year, indexes in 1946 and 1958 would have been 51.9 and 90.1 respectively. Table 17 compares the indexes which result when each year, in turn, is used as a base. It should be observed that the range narrows as the price total in the base year increases. This is a deceptive feature of percentages. It arises because numbers can increase indefinitely but

TABLE 17. Comparison of lumber wholesale price indexes computed from different base years

Base year	1946	1950	1952	1954	1956	1958
1946	100.0	178.6	192.7	174.8	192.2	173.6
1950	56.0	100.0	107.8	97.8	107.6	97.2
1952	51.9	92.7	100.0	90.7	99.7	90.1
1954	57.2	102.2	110.7	100.0	110.0	99.3
1956	52.0	93.0	100.3	90.9	100.0	90.3
1958	57.6	102.9	111.0	100.7	110.7	100.0

Source: Computed from data in Table 16.

normally in business situations can decrease no further than to zero. The range of index values between 1946 and 1958, when 1946 was the base, was 73.6 as compared with a range of only 42.4 when 1958 was the base. However, it should be observed that the *percentage increase* from 57.6 (in 1946) to 100.0 (in 1958), when 1958 is the base, amounts to 73.6 per cent $\left[\frac{42.4}{57.6}(100)\right]$, the same percentage increase as prevailed when 1946 was used as the base.

The simple aggregative index is easy to compute and to understand, but it is subject to major defects. First, no recognition is given to the relative importance of the various commodities included in the index. If Douglas fir is used in larger quantities than Western pine, prices of Douglas fir should be accorded more weight. As will be shown later, this deficiency can be overcome by using a *weighted* aggregative index rather than a *simple* aggregative index.

A second weakness of this index is the influence exerted by the units in which prices are quoted. This deficiency is not serious when the prices of a group of homogeneous commodities are expressed in the same units, as was the case in Table 16. However, it is more likely that commodities included in indexes will be commonly expressed in a variety of different units, such as gallons, tons, dozens, cases, carloads, kilowatt hours, etc. The price of a commodity quoted in terms of a case will have much less influence on the index than will the price of the same commodity quoted in terms of a carload. Tables 18 and 19 illustrate this point. The quoted price of oats is per bushel in Table 18 and per ton in Table 19. The change in the unit for which the price of oats is quoted results in a different weight for oats in the index. The 1956 index was 99.4 when oats were priced in bushels; but changed to 107.0 when oats were priced in tons. An index which can be manipulated by quoting commodity prices for different units is not a satisfactory index.

TABLE 18. Computation of simple aggregative index of feed prices for a small zoo, 1955 = 100

		Price per unit		
Commodity	Unit	1955 (p_0)	1956 (p_1)	1957 (p_2)
Oats.	bu	$ .60	$ .69	$ .61
Hay, baled.	Ton	20.90	21.20	18.40
Horse meat.	100 lb	12.30	12.20	13.93
Carrots.	100 lb	3.18	2.65	3.20
	Totals:	36.98	36.74	36.14
	Index:	100.0	99.4	97.7

Source: Data adapted from *Agricultural Statistics, 1958*; horse meat prices estimated by the authors.

TABLE 19. Computation of simple aggregative index of feed prices for a small zoo, 1955 = 100

Commodity	Unit	Price per unit		
		1955 (p_0)	1956 (p_1)	1957 (p_2)
Oats	Ton	$ 36.00	$ 41.40	$36.60
Hay, baled	Ton	20.90	21.20	18.40
Horse meat	100 lb	12.30	12.20	13.93
Carrots	100 lb	3.18	2.65	3.20
	Totals:	72.38	77.45	72.13
	Index:	100.0	107.0	99.7

Source: See Table 18.

SIMPLE AVERAGE OF RELATIVES METHOD

The undesirable influence exerted by the units in which prices are quoted is eliminated by the simple average of relatives method. This method requires that each price series to be included in the index first be expressed in per cents of its respective base period price. This has been done in Table 20 for the data which appeared in Tables 18

TABLE 20. Computation of simple average of relatives index of feed prices for a small zoo, 1955 = 100

Commodity	Price relatives		
	1955 $\left(\frac{p_0}{p_0}\right)(100)$	1956 $\left(\frac{p_1}{p_0}\right)(100)$	1957 $\left(\frac{p_2}{p_0}\right)(100)$
Oats	100.0	115.0	101.7
Hay, baled	100.0	101.4	88.0
Horse meat	100.0	99.2	113.3
Carrots	100.0	83.3	100.6
Totals:	400.0	398.9	403.6
Index:	100.0	99.7	100.9

Source: See Table 18.

and 19. It should be noted that the same percentage change in price of oats occurred when prices were quoted per bushel (Table 18) as when prices were quoted per ton (Table 19). It should be noted also that the greatest percentage increase in oat prices occurred in 1956. This explains the increase in the 1956 index which occurred when prices of oats were quoted per ton (Table 19); had the relative increase in the price of oats been less than the relative increases in the prices of the other commodities, the 1956 index in Table 19 would have been less than the 1956 index in Table 18.

The second step in the simple average of relatives method is to total the price relatives for each year. The third and final step is to compute a simple average of the price relatives; the resulting indexes in Table 19 are 100.0, 99.7, and 100.9 for 1955, 1956, and 1957 respectively. A formula for these computations may be expressed as follows:

$$\text{simple average of relatives index for period } n = \frac{\Sigma\left[\frac{p_n}{p_0}(100)\right]}{N}$$

Although the simple average of relatives method overcomes the second weakness of the simple aggregative method, it also suffers from the first weakness—that is, failure to recognize the relative importance of individual items included in the index. Fortunately, this weakness can be substantially overcome by employing specifically weighted indexes.

WEIGHTED AGGREGATIVE METHOD

Under this method, prices of individual commodities are weighted by appropriate quantities. A defect of the method lies in the difficulty of selecting appropriate quantities. The most common practice is to use quantities which were purchased, produced, stocked, shipped, or consumed in the base period. Sometimes weights are computed by averaging quantities for several years. Since the relative importance of commodities frequently shifts over a period of time, it is virtually impossible to select quantity weights which will remain appropriate for a long period of time. A partial solution is to reconstruct the index with new weights and on a recent base whenever the old relationships among commodities has been changed substantially.

The arithmetic computations required in the weighted aggregative method are illustrated in Table 21. The first step is to multiply prices

TABLE 21. Computation of weighted aggregative index of wholesale lumber prices, 1946 quantity weights, 1946 = 100

Lumber	Shipments, millions of board feet	Prices per thousand board feet (dollars)			Value of 1946 quantities at prices of indicated years (thousands of dollars)		
	1946 (q_0)	1946 (p_0)	1952 (p_{52})	1958 (p_{58})	1946 (p_0q_0)	1952 ($p_{52}q_0$)	1958 ($p_{58}q_0$)
Douglas fir.......	627	40.72	84.91	77.89	25.53	53.24	48.84
Western pine.....	502	39.49	81.82	68.70	19.82	41.07	34.49
Southern pine....	774	48.09	80.45	76.08	37.22	62.27	58.89
Totals:					82.57	156.58	142.22
Index:					100.0	189.6	172.2

of each commodity in 1946, 1952, and 1958 by their respective 1946 quantity weights. The resulting values are shown in the three right-hand columns. The second step is to total these value columns. The third and final step is to set the total value of the base year (1946) equal to an index of 100 and compute the index numbers for other years by expressing their respective value totals as relatives of the value total in the base year. Hence, the total of 156.58 in 1952 is 189.6 per cent of 82.57, and the 1958 total of 142.22 is 172.2 per cent of the base year total. A formula for these computations may be expressed as follows:

$$\text{weighted aggregative index for period } n = \frac{\Sigma p_n q_0}{\Sigma p_0 q_0}$$

The weighted aggregative index of wholesale lumber prices computed in Table 21 with 1946 quantity weights indicates a slightly smaller change in prices over this period than did the simple aggregative index computed in Table 16. This is because the relatively large shipments of Southern pine in 1946 result in the greatest weight being given to the price which increased least over this period.

A review of lumber statistics reveals that shipments of Douglas fir and Western pine have increased, while Southern pine shipments have declined. Thus the relationship among commodities in the index has been altered. As would be expected, substitution of 1958 quantity weights, with 1946 retained as 100, results in higher index values for both 1952 and 1958 (Table 22). The 1952 index changed from 189.6 to 194.0; the 1958 index from 172.2 to 174.4. The change in the index value for 1958 is not extreme, but since current trends in lumber shipments are expected to continue, 1946 quantity weights are unrealistic.

WEIGHTED AVERAGE OF RELATIVES METHOD

This method as illustrated obtains the same results as the weighted aggregative method.[3] It is employed when prices to be combined in the index have previously been expressed as relatives. Frequently movements of individual commodity prices are of much interest to businessmen and economists; as has been pointed out earlier, analysis of price movements is facilitated by expression of prices as percentage relatives.

Use of quantity weights for price relatives would be meaningless because the magnitude of prices has been "lost" in the conversion of unit prices to relatives. Therefore it became necessary to employ value weights. This has been done in Table 23 where a weighted average of relatives index has been computed for our set of wholesale lumber prices. The 1946 value weights were obtained from the 1946 value column of Table 22; price relatives are for prices in Table 22. The

TABLE 22. Computation of weighted aggregative index of wholesale lumber prices, 1958 quantity weights, 1946 = 100

	Shipments, millions of board feet	Prices per thousand board feet (dollars)			Value of 1958 quantities at prices of indicated years (thousands of dollars)		
Lumber	1958 (q_0)	1946 (p_0)	1952 (p_{52})	1958 (p_{58})	1946 (p_0q_0)	1952 ($p_{52}q_0$)	1958 ($p_{58}q_0$)
Douglas fir.......	679	40.72	84.91	77.89	27.65	57.65	52.89
Western pine.....	675	39.49	81.82	68.70	26.66	55.23	46.37
Southern pine....	585	48.09	80.45	76.08	28.13	47.06	44.51
Totals:					82.44	159.94	143.77
Index:					100.0	194.0	174.4

[3] The weighted aggregative and the weighted average of relatives methods obtain identical results if the weights assigned to the latter are proportional to the total values of the items in the base period.

TABLE 23. Computation of weighted average of relatives index of wholesale lumber prices, 1958 quantity weights, 1946 = 100

	1946 value wts. from table 22	Price relatives			Price relatives weighted by 1946 values		
		1946	1952	1958	1946	1952	1958
Lumber	(p_0q_0)	$\frac{p_0}{p_0}(100)$	$\frac{p_{52}}{p_0}(100)$	$\frac{p_{58}}{p_0}(100)$	$(p_0q_0)\frac{p_0}{p_0}(100)$	$(p_0q_0)\frac{p_{52}}{p_0}(100)$	$(p_0q_0)\frac{p_{58}}{p_0}(100)$
Douglas fir....	27.65	100.0	208.5	191.3	2,765	5,765	5,289
Western pine..	26.66	100.0	207.2	174.0	2,666	5,524	4,639
Southern pine..	28.13	100.0	167.3	158.2	2,813	4,706	4,450
Totals:					8,244	15,995	14,378
Index:					100.0	194.0	174.4

products of the 1946 value weights and the respective price relatives are shown in the three right-hand columns of Table 23. The amounts in these columns are approximately the same as the amounts in the three right-hand columns of Table 22 and, of course, the indexes are identical. A formula for this method may be expressed as follows:

$$\text{weighted average of price relatives for period } n = \frac{\Sigma\left[p_0q_0\left(\frac{p_n}{p_0}(100)\right)\right]}{\Sigma\, p_0q_0}$$

It may be observed that cancellation of the p_0 in the numerator of this formula results in $\frac{\Sigma\, p_nq_0}{\Sigma\, p_0q_0}(100)$, which is the formula for the weighted aggregative index. This explains why the two methods produce the same results if the same or proportionately equal base period weights are used.

SUMMARY OF METHODS FOR COMPUTING INDEXES

The four methods which have been described in the preceding sections are as follows:

1. Simple aggregative,

2. Simple average of relatives,
3. Weighted aggregative,
4. Weighted average of relatives.

It was demonstrated that the simple aggregative index could be manipulated merely by changing the units in which prices were expressed. Further, it was pointed out that neither the simple aggregative nor the simple average of relatives method gave recognition to the relative importance of the commodities included in the indexes.

As their names imply, the weighted aggregative and the weighted average of relatives indexes are computed by explicitly weighting the respective items in the index according to their economic importance. These methods, which produce identical results, are much superior to the other two methods and are widely used.

Illustrations of the four methods were limited to the construction of price indexes. However, quantity indexes may be computed by the same methods. In the case of a weighted aggregative quantity index, quantities are weighted by base period prices. Hence the weighted aggregative quantity index measures changes in value of *varying quantities* at constant (base period) prices, whereas the weighted aggregative price index measures changes in value of constant (base period) quantities at *varying prices*.

Choosing the right index

It was seen above that a number of indexes sometimes measure the same or very similar things. If a businessman is interested in determining the changes in construction costs, which of the three indexes is most appropriate? The answer to a set of five questions will help the businessman in selecting the right index.

First, what is the purpose for which the index number has been constructed? An index is designed to reflect changes in a particular composite. For instance, the *Consumer Price Index* is designed as a wage deflator to be used in estimating changes in real income. It does not show changes in the cost of maintaining a particular standard of living.

Second, are the items included in the index a representative sample of items relevant to the purpose for which the index is computed? This was discussed earlier in the section on selection of data (page 122).

Third, are the weights used in the index relevant to the purpose of the index, and are they taken from a period which is typical of the total period (or periods) covered by the index?

Fourth, are the basic data used in the construction of the index valid and accurate? For instance, are the prices which enter the consumer price index actually those paid by wage and clerical worker families in urban areas? What is the net price paid for a new electric range? an automobile? Certainly, it is often not the price listed on the price tag attached to the item as it sits in the show room. Also, are the same items being priced from month to month, so long as they are appropriate for inclusion in the index? To define an automobile by make is certainly not sufficient. The exact body style and accessories must remain the same if prices in different periods are to be comparable. Even then, a part of the change in price is likely to reflect a change in the quality of the product and not general inflation or general deflation.

Fifth, but far from last in importance, is the question of whether the index number has an appropriate base. This question was discussed on page 121 and 122.

Useful computations with index numbers

DETERMINATION OF DOLLAR PURCHASING POWER

Although yesterday's dollar and today's dollar contain 100 cents each, they are by no means the same dollars in terms of purchasing power. That is, the quantity of goods and services which can be purchased by a dollar fluctuates as the prices of goods and services fluctuate. In periods of inflation the value of the dollar declines; conversely, in periods of deflation the value of the dollar rises.

Since prices of all goods and services do not change uniformly, it is impossible to compute a *true* or *exact* dollar purchasing power. However, it is possible to compute the purchasing power of the dollar in terms of prices of a specific commodity or group of commodities. The Department of Commerce regularly computes and publishes the purchasing power of the dollar as measured by primary market prices and consumer prices. In recent years the value of the dollar has been somewhat lower in terms of consumer prices than in terms of primary market prices. However, by each measure the value of the dollar declined sharply in the years following 1946. Table 24 compares the

TABLE 24. Purchasing power of the dollar declines as prices rise (1947–1949 = 100)

	Consumer prices		Primary market prices	
Year	Price index	Dollar purchasing power	Wholesale price index	Dollar purchasing power
1946	83.4	119.9	78.7	127.1
1947	95.5	104.7	96.4	103.7
1948	102.8	97.3	104.4	95.8
1949	101.8	98.2	99.2	100.8
1950	102.8	97.3	103.1	97.0
1951	111.0	90.1	114.8	87.1
1952	113.5	88.1	111.6	89.6
1953	114.4	87.4	110.1	90.8
1954	114.8	87.1	110.3	90.7
1955	114.5	87.3	110.7	90.3
1956	116.2	86.1	114.3	87.5
1957	120.2	83.2	117.6	85.0
1958	123.5	81.0	119.2	83.9

Source: *Business Statistics, 1959*, U. S. Department of Commerce.

Consumer Price Index and *Wholesale Price Index* and the purchasing power of the dollar as measured by the two indexes. It will be observed that dollar purchasing power is merely the dollar (100 cents) expressed as a per cent of the consumer or wholesale price index.[4] For example, in 1946 the purchasing power of the dollar in terms of consumer prices was computed as follows:

$$\frac{100.0}{83.4}(100) = \mathbf{119.9}$$

On a 1947–1949 base, one consumer dollar in 1958 was equivalent to 81.0 cents in 1947–1949; one dollar in 1946 was equivalent to $1.199 in 1947–1949.

DEFLATION OF INCOME

Periods of inflation are characterized by rising incomes and prices and a consequent declining value of the dollar. If the relative increase

[4] An alternative method which produces the same result is, first, to compute the reciprocal of the consumer price index and, second, to express these reciprocals as percentages with the base period equal to 100.

in prices is greater than the relative increase in income, *real* income has declined. In Table 25 average weekly earnings in manufacturing industries for the period 1946–1958 have been deflated by using the *Consumer Price Index*. Deflated earnings are commonly referred to as *real* earnings. Deflated average weekly earnings for 1946 were computed as follows:

$$\frac{\$43.82}{83.4}(100) = \$52.54$$

Average weekly earnings of $83.50 in 1958 were required to buy the

TABLE 25. Deflation of average weekly earnings in manufacturing industries by index of consumer prices

Year	(1) Average weekly earnings, mfg. industries	(2) Consumer price index (1947–1949 = 100)	(3) Deflated avg. weekly earnings (Col. 1 ÷ Col. 2)
1946	$43.82	83.4	$52.54
1947	49.97	95.5	52.32
1948	54.14	102.8	52.67
1949	54.92	101.8	53.95
1950	59.33	102.8	57.71
1951	64.71	111.0	58.30
1952	67.97	113.5	59.89
1953	71.69	114.4	62.67
1954	71.86	114.8	62.60
1955	76.52	114.5	66.83
1956	79.99	116.2	68.84
1957	82.39	120.2	68.54
1958	83.50	123.5	67.61

Source: *Business Statistics, 1959*, U.S. Department of Commerce.

same quantities of goods and services as could have been purchased at a cost of only $67.61 in terms of 1947–1949 dollars. Average weekly earnings rose from $43.82 in 1946 to $83.50 in 1958, an increase of 90.6 per cent; real earnings increased by 28.7 per cent. Although weekly dollar earnings increased from $43.82 in 1946 to $49.97 in 1947, real earnings declined slightly from $52.54 to $52.32 because consumer prices increased sharply from an index of 83.4 to an index of 95.5.

DEFLATION OF DOLLAR SALES

During periods of significant price changes, dollar sales may be deceiving when used as a measure of business volume. When prices are rising, it is quite possible that a decline in physical volume of sales may be concealed by the rise in prices which causes an increase in the dollar value of sales. Firms which sell hundreds or thousands of different items often can estimate changes in their physical volume of sales only by deflating their dollar sales with an appropriate index of retail or wholesale prices.

TABLE 26. Deflation of retail sales in United States by index of retail prices

Year	(1) Estimated retail sales (millions)	(2) Retail price index* (1935–39 = 100)	(3) Deflated retail sales col. 1 ÷ col. 2 (millions)
1946	$ 8,541	155.2	$5,503
1947	9,967	180.1	5,534
1948	10,877	192.7	5,645
1949	10,893	187.7	5,803
1950	11,974	189.0	6,335
1951	12,748	206.8	6,164
1952	13,046	210.4	6,201
1953	13,529	209.1	6,470
1954	14,029	208.5	6,729
1955	14,094	208.0	6,776
1956	15,321	211.2	7,254
1957	15,811	217.2	7,279
1958	16,667	220.1	7,572

* Publication of this index was discontinued after February, 1959.

Source: *Business Statistics, 1957,* and selected issues of the *Survey of Current Business,* U. S. Department of Commerce.

In Table 26, estimated retail sales in the United States during the period 1946–1958 have been deflated by the Department of Commerce *Index of Retail Prices.* Substantial increases in retail prices caused dollar sales to rise much more rapidly than *real* sales. From 1946–1958 dollar sales increased 95 per cent as compared with an increase of only 38 per cent in real sales. Real sales reached only $7,572 million in

1958; however, due to marked advances in retail prices, dollar sales increased to $16,667 million during this period. Also, it is apparent that real sales declined from 1950 to 1951 although dollar sales increased.

SHIFTING THE INDEX BASE

Published indexes do not all have the same base periods. Comparison of relative changes in indexes with different base years is facilitated by shifting indexes to a single base. This is illustrated in Table 27

TABLE 27. Illustration of shifting an index base to facilitate comparison of indexes with different base periods

Year	Dept. of Commerce composite index (1947–1949 = 100)	Associated General Contractors' index (1913 = 100)	Associated General Contractors' index (1947–1949 = 100)
1946	77	256	79
1947	93	296	92
1948	104	331	102
1949	103	342	106
1950	107	357	111
1951	116	377	117
1952	119	387	120
1953	122	408	126
1954	122	426	132
1955	125	439	136
1956	132	461	143
1957	137	483	150
1958	139	499	154

Source: Indexes from *Business Statistics, 1959,* U. S. Dept. of Commerce.

where a comparison is made of two construction cost indexes, one with a base of 1947–1949, and the other with a base of 1913. Construction costs in 1958 as measured by the Associated General Contractors' index (499) appear to be much higher than construction costs as measured by the Department of Commerce composite index (139). This illusion prevails because the contractors' index was computed on a base of 1913, a year in which construction costs were much lower than in 1947–1949. A more valid comparison may be achieved by shifting the base of the contractors' index from 1913 to 1947–1949. This was done in the right-hand column of Table 27. The method employed was to express the contractors' index (1913 = 100) of each year as a per cent of the average contractors' index in 1947–1949 (323). For example, $\frac{256}{323}(100) = 79$, the new index for 1946, likewise, $\frac{499}{323}(100) = 154$, the new index for 1958. It is apparent that construction costs as measured by the contractors' index have increased more since 1946 than have construction costs as measured by the Department of Commerce index, which is a composite of various construction cost indexes, including some of the components in the Associated General Contractors' index.

Forecasting general business conditions

INADEQUACY OF MATHEMATICAL FORMULAS

Forecasting business conditions is a complex task which cannot be accomplished with exactness. The economic, social, and political forces which shape the future are many and varied; their relative importance changes almost constantly. As yet, no one has discovered a means of accurately measuring businessmen's expectations; this is a most important factor since current decisions are based on expectations for the future. It is not surprising, therefore, that mathematical formulas are of limited value in forecasting the future. Businessmen must rely heavily on judgment in interpretation of current business trends.

All forecasts are based on certain assumptions. The forecaster attempts to anticipate future economic trends which logically follow from his assumptions. As a practical matter, it is desirable to have more than one set of assumptions. The businessman then is better prepared to adjust operations rapidly in the event his preferred set of assumptions should prove to be in error. Assumptions must be made concerning war, peace, government regulations, taxes, employment, income, crop production, weather, population growth, foreign and domestic trade, and a host of other factors. Actually, most businessmen either consciously or unconsciously do make assumptions pertaining to the future. What many businessmen fail to do is to acquaint themselves with readily available data on business trends. This knowledge would enable them to make more realistic assumptions and also better to anticipate the economic consequences of their assumptions.

BASIC DATA REQUIRED

As indicated in earlier sections of this chapter, numerous business indexes or indicators are published regularly by both private and governmental organizations. It is neither necessary nor desirable for businessmen to attempt to analyze changes in all these indicators. Rather, businessmen should select a few key series for regular observation and supplement these from time to time with other series which have current significance. Just as it is unwise to rely blindly on mathematical formulas, so is it unwise to rely solely on any single indicator or any particular set of indicators.

Among the more important indexes which aid businessmen in forecasting are the following:

1. *Gross National Product* and its components are computed by the Department of Commerce and measure the dollar value of goods and services produced in the economy.
2. *Wholesale Price Index* is calculated by the Bureau of Labor Statistics and measures changes in primary market prices, prices at the first major point of entry for a commodity into the marketing system.
3. *Consumer Price Index* is also released by the Bureau of Labor Statistics. It measures changes in prices of items purchased by wage and clerical worker families in urban areas.
4. *Index of Industrial Production* as compiled by the Federal Reserve Board measures changes in physical output in mining, manufacturing, and utility industries.
5. *Index of Prices Received by Farmers*, *Index of Prices Paid by Farmers*, and *Farm Price Parity Ratio* are computed in the Department of Agriculture and are designed to measure changes in prices of items sold and purchased by farmers.
6. *Indexes of Common Stock Prices:* the Dow-Jones and Standard and Poor indexes measure changes in the prices of common stocks traded on the New York Stock Exchange.

Other important series which businessmen can use to advantage in forecasting are the following:

1. Population, labor force, employment, and unemployment from the Bureau of the Census and Bureau of Labor Statistics.
2. Average hours worked per week and average hourly and weekly

earnings of production workers released by the Bureau of Labor Statistics.

3. Consumer credit is measured by the Federal Reserve Board.
4. Department store sales are reported by the Federal Reserve Board.
5. Bond yields are computed by the Federal Reserve Board.

This list is by no means exhaustive; nor is the arrangement necessarily in order of importance. Several of the above series are composite averages or totals—or indexes of these averages or totals. Analyses also should be made of some of the major components of these series. For example, the gross national product of 479.5 billion in 1959 consisted of the following components:

	Billions
1. Personal consumption expenditures	$311.6
2. Gross private domestic investment	71.1
3. Net exports of goods and services	−0.8
4. Government purchases of goods and services	97.6
Total GNP:	$479.5

Although personal consumption expenditures are largest in amount, the items which attract most forecasters' attention are gross private domestic investment and government purchases of goods and services. This is true because most changes in income (and business conditions) are held to arise from changes in investment or government expenditures rather than from changes in consumer spending; expansion of national income requires new investment, which leads to increased production of goods and services.

Government expenditures receive particular attention during periods of war and national defense. At times when substantial cuts in government expenditures appear imminent, forecasters attempt to predict the extent to which these curtailments will be offset by increased private investment. Hence the forecaster becomes concerned with changes in the major components of gross private domestic investment. These components and their respective amounts for 1959 were as follows:

	Billions
1. New construction	$40.2
2. Producers' durable equipment	26.1
3. Change in business inventories	4.8
Gross private domestic investment:	71.1

Each of these series holds much significance for the future. Excessive accumulation of inventories is deflationary in nature. Declining construction activity and production of producers' durable equipment also are deflationary. However, a decline in construction activity arising from strikes or from shortages of material and/or labor may soon be offset by a burst of new construction; this situation should not be confused with a decline in demand.

Similar attention must be directed toward trends in employment, prices, the availability and cost of credit, and other economic series. Although this task may at first seem overwhelming, it should be noted that each of several publications regularly report data on a great many trends. Foremost among these publications is the *Survey of Current Business* published by the Department of Commerce.

MAJOR METHODS OF FORECASTING

Historical analysis. As the name implies, this method involves a projection of general business conditions and of individual series based on the pattern which has prevailed in past years. Reliance is placed on the continuation of trend and cyclical patterns. Illustrations of cycles which receive considerable attention are the 18-year residential building cycle, the 40-month heavy industry cycle and the 23-month cotton consumption cycle. A disconcerting aspect of cycle analysis is the fact that cyclical patterns are frequently upset by wars, prolonged depressions, crop failures, shifts in international economic relationships, and other disturbing forces.

An alternative or supplemental method to cycle analysis is the comparison of the current situation with a similar situation in the past. After World War II many persons forecast a depression because World War I had been followed by a depression. Actually these two periods were characterized by more dissimilarities than similarities, and the depression which was predicted failed to materialize.

Cross section analysis. This method is based on knowledge and interpretation of current forces rather than projection of past trends. Immediate recognition is given to the fact that business conditions are shaped by simultaneous expanding and contracting forces. Predominance of expanding forces results in booms, whereas predominance of contracting forces leads to depressions. The forecaster who utilizes this method prepares three lists: one which itemizes expanding forces, a second which enumerates stable forces, and a third which sets forth contracting forces. Weights are assigned to these forces on the basis of judgment.

Obviously the dominant forces change from time to time. Factors which may be considered include technological developments, supply-demand relationships, governmental policies, and businessmen's expectations. In regard to the latter, several organizations regularly conduct surveys of executive opinions concerning future trends of general business conditions and selected series of business data.

APPLICATION OF FORECASTING METHODS

In actual practice, businessmen should combine the historical and cross section methods. Valuable lessons can be learned from study of past trends, but future projections must be based on an analysis of current economic forces as well. The forecaster must also give cognizance to the international position of the United States and its bearing upon the business outlook. Likewise, consideration must be given to recent and prospective policies of the federal government with respect to government spending, public debt, monetary and credit policies, agricultural price supports, wage and price controls, and taxation

Large firms often assign responsibility for preparation of general business forecasts to research units staffed with professional economists and statisticians. Presidents and executives of small firms must assume personal responsibility for forecasting. Both large and small firms may engage private consultants, and more commonly, subscribe to one or more forecasting services which issue frequent forecasts to their clients. Since judgment plays such an important role in forecasting, it is to be expected that differences will exist even among professional forecasters. Hence, some firms arrive at their forecast by applying cross section analysis to forecasts prepared by several research organizations.

An obvious question at this point is "Why should a businessman concern himself with index number construction, sources of data, and forecasting methods if published forecasts by professional economists are readily available?" Part of the answer to this question lies in the fact that businessmen without this knowledge are severely handicapped in their efforts to read intelligently and understand these forecasts. Another part of the answer is that businessmen require this knowledge in order to make forecasts when substantial disagreement prevails among professional forecasters; also, differences which develop among executives of the same firm can be reconciled more easily if the executives possess some knowledge of forecasting techniques. Still another part of the answer lies in the fact that no professional outside consulting service can be personalized and tailored to interpret fully the impact of economic developments on individual firms. The business executive cannot escape the responsibility for making decisions; and decisions pertaining to future operations are based on forecasts. A forecast based on pertinent data interpreted in the light of current and anticipated conditions, though by no means infallible, is far superior to a forecast based on hunches and rumors.

Application of results

The forecast of general business conditions serves as the foundation for other forecasts which a firm requires. Forecasts of business conditions on the national level must be reduced to forecasts of business conditions in the area or areas where a firm operates. Closely allied to the general business forecast is the forecast for the industry of which an individual firm is a part. This forecast may be made by the same methods as used in arriving at the forecast for general business conditions. A wealth of data is available for every major industry and for many minor industries.

Forecasts of general business conditions and industry conditions provide a basis for sales forecasts. There is an important relationship between general economic conditions and a firm's sales, although sales of certain products react differently to changing economic conditions. In large organizations responsibility for general business forecasts is often placed in an economic research unit, and responsibility for sales forecasts may be placed in a market research unit closely allied with the sales department. However, separation of responsibility for preparation of these forecasts in no way reduces the dependence of the sales forecast on the general business forecast. This division of labor is a logical one which permits desirable specialization. The market research unit engages in surveys of consumer reaction and studies trends of sales by products, territories, and salesmen. Forecasts of future trends are adjusted on the basis of the forecast of general business conditions. Chapters 7 and 8 describe some of the techniques which may be used to forecast sales.

Questions and Exercises

1. Discuss the importance of forecasting general business conditions for management planning.

2. List and briefly describe at least eight published indicators of general business conditions.

3. What are index numbers?

4. Describe the nature and purpose of the following types of indexes:
   (a) Price indexes,
   (b) Quantity indexes,
   (c) Value indexes,
   (d) Business activity indexes.

5. There are a number of indexes designed to measure changes in construction costs. What factors should be considered in selecting an index from this group?

6. Explain briefly the following methods of computing index numbers:
   (a) Simple aggregative method,
   (b) Simple average of relatives method,
   (c) Weighted aggregative method,
   (d) Weighted average of relatives method.

7. Compute price (and/or quantity) index numbers using data which are appropriate in the tabulation below. Compute indexes by each of the methods listed in question 6. Experiment with various base periods.

	Quantity sold			*Price per unit*		
Commodity	*1958*	*1959*	*1960*	*1958*	*1959*	*1960*
A	30	40	50	$2.00	$2.20	$2.25
B	20	30	35	1.80	1.90	2.00
C	50	40	45	1.00	1.10	0.80

8. (a) Referring to appropriate sources, study the composition of the following indexes:
   (1) Bureau of Labor Statistics *Consumer Price Index*
   (2) Federal Reserve Board *Index of Industrial Production*
   (3) *Gross National Product*
   (4) The Dow-Jones indexes of industrial, rail, and utility stocks
   (5) Index of prices received by farmers

   (b) For each of the above indexes, answer the following questions:
   (1) What is the index designed to measure?

(2) What general types of items are included in the index? i.e., what are the major components?

(3) What criticism do you have of the manner in which the indexes are constructed?

9. (a) Deflate annual sales for company A by the index of retail prices.

Year	*Annual sales (thousands)*	*Index of retail prices (1935–1939 = 100)*
1950	$40	189.0
1951	44	206.8
1952	45	210.4
1953	47	209.1
1954	48	208.5
1955	52	208.0
1956	54	211.2
1957	58	217.2
1958	60	220.1

(b) Explain the significance of your computations in (a).

(c) Shift the base of the index of retail prices to 1952–1954.

(d) Use the index on the new base to deflate the 1950 and 1958 sales figures. Explain the differences in deflated sales which result.

10. Prepare a forecast of general business conditions based on an analysis of recent trends and current economic and political developments. Your report may be developed from the following outline. This exercise, in expanded form, may be assigned as a term project in lieu of exercise 4, Chapter 2.

I. Introduction—Purpose, scope, method
II. Trends in Business as Revealed by Major Indicators
  A. Quantitative indicators
    1. Gross national product and its components
      a. Personal consumption expenditures
      b. Gross private domestic investment
        (1) New construction
        (2) Producers' durable equipment
        (3) Change in business inventories
      c. Net foreign investment
      d. Government purchases of goods and services
    2. Industrial production
    3. Employment
  B. Price indicators
    1. Wholesale prices
    2. Consumer prices
  C. Financial indicators
    1. Volume of bank deposits and currency outstanding
    2. Interest rates, the capital market
    3. Consumer credit
III. Impact of the Federal Government on Business
  A. Government spending, taxation, and the public debt

B. Monetary and credit policies
C. Regulation and control of business and agriculture
D. Attitude of government toward private enterprise

IV. Impact of the International Situation on Business

V. Summary and Conclusions
A. General outlook for production, employment and prices
1. United States
2. Your state
3. Your community

SOURCE OF INFORMATION

1. Recent issues of *Federal Reserve Bulletin* and the *Federal Reserve Chartbook.*
2. Recent issues of *Survey of Current Business.*
3. Recent issues of news letters of leading commercial banks and Federal Reserve banks; for example, National City Bank monthly letter or *Business Conditions* report of Federal Reserve Bank of Chicago.
4. Reports of the President's Council of Economic Advisers.
5. Miscellaneous business services and business magazines.

7 *Forecasting business activity: time series analysis*

The analysis of movements of series of data over periods of time is referred to as *time series analysis.* A major purpose of such analysis is to improve forecasts of the future and thereby facilitate executive planning of business operations. Techniques of time series analysis may be utilized in forecasting movements of aggregates such as national industrial production, employment, and department store sales. However, analyses of these series are made by both public and private research organizations which regularly publish their findings. Hence the businessman's principal concern is with application of time series analysis to the sales of the individual firm.

At the outset it should be stated that methods of analysis provide at best only approximations of future activity. Results from application of mathematical formulas must always be tempered by judgment and knowledge of factors which cannot be reduced to mathematical terms. Nevertheless, study of these methods provides businessmen with a clearer understanding of the nature of the forces affecting the level of economic activity over time. It is this understanding, rather than any mathematical formulas, which is a prerequisite to sound forecasting.

Major factors which influence business activity

Business activity at any given point in time is influenced by four major factors: (1) long-time trend, (2) cyclical variation, (3) seasonal variation, and (4) irregular fluctuations. Analysis of the historical patterns of the first three factors may prove helpful in forecasting sales and business activity; the fourth factor, irregular fluctuations, has no pattern and defies attempts at systematic forecasting.

LONG-TIME TREND

The pattern of growth of industries and firms over a considerable period of years is referred to as the *secular* or *long-time trend.* Frequently this trend for an individual firm or industry takes the shape of an elongated *S*, as illustrated in Chart 5. Slow growth in the early years of existence is often followed by a period of rapid growth until a point of market saturation when a period of slower growth or stability is encountered. Eventually a period of decline may set in which ulti-

CHART 5. Illustration of a long-time trend

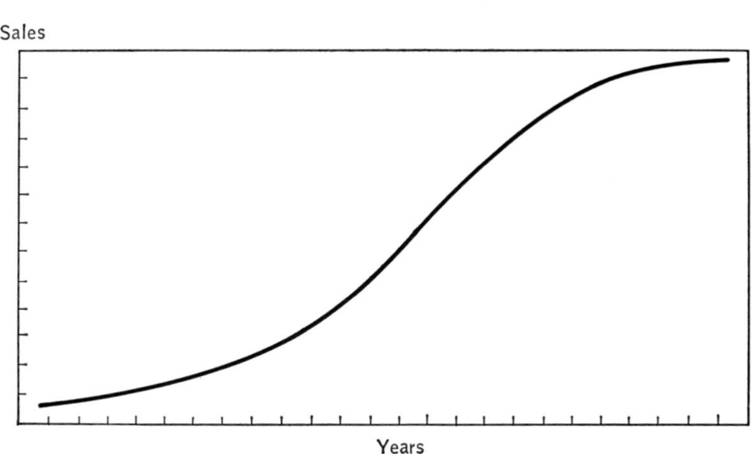

mately may terminate in the dissolution of the firm or death of the industry.

Long-time trend is illustrated graphically by a smooth line which may be straight or curved, depending upon the rate of growth or decline during the specific period which is being analyzed. Departures of actual sales from the long-time trend are assumed to result from cyclical, seasonal, or irregular forces.

CYCLICAL VARIATION

Business cycles may be described as consisting of four phases: (1) prosperity, (2) recession, (3) depression, (4) recovery. Although much

CHART 6. Illustration of cyclical variation

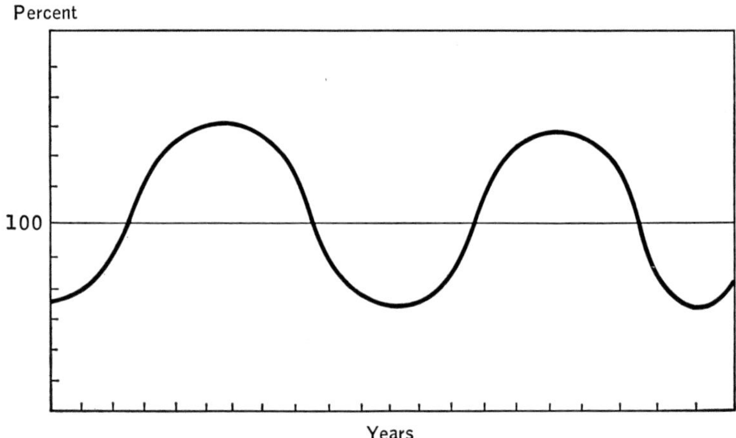

research has been devoted to cycle analysis, no method has been discovered which can be used to predict with exactness the duration or amplitude of a cycle or its component phases. Wars, technological developments, widespread crop failures, and other irregular forces seriously disrupt historical cyclical patterns. Consequently, the businessman must rely more on his analysis of current economic conditions than on historical patterns when he forecasts future cyclical movements.

Cyclical variation may be illustrated graphically by a line which undulates around *normal* activity. In Chart 6 *normal* has been designated as 100 per cent and cyclical activity has been expressed as varying per cents of *normal*.

SEASONAL VARIATION

Variation in business activity from month to month arises from climatic factors and from custom. Changes in climate cause sharp seasonal fluctuations in agriculture, logging, fishing, construction, and tourist industries. Retail sales show marked increases at Christmas, Easter, and at other times because of the impact of custom on buying habits.

Seasonal variations are much more regular and frequent in their occurrence than are cyclical variations. Hence, historical seasonal patterns provide a reasonably reliable basis for forecasting future

CHART 7. Illustration of seasonal variation

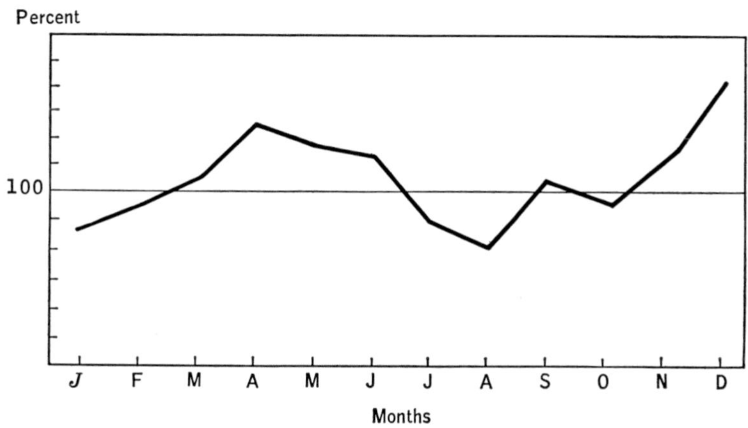

seasonal patterns. It is customary to express seasonal variation in any given month as a per cent, or *index*, of average monthly sales for a year. This is illustrated in Chart 7 where annual average monthly sales are indicated by the 100 per cent line.

Patterns of seasonal variation differ widely, depending largely on the nature of business operations and depending also on location. Seasonal patterns may shift over a period of time. This is true if advertising leads to shifts in buying habits or if manufacturers shift the dates when new models are placed on the market. In general, however, seasonal patterns remain relatively constant.

IRREGULAR FLUCTUATIONS

Wars, strikes, and "acts of God" are erratic in their occurrence. Over a period of time the effects of minor irregular fluctuations tend to cancel or average out. Large-scale wars or devastating disasters may completely alter the long-time trend and cyclical variations. Wars result in booms for some firms and depressions for others. A hurricane or flood may cause millions of dollars' loss in stricken areas but cause a subsequent boom for the construction industry. Political decisions involving expenditure of funds, taxation, or business regulation may have a pronounced though varied impact on business firms.

Although businessmen cannot predict the occurrence of irregular fluctuations they can improve their ability to adjust to them by anticipating fluctuations due to trend, cycles, and seasons.

METHODS OF ESTIMATING MAJOR FACTORS

Measures of trend, cyclical, and seasonal variation are computed by methods of averaging. Trend is longest in duration, cycles are of shorter duration, and a complete pattern of seasonal variation occurs every twelve months. Irregular fluctuations are of varying lengths but are usually of shorter duration than cycles and often are shorter than seasonal variations. By averaging data over a long period of years, cyclical, seasonal, and irregular fluctuations are canceled, and a smooth trend line results. Methods of averaging to determine trend are described in succeeding sections of this chapter.

Past cyclical variations may be estimated by first eliminating trend and seasonal influences from original data (sales) and then averaging out the irregular fluctuations. This may be best illustrated by using the following symbols:

T = long-time trend
C = cyclical variation
S = seasonal variation
I = irregular fluctuations

Original data, such as sales, are regarded as the product of these several forces. Hence, data for each month may be symbolized as

$T \times C \times S \times I$, or simply *TCSI*. Annual data are expressed as *TCI* since seasonal variations are not reflected in yearly totals or annual monthly averages. Division of annual data (*TCI*) by trend (*T*) results in a measure of cyclical and irregular variation (*CI*).[1]

$$\frac{TCI}{T} = CI$$

Smoothing the *CI*'s with a moving average tends to cancel out the irregular fluctuations (*I*) and results in a measure of cyclical variation (*C*).[2]

Measures of seasonal variation may be obtained by the same general method as used to estimate cyclical movements. Monthly data (*TCSI*) are divided by trend and cyclical fluctuations (*TC*) to arrive at estimates of seasonal and irregular variations.

$$\frac{TCSI}{TC} = SI$$

For each month of the year, an average of several *SI*'s from different years tends to eliminate the irregular fluctuations and results in a measure of seasonal variation (*S*).

Actual computation of estimates of trend, cycles, and seasonal movements involves numerous steps which often confuse the beginner. This preview of general method should be used by the reader as an aid to the understanding of the details of computation described in the sections which follow.

Methods of estimating trend

GENERAL CONSIDERATIONS

Since trend is considered as the pattern of general movement over a long period, it is necessary to determine how many years constitute a long period. Trend can be more rigorously defined as a generally irreversible movement which persists for a period which is long in relation to the cycle. Since the cycle varies from approximately 23 months in cotton goods production to almost 18 years in residential housing, it is difficult to specify just how many years of data are

[1] In the case of monthly data, which must be used if cycle turning points are to be pinpointed, *TCSI* would be divided by *TS* to arrive at *CI*.

[2] The method for computing a moving average is described in the following section of this chapter.

necessary to the successful isolation of the secular (long-run) trend. In most cases, the period covered probably should not include less than eight to ten years and, ideally, should include at least 20 years. Care must be exercised, however, not to include completely dissimilar periods in the computation. The occurrence of a war or other major economic upheaval or significant technological advances can cause the trend to change radically in nature between two periods. These remarks should not be interpreted to mean that new firms cannot make use of trend analysis in forecasting. Trends over brief periods can be recomputed easily as experience increases. Also, trends for the industry or older competing firms can be studied to advantage.

FREEHAND METHOD

Plotting actual data on a chart and drawing a freehand line through the data in effect represents a visual averaging process. This method is easy to apply and may be superior to other methods when performed by a person who possesses mature judgment and thorough knowledge of a firm's operations and of general business conditions. Application of the freehand method should not be attempted by persons who are unfamiliar with the operating characteristics of a firm.

METHOD OF SEMI-AVERAGES

The method of semi-averages is quite simple but not very satisfactory. Computational steps are illustrated in Table 28. The period of years is divided into two equal parts; where the period contains an odd number of years, the middle year is disregarded. Totals are next computed for each half of the period. Semi-averages are computed by dividing each total by the number of years in the semi-period. For example, in Table 28, the total sales for the period 1938–1947 were $4,939.6 million; average annual sales during this period were $4,939.6 divided by 10 years, or $494.0 million. Note that semi-totals and semi-averages are placed opposite the mid-points of their respective periods in Table 28. The final step is to plot the semi-averages on a chart and draw a straight line through them. A comparison of actual sales and trend as computed by the method of semi-averages is graphically illustrated in Chart 8.

Selection of the period of years has a direct bearing on the slope of the line. If a depression prevailed during the first half of the period

TABLE 28. Long-time trend of J. C. Penney Company net sales, 1938–1958, computed by the method of semi-averages

(Millions of Dollars)

Year	Net sales	Semi-totals	Semi-averages
1938	$ 258.0		
1939	282.1		
1940	304.5		
1941	377.6		
1942	490.4	$ 4,939.6	$ 494.0
1943	489.9		
1944	535.4		
1945	549.2		
1946	676.6		
1947	775.9		
1948	885.2		
1949	880.2		
1950	949.7		
1951	1,035.2		
1952	1,079.3		
1953	1,109.5	11,395.3	1,139.5
1954	1,107.2		
1955	1,220.0		
1956	1,291.9		
1957	1,312.3		
1958	1,410.0		

Source: *Moody's Industrial Manual*, selected issues.

and prosperity characterized the second half, the straight-line trend would be steeper than appropriate. If prosperity occurred during the first half and depression during the second half, the line would be unduly depressed. It is desirable that each half of the period contain the same number of prosperous and depressed years. Unfortunately it is frequently impossible to select periods which meet this requirement and which also are significant in other respects. Operations of many firms have not spanned several business cycles, or even a single business cycle. Since it is important for all firms to predict trend, it becomes apparent that the method of semi-averages is unsatisfactory for many firms.

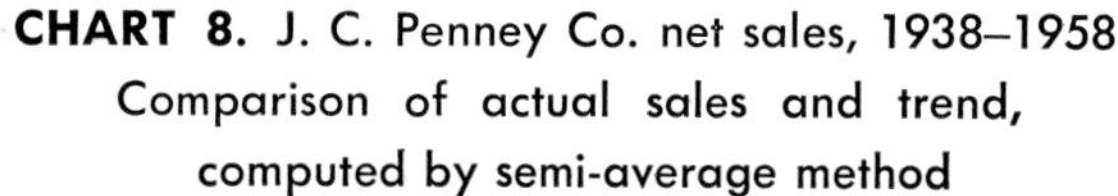

CHART 8. J. C. Penney Co. net sales, 1938–1958. Comparison of actual sales and trend, computed by semi-average method

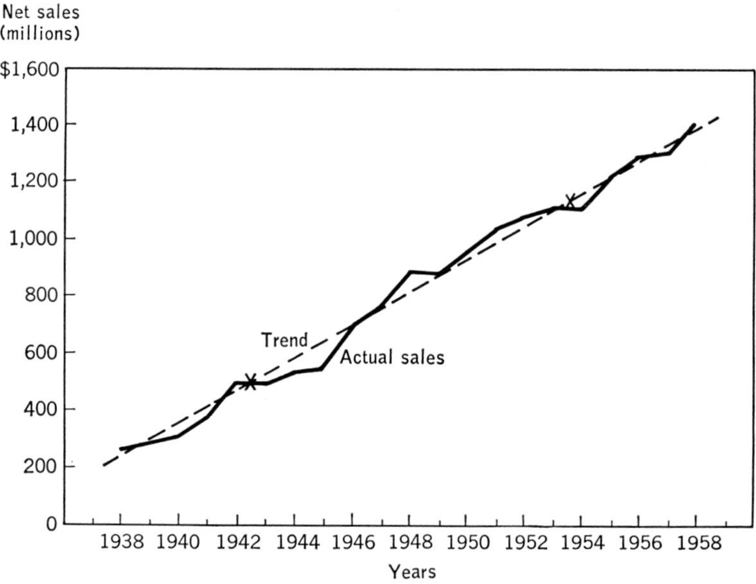

Source: Table 28.

MOVING-AVERAGE METHOD

Table 29 shows this method of computing long-time trend. First compute a series of moving totals for periods consisting of a predetermined number of years—five years in this illustration. Referring to Table 29 it may be observed that total sales for 1938–1942 amounted to $1,712.6 million; total sales for 1939–1943 were $1,944.5 million, etc. Each succeeding moving total is computed by omitting the first year of the preceding period and including the year which follows the last year of the preceding period. The total of $1,712.6 million for 1938–1942 is placed opposite 1940, the middle year of the period. The moving average for 1938–1942 is computed by dividing the total sales by the number of years, $1,712.6 million divided by 5 years equals $342.5 million. The original data and the moving-average trend line are shown in Chart 9.

Theoretically, the length of the moving period should coincide with the length of the business cycle which characterizes the data series.

TABLE 29. Long-time trend of J. C. Penney Company net sales, 1938–1958 computed by five-year moving average

(Millions of Dollars)

Year	Net sales	Five-year moving total	Five-year moving average
1938	$ 258.0		
1939	282.1		
1940	304.5	$1,712.6	$ 342.5
1941	377.6	1,944.5	388.9
1942	490.4	2,197.8	439.6
1943	489.9	2,442.5	488.5
1944	535.4	2,741.5	548.3
1945	549.2	3,027.0	605.4
1946	676.6	3,422.3	684.5
1947	775.9	3,767.1	753.4
1948	885.2	4,167.6	833.5
1949	880.2	4,526.2	905.2
1950	949.7	4,829.6	965.9
1951	1,035.2	5,053.9	1,010.8
1952	1,079.3	5,280.9	1,056.2
1953	1,109.5	5,551.2	1,110.2
1954	1,107.2	5,807.9	1,161.6
1955	1,220.0	6,040.9	1,208.2
1956	1,291.9	6,341.4	1,268.3
1957	1,312.3		
1958	1,410.0		

Source: Table 28 and related computations.

This is required in order to average out the cyclical fluctuations; irregular fluctuations which are shorter than cyclical fluctuations also tend to be cancelled by this averaging process. In actual practice it is rarely possible to select a period of years which satisfies these theoretical considerations, because successive business cycles vary considerably in their duration. The five-year period in Table 29 was selected for illustrative purposes only.

The moving-average computed in Table 29 has been plotted in Chart 9. Although the slope of the line changes from year to year, it maintains a course which is below the peaks and above the low points of the line depicting actual sales. Presumably these high and low points resulted from cyclical and/or irregular forces which have been smoothed out by the five-year moving-average. Note that a moving-

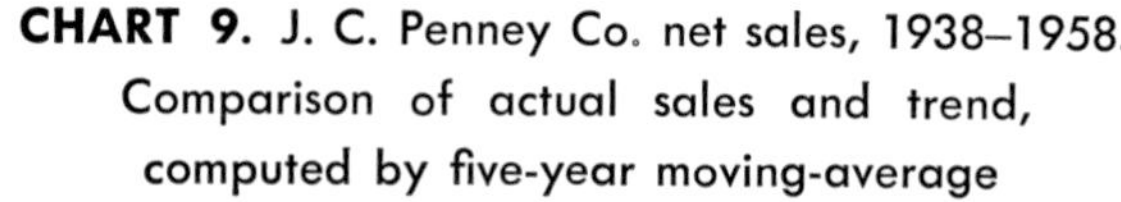

CHART 9. J. C. Penney Co. net sales, 1938–1958. Comparison of actual sales and trend, computed by five-year moving-average

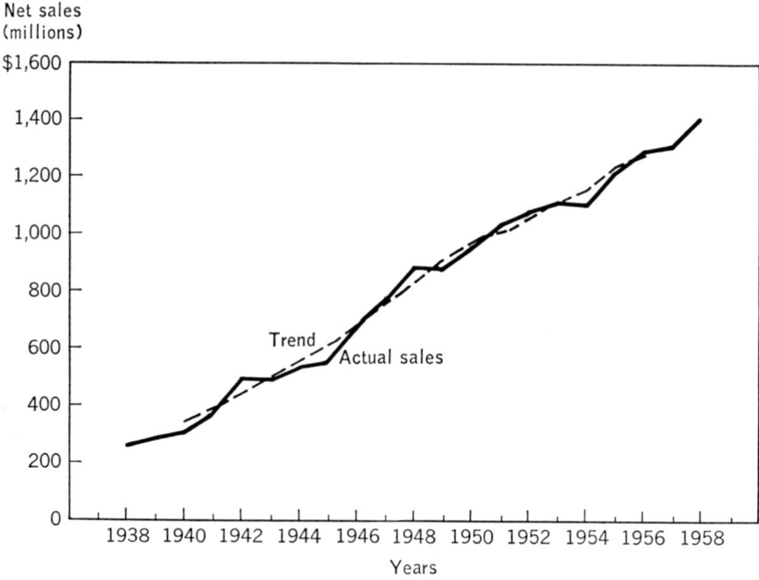

Source: Table 29.

average trend estimate for 1957 could not be computed until sales for 1959 had been determined. Had a seven-year moving-average been used, the latest year for which trend could have been estimated would have been 1955.

The moving-average method has two serious limitations. First, the variation in the length and amplitude of business cycles usually makes it impossible to select a wholly satisfactory moving-period. A moving-average can properly smooth cyclical fluctuations only if the moving-period is equal to the length of the cycle. Second, it is impossible to compute estimates of trend for the most recent year or years; the number of years for which estimates cannot be computed increases as the length of the moving-period increases.

METHOD OF LEAST SQUARES

This method may be used to compute either straight or curved trend lines. Estimates of trend are calculated in such a manner that the sum of *squared* deviations of actual sales from estimated sales are at a minimum; hence the term *least squares*.

The discussion in this text is limited to a description of the method for computing a straight-line trend by the method of least squares. Calculation of curved-line trends employs the same principle but involves more complex mathematics. Also, curve-line trends can often be approximated satisfactorily with straight-line trends after suitable transformation of the data.

Straight-line equation. The formula for a straight line is

$$Y = a + bX.$$

In time series analysis, X symbolizes time periods and Y represents sales, production, inventory, i.e., the variable whose fluctuations over time are being studied. Whereas Y and X vary, a and b remain constant and may be defined as follows:

a = The value of Y when X equals zero, the determinant of the height of the straight line above the horizontal (X) axis.

b = The amount of change in Y which occurs with each unit change in X (b indicates the slope of the straight line).

Since the X values represent time periods (years) and are known to the analyst, estimated values of long-time trend may be calculated as soon as the values of a and b have been determined. Fortunately these values are easy to compute if certain conditions are rigidly observed. These conditions may best be described by reference to Table 30. The first two columns show years and actual sales, respectively. The third column from the left is headed by the symbol X. This may be confusing to the reader since the first line of this paragraph states that X values represented years. Actually, the figures in the X column do represent time, or years. In fact, they are substitutes for the cumbersome four-digit numbers of 1938, 1939, 1940, etc. Values of a and b may be determined by this short method *only if* the center of the period is assigned a substitute value of zero and if the years on either side are assigned values which cancel each other, i.e., if $\Sigma X = 0$. Hence in Table 30 the year 1948 is assigned an X value of zero; 1949 is assigned an X value of 1; 1947 is assigned an X value of -1; etc. Under these conditions the values of a and b may be calculated by the following formulas:

$$a = \frac{\Sigma Y}{N}, \qquad b = \frac{\Sigma XY}{\Sigma X^2}$$

TABLE 30. Straight-line trend of J. C. Penney Company net sales

Computed by Method of Least Squares for Odd Number of Years, 1938–1958

Year	Net sales (millions) Y	Deviations in years X	Sales weighted by deviations XY	Deviations squared X^2	Long-term trend of net sales T
1938	$ 258.0	−10	−2,580.0	100	$ 217.5
1939	282.1	−9	−2,538.9	81	276.8
1940	304.5	−8	−2,436.0	64	336.1
1941	377.6	−7	−2,643.2	49	395.4
1942	490.4	−6	−2,942.4	36	454.7
1943	489.9	−5	−2,449.5	25	514.0
1944	535.4	−4	−2,141.6	16	573.3
1945	549.2	−3	−1,647.6	9	632.6
1946	676.6	−2	−1,353.2	4	691.9
1947	775.9	−1	−775.9	1	751.2
1948	885.2	0	0.0	0	810.5
1949	880.2	1	880.2	1	869.8
1950	949.7	2	1,899.4	4	929.1
1951	1,035.2	3	3,105.6	9	988.4
1952	1,079.3	4	4,317.2	16	1,047.7
1953	1,109.5	5	5,547.5	25	1,107.0
1954	1,107.2	6	6,643.2	36	1,166.3
1955	1,220.0	7	8,540.0	49	1,225.6
1956	1,291.9	8	10,335.2	64	1,284.9
1957	1,312.3	9	11,810.7	81	1,344.2
1958	1,410.0	10	14,100.0	100	1,403.5
Total:	$17,020.1	0	45,670.7	770	$17,020.5

Source: *Moody's Industrial Manual*, selected issues.

$$a = \frac{\Sigma Y}{N} = \frac{17{,}020.1}{21} = \mathbf{810.5}, \qquad b = \frac{\Sigma XY}{\Sigma X^2} = \frac{45{,}670.7}{770} = \mathbf{59.3}$$

T (Trend) $= 810.5 + 59.3X$, with origin in 1948 and with units of X expressed in terms of years and T in millions of dollars.

It is now apparent that a is simply the average sales for the period. Columns of XY and X^2 in Table 30 must be computed before the slope of the line, b, can be determined. When this has been accomplished, the long-time trend estimates of sales (T) in the right-hand column may be calculated by substituting appropriate values for a, b, and X in the equation.

$$Y = a + bX$$

or, substituting a meaningful symbol T (trend) for calculated Y.

$$T = a + bX$$

Computation of estimated trend values. The least squares straight-line trend equation for the data in Table 30 is

$$T = 810.5 + 59.3X$$

with origin in 1948 and with units of X expressed in years and T in millions of dollars. This equation, in effect, states the following:

1. In 1948 (when $X = 0$), estimated sales due to trend amount to \$810.5 million ($a = 810.5$).
2. An increase of \$59.3 million (\$59,300,000) in sales will occur each year due to trend ($b = 59.3$). However, the reader must recognize that actual sales may increase more, less, or even decrease as a result of the additional effects of cyclical and/or irregular forces.

Estimated trend for 1938 is solved by substituting -10 for X:

$$T = 810.5 + 59.3(-10) = 810.5 - 593.0 = \mathbf{217.5}$$

Trend values for other years may be determined in similar fashion, or by merely adding the value of b to each preceding trend value. For purposes of plotting a least squares straight-line trend on a chart, it is necessary to compute trend values for but two years and connect these points with a straight line; this has been illustrated on Chart 10.

Meaning of trend estimates. Theoretically, the long-time trend of sales appearing in the right-hand column of Table 30 reflects the volume of sales resulting from trend forces alone. For example, in 1950 it was estimated that sales should have amounted to \$929.1 million in the absence of cyclical and/or irregular forces. The fact that actual sales in 1950 were \$949.7 million indicates that cyclical and/or irregular forces pushed actual sales above their normal long-time trend. Based on a projection of trend alone, 1959 sales would be forecast at \$1,462.8 million. It should be recognized that trend estimates are truly *estimates*; the influence of cyclical and irregular forces may not be wholly removed.

Computation of trend for period with even number of years. The method for calculating trend for a period with an odd number of years was illustrated in Table 30. The important condition that the X value for the center of the period be zero was satisfied by assigning an X value of zero to 1948, the middle year in the series. This made it possible

CHART 10. Net sales of J. C. Penney Co., 1938–1958. Comparison of actual sales and trend computed by method of least squares

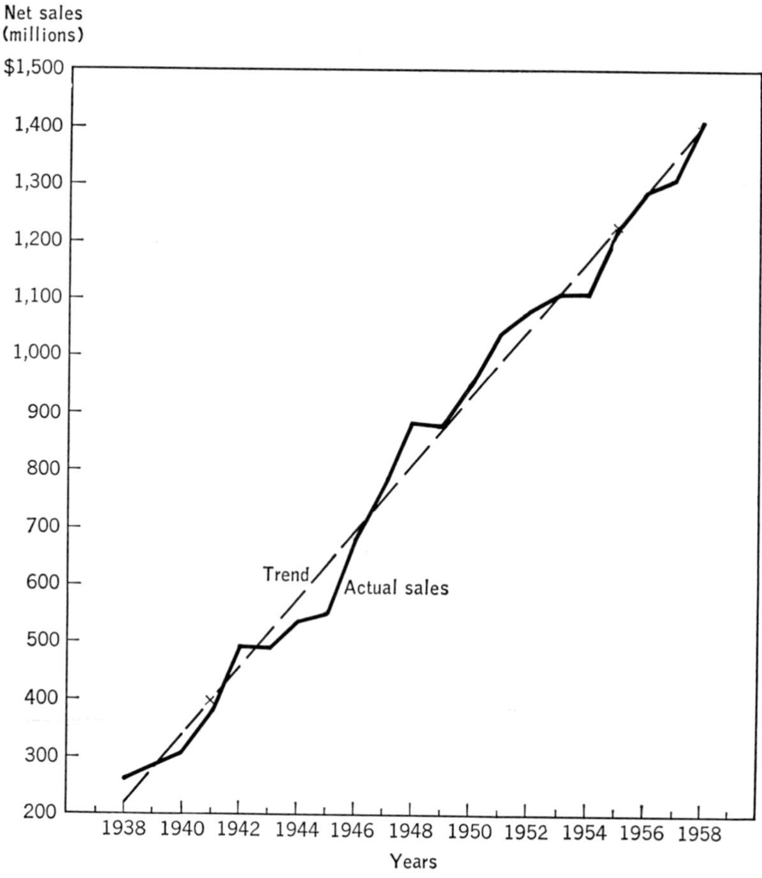

Source: Table 30.

to satisfy the condition that X values assigned to years on both sides of the zero point must cancel out, i.e., that $\Sigma X = 0$.

Table 31 shows how these conditions may be met when the period contains an even number of years. The mid-point of the period 1939–1958 is January 1, 1949. By assigning each six-month interval a value of 1, we can designate X values for 1948 and 1949 (each at July 1) as -1 and $+1$, respectively. It logically follows that the X value for 1950 (July 1) must be $+3$, since it is two six-month periods from 1949. This device permits us to satisfy the mathematical conditions upon

TABLE 31. Straight-line trend of J. C. Penney Company net sales

Computed by Method of Least Squares for Even Number of Years 1939–1958

Year	Net sales (millions) Y	Deviations in 6-month intervals X	Sales weighted by deviations XY	Deviations squared X^2	Long-term trend of net sales T
1939	$ 282.1	−19	−5,359.9	361	$ 268.1
1940	304.5	−17	−5,176.5	289	328.1
1941	377.6	−15	−5,664.0	225	388.1
1942	490.4	−13	−6,375.2	169	448.1
1943	489.9	−11	−5,388.9	121	508.1
1944	535.4	−9	−4,818.6	81	568.1
1945	549.2	−7	−3,844.4	49	628.1
1946	676.6	−5	−3,383.0	25	688.1
1947	775.9	−3	−2,327.7	9	748.1
1948	885.2	−1	−885.2	1	808.1
1949	880.2	1	880.2	1	868.1
1950	949.7	3	2,849.1	9	928.1
1951	1,035.2	5	5,176.0	25	988.1
1952	1,079.3	7	7,555.1	49	1,048.1
1953	1,109.5	9	9,985.5	81	1,108.1
1954	1,107.2	11	12,179.2	121	1,168.1
1955	1,220.0	13	15,860.0	169	1,228.1
1956	1,291.9	15	19,378.5	225	1,288.1
1957	1,312.3	17	22,309.1	289	1,348.1
1958	1,410.0	19	26,790.0	361	1,408.1
Totals:	$16,762.1	0	79,739.3	2,660	$16,762.0

Source: *Moody's Industrial Manual*, selected issues.

$$a = \frac{\Sigma Y}{N} = \frac{16{,}762.1}{20} = \mathbf{838.1}$$

$$b = \frac{\Sigma XY}{\Sigma X^2} = \frac{79{,}739.3}{2{,}660} = 29.98 = \mathbf{30.0}$$

T (Trend) $= 838.1 + 30.0X$, with origin on January 1, 1949, and with units of X expressed in terms of six-months intervals and T in millions of dollars.

which the short formulas for a and b depend. Note that the two equations for long-time trend of J. C. Penney Company sales are closely comparable.

Odd years:

$T = 810.5 + 59.3X$; Origin, July 1, 1948; $X =$ one year

Even years:

$T = 838.1 + 30.0X$; Origin, January 1, 1949; X = six months

Even years converted to same origin as odd-year trend:

$T = 808.1 + 60.0X$; Origin, July 1, 1948; X = one year

LIMITATIONS OF RIGID METHODS

Projection of future trends should never be based solely upon historical trend lines computed by rigid mathematical methods. This is true because vastly different results may be obtained merely by selecting different periods of years. In Chart 11 least squares straight lines have been fitted to sales of J. C. Penney Company for four different periods. Trend I (1945–1952) has a steep slope, with sales due to trend increasing $71.7 million each year. At the other extreme is Trend IV (1948–1954), which has a slope of sales increasing only $44.8 million per year. Each of these lines is mathematically correct. Yet it is possible that none of them may prove to be the pattern of future growth.

Table 32 compares estimates of 1959 sales as computed by various methods. Estimated 1959 sales range from $1,364.9 million to $1,606.3 million. This range of forecast sales will become wider each year. Obviously five of the six forecasts must be incorrect and it is quite possible that none of them is right.

On several occasions the author has observed the use of straight-line trends where curved-line trends or linear transformations of

TABLE 32. Estimated 1959 sales of J. C. Penney Company

Based on Various Methods of Computing Trend

Method of estimating trend	Net sales (millions)
Semi-average	$1,465.0
Moving-average	*
Least-squares:	
1938–1958	1,462.8
1939–1958	1,468.1
1940–1950	1,537.2
1945–1952	1,606.3
1948–1954	1,364.9

* Mathematical projection of moving average is not possible.

CHART 11. Net sales of J. C. Penney Co., 1939–1958. Comparison of actual sales and four straight-line trends computed by methods of least squares

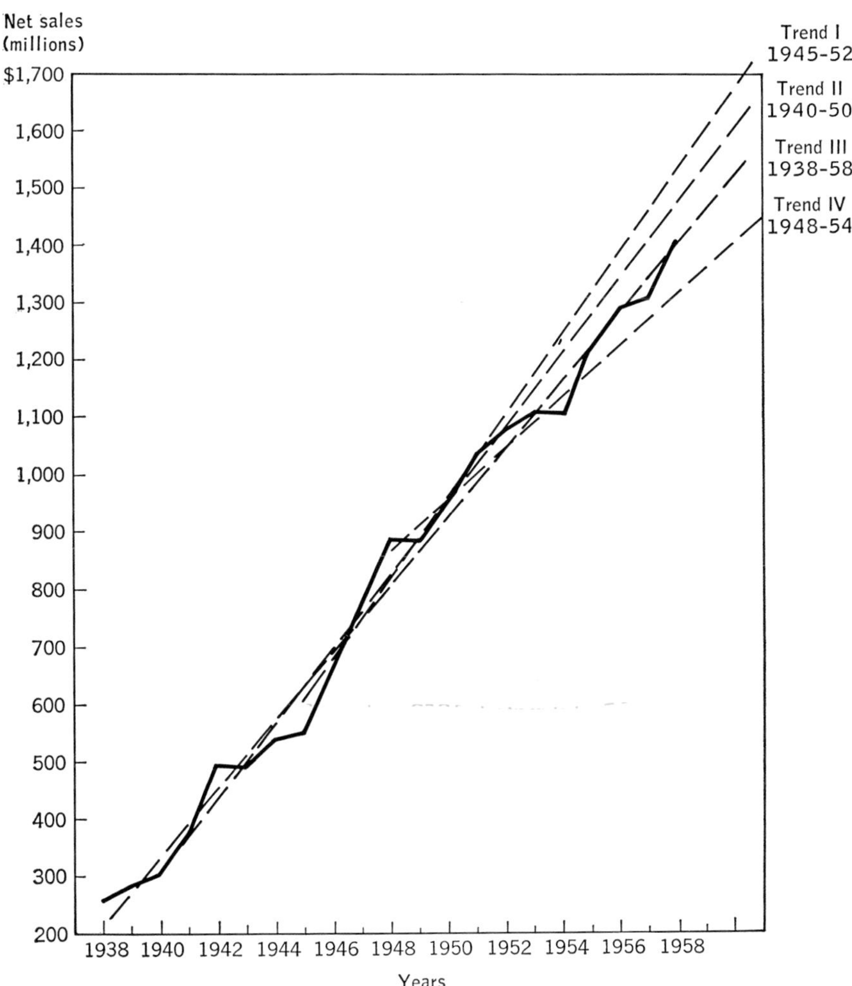

Source: Basic data from Table 30.

curved-line trends would have been more appropriate. For example, a straight-line trend fitted to a series of data rising rapidly in the pattern of a curve will result in lower projected values than would have been obtained with a curved line. If such a series would plot as a straight line on a semilogarithmic or ratio chart, then a straight line fitted to the logarithms would be appropriate.[3]

summary

Mathematical methods of estimating trend generally produce such a variety of results that a serious question is raised concerning their validity. When employed by persons uninformed concerning the nature of the data and the nature of economic conditions, the results may be dangerously misleading.

However, the above methods may be useful as an aid to a person who possesses the requisite knowledge of a firm's operations and economic affairs. Such a person is in a favorable position to select a period of years as a base which is likely to reflect the pattern of future growth. Even so, the computed trend line can serve only as a point of departure in predicting future trend. Recent technological developments, population shifts, and political conditions on local, national, and international levels may significantly alter the long-time trend of an industry or a firm. These and other pertinent factors must receive due attention by all who attempt to make realistic projections of future trends.

Method of estimating cyclical variation

The irregularity of cyclical patterns is such that future cyclical movements can better be predicted by an analysis of current economic and political forces than by reliance on a continuation of past cyclical behavior. Methods for analyzing general business conditions were described in Chapter 6.

However, a fuller understanding of the concepts of trend and cyclical forces may be obtained by mathematically adjusting data for trend; the adjusted figures reflect fluctuations which presumably occurred because of cyclical and/or irregular forces. If original annual data are regarded as the product of trend, cyclical and irregular forces (*TCI*), an estimate of the impact of cyclical and irregular forces (*CI*) may be computed by dividing the original data by estimates of

[3] The semilogarithmic, or ratio chart, is described in Chapter 10.

long-time trend (T). This procedure may be illustrated symbolically as follows:

$$\frac{TCI}{T} = CI$$

Smoothing CI with a moving average results in an indication of cyclical variation (C).

Annual sales of J. C. Penney Company have been adjusted for trend in Table 33. Net sales (TCI) have been divided by trend estimates (T), as calculated in Table 30, to obtain adjusted sales (CI). It will be noted that adjusted sales (CI) are expressed as per cents rather than as dollar amounts. Hence, in 1938, net sales ($258.0 million) were 18.6 per cent higher than *normal* (100 per cent), or

TABLE 33. Adjustment of J. C. Penney Company sales for trend, 1938–1958

Year	Net sales (millions) TCI	Trend (millions) T	Adjusted sales ($TCI \div T$) CI	Three-year moving average adjusted sales C
1938	$ 258.0	$ 217.5	118.6	
1939	282.1	276.8	101.9	103.7
1940	304.5	336.1	90.5	96.0
1941	377.6	395.4	95.5	98.0
1942	490.4	454.7	107.9	99.6
1943	489.9	514.0	95.3	98.9
1944	535.4	573.3	93.4	91.8
1945	549.2	632.6	86.8	92.7
1946	676.6	691.9	97.8	96.0
1947	775.9	751.2	103.3	103.4
1948	885.2	810.5	109.2	104.6
1949	880.2	869.8	101.2	104.2
1950	949.7	929.1	102.2	102.7
1951	1,035.2	988.4	104.7	103.3
1952	1,079.3	1,047.7	103.0	102.6
1953	1,109.5	1,107.0	100.2	99.2
1954	1,107.2	1,166.3	94.5	98.1
1955	1,220.0	1,225.6	99.6	98.2
1956	1,291.9	1,284.9	100.5	99.2
1957	1,312.3	1,344.2	97.6	99.5
1958	1,410.0	1,403.5	100.5	

Source: Table 30.

trend sales ($217.5 million). It is reasoned that deviations from *normal* were due to cyclical or irregular forces.

Chart 12 portrays the movement of cyclical and irregular forces in relation to *normal* (trend) as 100 per cent; each estimate of trend is equivalent to 100 per cent. Trend is indicated by the solid straight line at the 100 per cent level. Adjusted sales, which are an index of cyclical and irregular forces, are depicted by the solid irregular line. Fluctuations due to cyclical forces can best be distinguished from

CHART 12. J. C. Penny Co. net sales adjusted for trend, 1938–1958

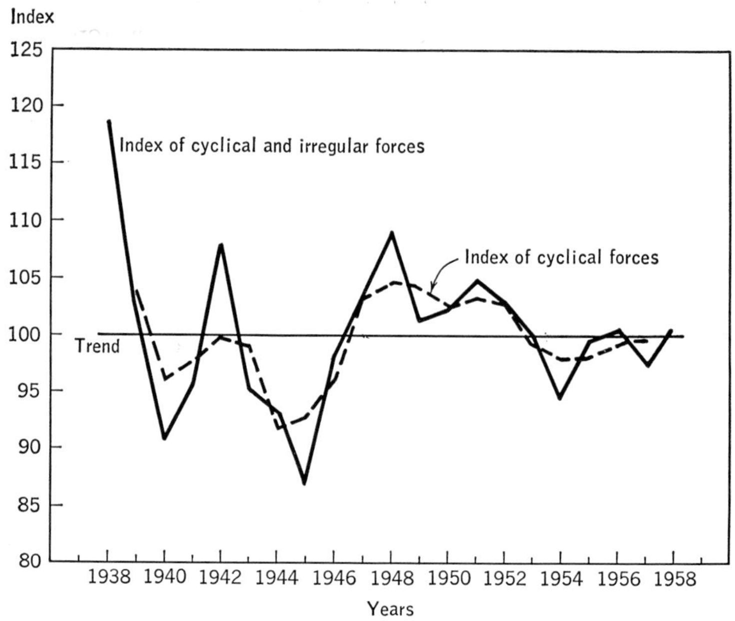

Source: Table 33.

fluctuations caused by irregular forces by knowledge of business conditions and circumstances which influenced the firm's sales.

Adjusted sales (*CI*) may be smoothed by computing a moving-average as was done in the right-hand column of Table 33; the resulting estimate of cyclical forces (*C*) is illustrated by the dotted line on Chart 12. The length of the moving-average must be determined subjectively by inspection; ideally it should be equal in length to the longest irregular fluctuation but it must not be of such length that it will remove the cyclical pattern.

Methods of estimating seasonal variation

Estimates of trend and cyclical forces are adequate for long-range planning, as required for expansion of plant facilities, but estimates of seasonal variation are important for short-run planning. Buyers purchasing stock for sales during a specific season in the coming year are concerned with seasonal variations as well as cyclical and trend movements.

Earlier in this chapter it was mentioned that seasonal fluctuations occur because of climatic patterns and because of customs such as Christmas and Easter. For most firms, sales in certain months almost always tend to be higher than sales in other months of the same year, although the average monthly level of sales may change appreciably from year to year. What is needed is an index which reflects the typical relationship of sales of each month to average sales for the year.

Various methods may be employed to compute a seasonal index. One method is to (1) select a specific year which appears to be typical, (2) compute the average monthly sales, and (3) express actual sales each month as a per cent of average monthly sales. This method is simple but is unsatisfactory because trend, cyclical, and irregular forces are such that no single year can be considered *typical*. Rather, an index of seasonal variation which occurred in a particular year is a *specific* seasonal index.

A continuation and partial improvement of this method is to compute specific seasonal indexes for several years and then take an average of these as a measure of *typical* seasonal variation. If the period of years is long enough, this method has the advantage of averaging out irregular and cyclical fluctuations. However, it cannot eliminate trend which, unlike irregular and cyclical variations, moves in but one direction. In cases where sales are rising over the long-time trend, sales in later months are higher relative to earlier months than they would have been in the absence of trend. It therefore becomes necessary to eliminate trend as well as cyclical and irregular forces before a typical seasonal index may be obtained. The most satisfactory method which has been designed to achieve this purpose is the ratio-to-moving-average method.

RATIO-TO-MOVING-AVERAGE METHOD

This method consists of three basic steps:

1. Computation of a centered 12-month moving-average which does not reflect seasonal and irregular forces and hence is a measure of trend and cyclical forces (*TC*).
2. Computation for each month of a ratio of actual sales (*TCSI*) to the centered 12-month moving-average (*TC*). The resultant ratios (*SI*), expressed as relatives, are *specific* seasonal indexes which reflect irregular as well as seasonal fluctuations.
3. Computation of averages of specific seasonal indexes by months in order to substantially reduce, if not eliminate, variations due to irregular forces. These averages constitute the *typical* seasonal index.

The method obtains its name from the second step which involves computation of ratios of actual sales to moving-averages. The first step, the computation of a moving-average (*TC*) results in a series which reflects changes due to trend and cyclical factors. Removal of these influences from the data makes it possible to average out irregular influences to arrive at the seasonal. It would be impossible to compute a seasonal index by a direct averaging process since seasonal fluctuations are of shorter duration than cycles or trend and would be canceled out when averaging out these longer movements.

Computation of specific seasonal indexes. The first two basic steps of the ratio-to-moving-average method are illustrated in Table 34. The example is limited to seven years; a longer period is sometimes used. Months and years are shown in what is often referred to as the *stub* of the table; sales of the Small-Way Department Store for corresponding periods are shown in column 1. Actual sales include all elements of time series fluctuations (*TCSI*). Note that although sales fluctuated from month to month they increased substantially during this period. This increase reflects trend and cyclical forces which are isolated by computation of the 12-month centered moving-average which cancels out seasonal and irregular variations.

The top figure (000 omitted) in column 2, \$400, is total sales from January through December 1953. The second figure, \$405, is total sales from February 1953 through January 1954. Each succeeding 12-month total *moves* one month nearer to the present. The easiest method to obtain these totals is to deduct the first month's sales from the total for the preceding period and then add the sales for the following month. For example, the total of \$405 may be computed as follows:

	\$400	= sales from January through December 1953
minus	24	= sales in January 1953
	\$376	
plus	29	= sales in January 1954
	\$405	= sales from February 1953 through January 1954

The 1953 sales total of \$400 in column 2 has been placed on a level between June and July—specifically at July 1, the mid-point of the twelve-month period for which it is the sum. In order to obtain an annual total which is *centered* at July 15, it would be necessary to take an average of the annual totals for July 1 and August 1, \$400 and \$405, respectively. The resulting average, \$402.50 would be centered on July 15, 1953. The total of \$402.50 would then be divided by 12 months to obtain the centered 12-month moving-average (TC) of \$33.5 for July 1953, the top amount in column 4. A computational simplification is possible by entering in Column 3 a two-month moving-total of the twelve-month moving-total in Column 1. The two divisions (by 2 to obtain the centered 12-month moving-total and by 12 to obtain the centered moving-average shown in column 4) can be accomplished in one step by dividing the two-month moving-total of the twelve-month moving-total by 24. Note that the two-month moving-total would actually be computed in obtaining the centered moving-total; thus, the number of divisions is decreased from two to one and the computational process is simpler by the illustrated method.

The final column on the right in Table 34 contains the specific seasonal indexes. These indexes were calculated for each month by expressing as per cents the ratio of sales ($TCSI$) to corresponding centered 12-month moving-averages (TC). This may be expressed symbolically as

$$\frac{TCSI}{TC}(100) = SI$$

The specific seasonal index of 86.6 for July 1953 was computed as follows:

$$\frac{\text{sales in July 1953}}{\substack{\text{12-month moving-average}\\ \text{centered on July 1953}}} = \frac{29}{33.5}(100) = 86.6$$

TABLE 34. Computation of specific seasonal indexes for Small-Way Department Store, 1953–1959, ratio-to-moving-average method

Year and month	(1) Sales (000) *TCSI*	(2) 12-month moving total	(3) 2-month moving total of the 12-month moving total	(4) Centered 12-month moving average (col. 3 ÷ 24) *TC*	(5) Specific seasonal indexes (*TCSI* ÷ *TC*) *SI*
1953					
Jan.	$24				
Feb.	25				
Mar.	29				
Apr.	32				
May	35				
June	34				
		$400			
July	29		$ 805	$33.5	86.6
		405			
Aug.	29		815	34.0	85.3
		410			
Sept.	35		822	34.2	102.3
		412			
Oct.	35		831	34.6	101.2
		419			
Nov.	43		839	35.0	122.9
		420			
Dec.	50		843	35.1	142.5
		423			
1954					
Jan.	29		849	35.4	81.9
		426			
Feb.	30		860	35.8	83.8
		434			
Mar.	31		874	36.4	85.2
		440			
Apr.	39		888	37.0	105.4
		448			
May	36		903	37.6	95.7
		455			
June	37		930	38.8	95.4
		475			
July	32		955	39.8	80.4
		480			
Aug.	37		962	40.1	92.3
		482			
Sept.	41		967	40.3	101.7
		485			
Oct.	43		971	40.5	106.2
		486			
Nov.	50		979	40.8	122.5
		493			
Dec.	70		991	41.3	169.5
		498			
1955					
Jan.	34		996	41.5	81.9
		498			
Feb.	32		1002	41.8	76.6
		504			
Mar.	34		1013	42.2	80.6
		509			
Apr.	40		1025	42.7	93.7
		516			
May	43		1034	43.1	99.8
		518			
June	42		1043	43.5	96.6
		525			
July	32		1050	43.8	73.1
		525			
Aug.	43		1053	43.9	97.9
		528			
Sept.	46		1062	44.2	104.1
		534			
Oct.	50		1071	44.6	112.1
		537			
Nov.	52		1077	44.9	115.8
		540			
Dec.	77		1083	45.1	170.7
		543			
1956					
Jan.	34		1090	45.4	74.9
		547			
Feb.	35		1097	45.7	76.6
		550			
Mar.	40		1112	46.3	86.4
		562			
Apr.	43		1121	46.7	92.1
		559			
May	46		1129	47.0	97.9
		570			
June	45		1145	47.7	94.3
		575			

TABLE 34 (cont.).

Year and month	(1) Sales (000) *TCSI*	(2) 12-month moving total	(3) 2-month moving total of the 12-month moving total	(4) Centered 12-month moving average (col. 3 ÷ 24) *TC*	(5) Specific seasonal indexes (*TCSI* ÷ *TC*) *SI*
1956					
July	$ 36	$579	$1154	$48.1	74.8
Aug.	46	587	1166	48.6	94.7
Sept.	58	593	1180	49.2	117.9
Oct.	47	597	1190	49.6	94.8
Nov.	63	605	1202	50.1	125.7
Dec.	82	611	1216	50.7	161.7
1957					
Jan.	38	623	1234	51.4	73.9
Feb.	43	627	1250	52.1	82.5
Mar.	46	622	1249	52.0	88.5
Apr.	47	633	1255	52.3	89.9
May	54	631	1264	52.7	102.5
June	51	650	1281	53.4	95.6
July	48	651	1301	54.2	88.6
Aug.	50	645	1296	54.0	92.6
Sept.	53	644	1289	53.7	98.7
Oct.	58	652	1296	54.0	107.4
Nov.	61	654	1306	54.4	112.1
Dec.	101	658	1312	54.7	184.6
1958					
Jan.	39	661	1319	55.0	70.9
Feb.	37	659	1320	55.0	67.3
Mar.	45	664	1323	55.1	81.7
Apr.	55	668	1332	55.5	99.1
May	56	684	1352	56.3	99.5
June	55	700	1384	57.7	95.3
July	51	703	1403	58.5	87.2
Aug.	48	711	1414	58.9	81.5
Sept.	58	714	1425	59.4	97.6
Oct.	62	721	1435	59.8	103.7
Nov.	77	718	1439	60.0	128.3
Dec.	117	728	1446	60.2	194.4
1959					
Jan.	42	733	1461	60.9	69.0
Feb.	45	744	1477	61.5	73.2
Mar.	48	760	1504	62.7	76.6
Apr.	62	768	1528	63.7	97.3
May	53	770	1538	64.1	82.7
June	65	775	1545	64.4	100.9
July	56				
Aug.	59				
Sept.	74				
Oct.	70				
Nov.	79				
Dec.	122				

Source: Hypothetical.

This may be interpreted as indicating that sales in July 1953 ($29) were 86.6 per cent of average monthly sales for the 12-month period centered on July 1953. However, we observe that specific seasonal indexes fluctuate a great deal from year to year. Consider the following tabulations of specific seasonal indexes for July during the period 1953–1958:

Year	*July Specific Seasonal Indexes*
1953	86.6
1954	80.4
1955	73.1
1956	74.8
1957	88.6
1958	87.2

These year-to-year fluctuations are presumably due, in large part, to irregular forces which have not been removed from the specific seasonal indexes. The third basic step of the ratio-to-moving-average method is designed to eliminate or substantially reduce fluctuations attributable to erratic factors.

Computation of typical seasonal indexes. Specific seasonal index numbers in the right-hand column of Table 34 have been arrayed by months in Table 35. The array is used because any specific seasonal

TABLE 35. Computation of typical seasonal index for Small-Way Department Store sales by averaging specific seasonal indexes by months (1953–1959)

Rank	Jan.	Feb.	Mar.	Apr.	May	June	July	Aug.	Sept.	Oct.	Nov.	Dec.	Total
1	69.0	67.3	76.6	89.9	82.7	94.3	73.1	81.5	97.6	94.8	112.1	142.5	
2	70.9	73.2	80.6	92.1	95.7	95.3	74.8	85.3	98.7	101.2	115.8	161.7	
3	73.9	76.6	81.7	93.7	97.9	95.4	80.4	92.3	101.7	103.7	122.5	169.5	
4	74.9	76.6	85.2	97.3	99.5	95.6	86.6	92.6	102.3	106.2	122.9	170.7	
5	81.9	82.5	86.4	99.1	99.8	96.6	87.2	94.7	104.1	107.4	125.7	184.6	
6	81.9	83.8	88.5	105.4	102.5	100.9	88.6	97.9	117.9	112.1	128.3	194.4	
Total	452.5	392.7	499.0	472.1	495.4	477.2	490.7	364.9	504.4	418.5	486.9	686.5	
Ave.:	75.4	78.5	83.2	94.4	99.1	95.4	81.8	91.2	100.9	104.6	121.7	171.6	1,197.8
Seasonal index	75.5	78.6	83.4	94.6	99.3	95.6	82.0	91.4	101.1	104.8	121.9	171.9	1,200.1

$$\text{Leveling factor} = \frac{1{,}200.0}{1{,}197.8} = 1.001837$$

index which can be seen to be extreme as a result of very irregular factors should be disregarded in computing the *typical* pattern of seasonal variation. The array makes immediately obvious those specifics which may have been affected by such factors. Such unusual specifics have been crossed out in Table 35 and have not been used in computing the typical seasonal indexes. The values remaining in the column for each month are totaled and an average computed. It is necessary to adjust these averages so that their sum will be 1,200, or nearly 1,200. This adjustment is required because the seasonal index only indicates how total sales for the year are distributed among the several months; if exactly the total amount of activity is to be distributed the *average* monthly index must be 100 per cent.

In Table 35, the total of the row of initial averages is 1,197.8. The total of the adjusted averages (typical seasonal indexes) in the bottom row of the table is 1,200.1. The adjusting, or leveling, factor was computed by dividing the desired theoretical total of 1,200 by the total of the average row (1,197.8). Since 1,200 is 1.001837 times the total of the unadjusted averages, it is reasoned that each monthly average should be increased by multiplying it by 1.001837. The adjusted (leveled) averages obtained in this final step are considered *typical seasonal indexes*.

The typical seasonal indexes, which are commonly referred to as simply the *seasonal indexes*, may be presented graphically as in Chart 13. The monthly pattern of sales therein reflected is *typical* for those years from which the indexes were computed. For example, from either Table 35 or Chart 13, we can ascertain that January sales are typically about 75.5 per cent of annual average monthly sales (100 per cent); December sales are typically about 71.9 per cent above average monthly sales (or 171.9 per cent of average).

ADJUSTMENT OF DATA FOR SEASONAL VARIATION

For analysis and comparison it is often useful to remove influences of seasonal variation from data. The influence of the seasonal factor obscures comparisons of rates of change and the recognition of changes in direction of a series. The process of adjustment is simple; raw data (the original series) reflect all components of time series variation (*TCSI*) and seasonal influences (*S*) may be eliminated by division:

$$\frac{TCSI}{S} = TCI$$

CHART 13. Typical seasonal indexes of Small-Way Department Store sales

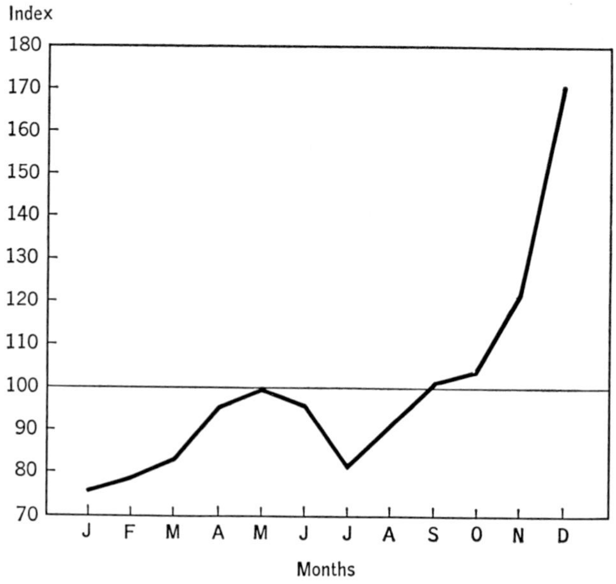

Source: Table 35.

Smoothing *TCI* with a moving average removes most of the effects of irregular forces (*I*) and leaves an indication of trend-cycle movements (*TC*).

Sales of the Small-Way Department Store from 1953 through 1959 have been adjusted for seasonal variation in Table 36 and the irregular variation smoothed out of the adjusted data to reveal the trend-cycle movements of sales. The seasonal index in Column 2 was obtained from Table 35. Seasonally-adjusted sales for January 1953 as shown in column 3 were computed as follows:[4]

$$\frac{24}{75.5\%} = \$31.8$$

In the absence of seasonal fluctuations, sales in January 1953 would have been $31,800; actual sales were only $24,000. Comparison of actual sales with seasonally-adjusted sales in Table 36 reveals much less fluctuation in seasonally adjusted sales. Changes which do occur are attributed to trend, cyclical, and irregular forces. Examination

[4] Note that 75.5 per cent may be written as 0.755; this explains the answer of $31.8 rather than $0.318.

of the smoothed seasonally-adjusted series (Column 5) indicates that the trend of Small-Way sales was decidedly upward during 1953–1959, although there were slight cyclical slow-downs in late 1953–1954 and again in 1957–1958.

ADJUSTMENT OF DATA FOR CALENDAR VARIATION

Where *rates* rather than total activity are to be compared it is frequently necessary to adjust data for variations in the length of the periods. Variation in the number of days in the months of a year is an example of this type of fluctuation. Total activity in February often is less than for January or March, not because the *rate* of activity has been less, but simply because there are fewer days in February.

Adjustment for calendar variation can be made by dividing monthly totals by the actual number of days in the month and then multiplying the result by the average number of days in each month. This may be illustrated by adjusting January and February 1958 sales of the Small-Way Department Store (Table 36) for calendar variation; actual sales in those months were \$39 thousand and \$37 thousand, respectively.

$$\text{Average days per month in 1958} = \frac{365}{12} = 30.42$$

$$\text{January:} \quad \frac{\$39}{31}(30.42) = \$38.3 = \text{sales adjusted for calendar variation}$$

$$\text{February:} \quad \frac{\$37}{28}(30.42) = \$40.2 = \text{sales adjusted for calendar variation}$$

It becomes evident that the *rate* of sales in February was actually above the *rate* of sales for January even though total sales were higher in January.

Adjustment of data for calendar variation is expedited by reference to a table of adjustment factors, such as Table 37. These factors are computed by dividing the average number of days per month by the actual number of days in specific months. Adjustment factors for February in an ordinary year and in a leap year are calculated as follows:

$$\text{February (ordinary year):} \quad \frac{30.41667}{28} = 1.086310$$

$$\text{February (leap year):} \quad \frac{30.5}{29} = 1.051724$$

TABLE 36. Adjustment of Small-Way Department Store sales for seasonal variation and computation of trend-cycle curve, 1953–1959

Year and month	(1) Sales (000) *TCSI*	(2) Seasonal index *S*	(3) Adjusted sales (000) (*TCSI* ÷ *S*) *TCI*	(4) 5-month moving total of seasonally-adjusted sales	(5) 5-mo. moving avg. of seasonally-adj. sales (*TC*)
1953					
Jan.	$24	75.5	$31.8		
Feb.	25	78.6	31.8		
Mar.	29	83.4	34.8	$167.4	$33.5
Apr.	32	94.6	33.8	171.2	34.2
May	35	99.3	35.2	174.8	35.0
June	34	95.6	35.6	171.7	34.3
July	29	82.0	35.4	172.5	34.5
Aug.	29	91.4	31.7	170.7	34.1
Sept.	35	101.1	34.6	170.4	34.1
Oct.	35	104.8	33.4	164.1	32.8
Nov.	43	121.9	35.3	170.8	34.2
Dec.	50	171.9	29.1	174.4	34.9
1954					
Jan.	29	75.5	38.4	178.2	35.6
Feb.	30	78.6	38.2	184.1	36.8
Mar.	31	83.4	37.2	191.3	38.3
Apr.	39	94.6	41.2	191.6	38.3
May	36	99.3	36.3	192.4	38.5
June	37	95.6	38.7	195.7	39.1
July	32	82.0	39.0	195.1	39.0
Aug.	37	91.4	40.5	199.8	40.0
Sept.	41	101.1	40.6	202.1	40.4
Oct.	43	104.8	41.0	203.8	40.8
Nov.	50	121.9	41.0	208.3	41.7
Dec.	70	171.9	40.7	208.4	41.7
1955					
Jan.	34	75.5	45.0	208.2	41.6
Feb.	32	78.6	40.7	209.5	41.9
Mar.	34	83.4	40.8	212.1	42.4
Apr.	40	94.6	42.3	211.0	42.2
May	43	99.3	43.3	209.3	41.9
June	42	95.6	43.9	215.5	43.1
July	32	82.0	39.0	218.7	43.7
Aug.	43	91.4	47.0	223.1	44.6
Sept.	46	101.1	45.5	221.9	44.4
Oct.	50	104.8	47.7	227.7	45.5
Nov.	52	121.9	42.7	225.7	45.1
Dec.	77	171.9	44.8	224.7	44.9
1956					
Jan.	34	75.5	45.0	225.0	45.0
Feb.	35	78.6	44.5	227.8	45.6
Mar.	40	83.4	48.0	229.3	45.9
Apr.	43	94.6	45.5	231.4	46.3
May	46	99.3	46.3	230.8	46.2
June	45	95.6	47.1	233.1	46.6

TABLE 36. (cont.)

Year and month	(1) Sales (000) *TCSI*	(2) Seasonal index *S*	(3) Adjusted sales (000) (*TCSI* ÷ *S*) *TCI*	(4) 5-month moving total of seasonally-adjusted sales	(5) 5-mo. moving avg. of seasonally-adj. sales (*TC*)
1956					
July	$ 36	82.0	$43.9	$245.0	$49.0
Aug.	46	91.4	50.3	243.5	48.7
Sept.	58	101.1	57.4	248.1	49.6
Oct.	47	104.8	44.8	251.9	50.4
Nov.	63	121.9	51.7	251.9	50.4
Dec.	82	171.9	47.7	249.2	49.8
1957					
Jan.	38	75.5	50.3	259.6	51.9
Feb.	43	78.6	54.7	257.6	51.5
Mar.	46	83.4	55.2	264.3	52.9
Apr.	47	94.6	49.7	267.3	53.5
May	54	99.3	54.4	271.1	54.2
June	51	95.6	53.3	270.6	54.1
July	48	82.0	58.5	273.3	54.7
Aug.	50	91.4	54.7	274.2	54.8
Sept.	53	101.1	52.4	270.9	54.2
Oct.	58	104.8	55.3	271.2	54.2
Nov.	61	121.9	50.0	268.2	53.6
Dec.	101	171.9	58.8	262.9	52.6
1958					
Jan.	39	75.5	51.7	261.6	52.3
Feb.	37	78.6	47.1	269.7	53.9
Mar.	45	83.4	54.0	267.3	53.5
Apr.	55	94.6	58.1	273.1	54.6
May	56	99.3	56.4	288.2	57.6
June	55	95.6	57.5	286.7	57.3
July	51	82.0	62.2	286.0	57.2
Aug.	48	91.4	52.5	288.8	57.8
Sept.	58	101.1	57.4	294.5	58.9
Oct.	62	104.8	59.2	300.4	60.1
Nov.	77	121.9	63.2	303.5	60.7
Dec.	117	171.9	68.1	303.4	60.7
1959					
Jan.	42	75.5	55.6	301.8	60.4
Feb.	45	78.6	57.3	304.1	60.8
Mar.	48	83.4	57.6	289.4	57.9
Apr.	62	94.6	65.5	301.8	60.4
May	53	99.3	53.4	312.8	62.6
June	65	95.6	68.0	319.8	64.0
July	56	82.0	68.3	327.5	65.5
Aug.	59	91.4	64.6	340.9	68.2
Sept.	74	101.1	73.2	337.7	67.5
Oct.	70	104.8	66.8	340.4	68.1
Nov.	79	121.9	64.8		
Dec.	122	171.9	71.0		

TABLE 37. Adjustment factors for monthly calendar variation

Month	Ordinary year		Leap year	
	Days	Adjustment factor	Days	Adjustment factor
January	31	0.981183	31	0.983871
February	28	1.086310	29	1.051724
March	31	0.981183	31	0.983871
April	30	1.013889	30	1.016667
May	31	0.981183	31	0.983871
June	30	1.013889	30	1.016667
July	31	0.981183	31	0.983871
August	31	0.981183	31	0.983871
September	30	1.013889	30	1.016667
October	31	0.981183	31	0.983871
November	30	1.013889	30	1.016667
December	31	0.981183	31	0.983871
Total:	365	...	366	...
Average:	30.41667	...	30.5	...

Adjusted sales of Small-Way Department Store for February 1958 could then be computed:

$$\$37 \times 1.086310 = \$40.2 = \text{sales adjusted for calendar variation}$$

This result is identical with the adjusted sales as computed in the preceding paragraph.

Similar adjustment of data may be made for variation in number of working days; this is sometimes important when analyzing production data. Variations in holidays and number of week ends often require that data be adjusted; Easter, which may occur in either March or April, is particularly troublesome. Appropriate adjustments for all cases must be determined on an individual basis.

Method of forecasting sales by time series analysis

LONG-RANGE FORECASTING

Computation of trend. When planning construction of costly facilities it is essential to make forecasts of future trends. Large factories, office buildings, store buildings, costly equipment, and other capital investments are planned in anticipation of the future. Therefore it becomes important to have the best possible estimate of future business activity.

A technique of long-range forecasting may be demonstrated by reference to Small-Way Department Store, whose monthly sales for 1953–1959 were shown in Tables 34 and 36. The first step is to estimate long-range trend. Since seasonal variation is of no concern in the determination of trend, computations may be simplified by using annual rather than monthly sales. Hence annual totals of monthly sales for the period 1947–1959 are listed in Column 1 of Table 38. The straight-line trend equation has been calculated in Table 38; estimated trend for any future year may be obtained by substituting

TABLE 38. Straight-line trend of Small-Way Department Store sales 1947–1959 (computed by method of least squares)

Year	(1) Sales (000) *TCI* *Y*	(2) Deviations in years *X*	(3) Sales weighted by deviations *XY*	(4) Deviations squared X^2	(5) Long-time trend of sales (000) *T*
1947	$ 70	−6	−420	36	$ 67.5
1948	150	−5	−750	25	125.1
1949	175	−4	−700	16	182.7
1950	250	−3	−750	9	240.3
1951	275	−2	−550	4	297.9
1952	350	−1	−350	1	355.5
1953	400	0	0	0	413.1
1954	475	+1	+475	1	470.7
1955	525	+2	+1,050	4	528.3
1956	575	+3	+1,725	9	585.9
1957	650	+4	+2,600	16	643.5
1958	700	+5	+3,500	25	701.1
1959	775	+6	+4,650	36	758.7
Total:	$5,370		10,480	182	$5,370.3

Source: Hypothetical

$$a = \frac{\Sigma Y}{N} = \frac{5,370}{13} = \mathbf{413.1}, \qquad b = \frac{\Sigma XY}{\Sigma X^2} = \frac{10,480}{182} = \mathbf{57.6}$$

$T = 413.1 + 57.6X$, with origin at July 1, 1953, each unit of X equal to one year, and T in thousands of dollars.

an appropriate value for X. Assume that executives desire a forecast for 1965. The X value for 1965 would be +12 since 1965 is twelve years later than the year of origin, 1953. Estimated sales for 1965 due to trend may then be computed:

$$T = 413.1 + 57.6\ (12) = 413.1 + 691.2 = \mathbf{1{,}104.3} \text{ thousand.}$$

In the absence of cyclical and irregular forces, a continuation of the past trend pattern would result in sales amounting to $1,104,300 in 1965.

Adjustment for cyclical variation. Irregular variations cannot be forecast because of their unpredictable character; but the forecaster should consider the effects of cyclical variation on trend when making long-range forecasts. If an analysis of business conditions and pertinent economic factors (Chapter 6) indicates that sales in 1965 will be about 5 per cent below trend, or normal, the following adjustment of trend will be made:

$$\text{trend} + \text{cyclical variation} = \text{forecasted sales}$$

$$\text{sales} = 1{,}104.3 - (5\% \text{ of } 1{,}104.3) = \mathbf{1{,}049.1}$$

Since forecasted sales of $1,049,100 for 1965 is much larger than 1959 sales of $775,000, directors of Small-Way Department Store may authorize expansion of facilities to accommodate the estimated increase in volume of business. It should be pointed out that the directors and management must also consider factors such as more intensive utilization of existing facilities, shifts in cost ratios resulting from increased sales, and independent analyses of future demand for commodities sold by Small-Way.

SHORT-RANGE FORECASTING

Annual trend equation reduced to monthly terms. Short-range forecasting usually refers to forecasting for specific months or seasons. Consequently, trend equations in annual terms must be changed to monthly terms. This procedure may be illustrated with the annual trend equation of Small-Way:

$$T = 413.1 + 57.6X,$$

with origin at July 1, 1953 and X in terms of years and b in terms of *annual* increments in *annual* sales. The first step is to divide the a and b values by 12, the number of months in a year. Then

$$T = 34.4 + 4.8X$$

with origin at July 1, 1953 and X in terms of years and b in terms of *annual* increments in *monthly* sales. However, this equation is unsatisfactory because the b value is equal to the amount of change in trend which occurs between a specific month in one year and the same month the *next year*. That is, sales in January 1954 would normally be \$4,800 larger than sales in January 1953. What is needed is a b value which expresses the change between a specific month and the succeeding month in the *same* year. To compute this b value it is necessary to again divide by 12:

$$\frac{4.8}{12} = \mathbf{0.4}$$

That is, sales due to trend in February 1953 would normally be \$400 larger than sales in January 1953. Now the trend equation is

$$T = 34.4 + 0.4X$$

with origin at July 1, 1953 and X in terms of months and b in terms of *monthly* increments in *monthly* sales.

One final adjustment is required to shift the origin from July 1, 1953 to July 15, 1953. July 1 is at the middle of 1953 and hence is *centered* for annual data. However, a shift must be made to July 15, since annual data have been reduced to monthly data and monthly data should be centered on the *middle* of each *month*. This is accomplished by increasing the value of a (the value of trend at the origin) by one-half (0.5) of the monthly b:

$$\text{centered } a = T\,(\text{July 15, 1953}) = 34.4 + (0.4)(0.5) = \mathbf{34.6}$$

Hence the a value at the July 15 origin is 34.6 and the trend equation is

$$T = 34.6 + 0.4X$$

with origin at July 15, 1953 and X in terms of months and b in terms of *monthly* increments in *monthly* sales.

Trend forecast. Short-range forecasting may be accomplished by first forecasting trend, then adjusting for seasonal variation, and finally adjusting for cyclical variations. Assume that in early 1960 executives of Small-Way wish to estimate sales in August 1960 in order to purchase adequate stock for inventories. Since August 1960 is 85 months from July 1953, the value 85 is substituted for X in the trend equation:

$$T = 34.6 + 0.4(85) = 34.6 + 34.0 = \mathbf{68.6}$$

If only trend forces were operative, sales of Small-Way would be \$68,600 in August 1960.

Adjustment for seasonal variation. The seasonal index of Small-Way sales for August is 91.4 as computed in Table 35. This means that seasonal factors usually cause August sales to be 91.4 per cent of sales estimated due to trend. The forecasted amount of sales in August due to a combination of trend and seasonal forces may be computed as follows:

$$T \times S = TS, \quad \text{or statistical normal}$$

$$68.6(0.914) = 62.70, \quad \text{or 62.7 thousand.}$$

Since trend and seasonal forces are *normal* for monthly data, sales of $62,700 may be forecast as *normal* for August 1960.

Adjustment for cyclical variation. On the basis of an analysis of general business conditions, a further adjustment may be required for estimated cyclical fluctuations. If Small-Way officials estimate cyclical variations will cause sales to be 10 per cent above *normal* in August 1960 dollar sales volume may be estimated as follows:

$$TS + (10\% \times TS) = \text{estimated sales}$$

$$62.7 + (0.10)(62.7) = 68.97 \quad \text{or} \quad \mathbf{69.0} \text{ thousand}$$

Buyers for Small-Way may now place orders for inventories for August sales of $69,000. However, a continuous analysis of business conditions is required in order to adjust plans rapidly to meet new developments.

Limitations of forecasting by time series analysis

The old adage that a chain is no stronger than its weakest link characterizes the limitations of forecasting by time series analysis. The four basic forces which shape business data—(1) trend, (2) seasonal, (3) cyclical, and (4) irregular—may be regarded as four links in a chain. None of these forces can be forecast with certainty. Most reliable are the forecasts of trend and seasonal movements. However, past trend and seasonal patterns often have been known to shift. Estimates of cyclical changes can best be made by an analysis of current economic factors as described in Chapter 6. Such analyses are, of necessity, subjective and therefore dependent upon the knowledge and skill of the forecaster. Finally, even though reasonable success is achieved in forecasting trend, seasonal, and cyclical forces, sales forecasts may be invalidated by events which are irregular and unpredictable in nature.

An obvious question at this point is, "Why forecast?" The answer is simply that forecasts cannot be avoided; *tomorrow's* operations are shaped by *today's* decisions. Forecasts based on intelligent analysis of available data, though fallible, are far superior to forecasts based on hunches and rumors. Also, study of forecasting methods provides businessmen with a clearer understanding of the nature of trend, cyclical, and seasonal forces. This knowledge is an invaluable aid to executives who must make rapid shifts in business plans to meet ever changing business conditions.

Questions and Exercises

1. Differentiate the following forces which influence business activity:
   (a) Long-time trend
   (b) Cyclical variation
   (c) Seasonal variation
   (d) Irregular fluctuations

2. Briefly describe the methods of estimating each of the above forces. What are some of the major limitations of these methods?

3. (a) Compute the straight-line trend equation for the data below by the method of least squares; determine the annual trend estimates for each year.

C-E CORPORATION SALES

Year	*Sales* (Thousands of dollars)
1948	25
1949	26
1950	28
1951	30
1952	33
1953	35
1954	37
1955	36
1956	40
1957	42
1958	43
1959	44

(b) What do the trend values measure?

(c) What volume of sales would you plan for in 1961 if you predict cyclical forces will push sales 10 per cent below normal?

(d) List major limitations of the least-squares method of estimating trend.

4. Repeat exercise 3 (a), (b), and (c), adding the year 1960 with sales of $48,000. Compare the results of exercises 3 and 4.

5. Fit trends by various methods (semi averages, moving averages, least squares) to the sales of Montgomery Ward & Co. and Sears, Roebuck and Co. as published by the U. S. Department of Commerce in *Business Statistics* and the *Survey of Current Business.* This exercise may be repeated with sales of other companies, which may be obtained from company annual reports and the publications of *Standard & Poor's Corporation* and *Moody's Investors Service.* Compare the trends of various companies. Compare the various trends for each company. Discuss fully the implications of your findings.

6. Adjust sales data in exercises 4 and 5 for trend. Explain why the resultant percentages may be regarded as an estimation of cyclical and irregular forces. Smooth the adjusted series with a moving average and fully interpret the results.

7. Compute an index of seasonal variation for the following series by the method of ratio-to-12-month-moving averages.

SALES OF E.Z. DUE COMPANY
($000 omitted)

Month	1954	1955	1956	1957	1958	1959
J	5	5	10	10	15	20
F	5	5	10	10	10	15
M	10	15	15	25	20	25
A	25	30	40	60	50	55
M	15	20	20	35	30	40
J	15	15	25	40	30	30
J	5	10	5	15	10	15
A	20	25	30	50	40	45
S	25	30	40	60	50	60
O	20	25	30	50	40	45
N	25	35	35	65	50	60
D	30	35	40	70	60	60

(a) Construct a worksheet with column headings arranged as in Table 34.
(b) All students enter data in Column 1 and compute data for Columns 2 and 3.
(c) The burden of computation of data for Columns 4 and 5 may be eased by dividing the period among several groups of students. For example, five groups of students may be given assignments as follows:

Group	*Fiscal Year* (July 1–June 30)
1	1954–1955
2	1955–1956
3	1956–1957
4	1957–1958
5	1958–1959

(d) All students compute seasonal index (see Table 35).

(e) All students adjust actual sales of E.Z. Due Company in 1959 for seasonal variation (see Table 36). What do the adjusted sales reflect?

8. (a) Adjust the following monthly sales for calendar variation. Use adjustment factors appearing in Table 37.

Month	*Sales* (000)
January	$20
February	19
March	21
April	21
May	20
June	19
July	18
August	19
September	22
October	21
November	23
December	30

(b) What is the meaning of the adjusted figures? Be specific.

9. R. D. Company 1960 monthly sales, the seasonal index, and 1960 monthly trend estimates were as follows:

Month	*Sales* (000)	*Seasonal Index*	*Trend Estimates*
January	($40	180	20.0
February	38	160	22.0
March	35	160	24.0
April	30	130	26.0
May	27	100	28.0
June	22	70	30.0
July	10	30	32.0
August	11	30	34.0
September	12	30	36.0
October	23	60	38.0
November	45	110	40.0
December	58	140	42.0
			372.0

(a) Were actual sales above or below *normal* in January? Was this also true in the other months? What do you conclude about sales in 1960?

(b) Did business improve or decline between January and February? By what percentage? Make a similar comparison between April and November. take out seasonal effect (increased)

(c) In 1959, what forecast of sales for April 1960 would have been made if R. D. Company executives had anticipated sales would be 10 per cent above *normal*? normal sales are the product of the trend & seasonal effect

(d) If R. D. Company executives expected sales in 1963 would be 5 per cent above normal, what dollar amount of sales would they forecast? (Note that the monthly increment in monthly trend estimates is 2.0. What is the annual increment in annual trend estimates?)

10. Discuss the limitations of forecasting by time series analysis.

Long Range Forecast = (1) computation of trend (T = a + bx)
(2) adjustment for cyclical effects
Trend Val × cyclical value = F/C

Short Range Forecast = (1) Put annual trend in monthly terms and adjust to middle of month.
(2) calculate trend F/C value
(3) adjust for seasonal variation
(4) adjust for cyclical variation or effect

8 *Forecasting sales: correlation analysis*

Correlation analysis is an additional technique which may be employed to forecast sales.[1] Since all forecasting methods are subject to error, a firm is wise to employ more than one method. A forecast based on time series analysis tends to be substantiated if a similar forecast is obtained by correlation analysis. Significantly different results cast doubt on each forecast and indicate the need for further analysis.

It is a recognized fact that certain lines of business or economic activity generate business in other fields. For example, sales of gasoline and auto supplies tend to increase with growth in auto registrations and miles of improved highways. Sales of building supplies fluctuate with changes in the number and value of building permits issued. Furniture sales follow the pattern of new home purchases. Population, employment, income, climate, and distribution of age, education, sex,

[1] Other applications of correlation analysis are briefly mentioned on pages 206-7.

and nationality are among other factors which may be used to forecast sales.

The reader is cautioned against *spurious* correlation, that is, the coincidental appearance of relationship between series of data which have no causal or logical connection. For example, similar fluctuations of annual Alaskan salmon catches and the price of lumber would not indicate meaningful correlation. This is in contrast to relationships between sales and such factors as income, population, and industrial production. Some writers have been critical of correlating time series, arguing (1) that values in succeeding years are not independent of values in preceding years and (2) that appearance of correlation may be due to similar effect of trend, cyclical, and seasonal forces on each of the series being correlated. However, insofar as sales forecasting is concerned, this writer is of the opinion that where a logical connection exists, as between sales and income, correlation of time series appears legitimate and highly useful.

TYPES OF CORRELATION

Analysis of the relationship between two sets of data is referred to as *simple correlation. Multiple correlation* analysis is designed to measure the influence of several series of data upon a particular series, such as sales. For example, sales of paint might be forecast for specific states or regions by analysis of (1) the number of residential structures with paintable surfaces, (2) the number of owner-occupied residences, and (3) the median value of owner-occupied residences. *Partial correlation* analysis is a technique by which the influence of one series upon another is measured while other pertinent series are recognized but *held constant.* For example, the influence of the number of residential structures upon paint sales may be analyzed while holding such factors as owner-occupancy and building values at constant levels. This text will deal only with simple correlation. Study of multiple and partial correlation must be reserved for advanced courses in statistics.

PATTERN OF CORRELATION

A line drawn on a chart to depict the relationship between series of data may be either *straight* (*linear*) or *curved* (*curvilinear*). The relationship is linear if the amount of change in one series remains in constant ratio to the amount of change in the other series. The relationship between J. C. Penney Co. net sales and total U. S. disposable income from 1938 to 1958 appears to approximate a straight line in Chart 14. It would, of course, be inappropriate to fit a curved line to data which have a linear relationship, and vice versa. This text will be limited to an introductory treatment of simple linear correlation.

DIRECTION OF CORRELATION

If an increase in one series is accompanied by an increase in the other series, the relationship is said to be *positive* or *direct*. Positively correlated data on a chart would proceed from the lower left to the upper right as in Chart 14. A *negative* or *inverse* correlation exists when increases in one series are accompanied by decreases in the other series. A line showing this relationship would proceed from the upper left of a chart toward the lower right.

Visual determination of correlation

TABULAR PRESENTATION

A rough approximation of the degree of correlation can be obtained by visual inspection of two series of data arranged in tabular form. Examination of the data in Table 39 reveals somewhat parallel increases in J. C. Penney Co. net sales and U. S. disposable personal income. Under closer scrutiny it is observed that the only divergences in the direction of movement in the two series occurred in 1954, a year of mild recession. Also, the ratio of store sales to income appears to remain quite stable. However, a better indication of the degree of correlation can be obtained by plotting the data in Table 39 in a scatter diagram.

SCATTER DIAGRAMS

The most valuable graphic device for illustrating correlation is the scatter diagram. In Chart 14, J. C. Penney Co. sales and disposable personal income have been plotted as a single point for each year from 1938 through 1958; a total of 21 points appears in the chart. Store sales are measured by the vertical axis on the left and disposable income amounts are measured by the horizontal axis at the base of the chart.[2] The lowest point at the left represents sales of $258 million

[2] It is customary to plot the variable which is to be forecast on the vertical axis.

TABLE 39. J. C. Penney Company net sales and U. S. disposable personal income, 1938–1958

Year	Net sales (millions)	Disposable personal income (billions)
1938	$ 258	$ 66
1939	282	70
1940	304	76
1941	378	93
1942	490	118
1943	490	134
1944	535	147
1945	549	150
1946	677	159
1947	776	169
1948	885	188
1949	880	188
1950	950	206
1951	1,035	226
1952	1,079	237
1953	1,110	250
1954	1,107	254
1955	1,220	270
1956	1,292	287
1957	1,312	308
1958	1,410	316

Source: J. C. Penney Company data from *Moody's Industrial Manual*, selected issues; U. S. disposable personal income amounts from *Business Statistics 1959*, U. S. Department of Commerce.

and disposable income of $66 billion, which occurred in 1938 (see Table 39). The straight-line relationship between sales and disposable income is at once apparent. Points which noticeably deviate from the straight-line pattern represent sales and income for the war years of 1943, 1944, and 1945; even so, the deviation from the long-run pattern is slight. Furthermore, the three points for 1943, 1944, and 1945 appear to fit a separate straight line. J. C. Penney Co. deals principally in soft goods, hence its sales were not so adversely affected by World War II as were the sales of many companies which manufactured and sold hard goods.

Data for years in which war or other factors have disturbed normal relationships should always be scrutinized and may be omitted from

CHART 14. Scatter diagram illustrating relationship of J. C. Penney Co. sales and U. S. disposable personal income, 1938–1958

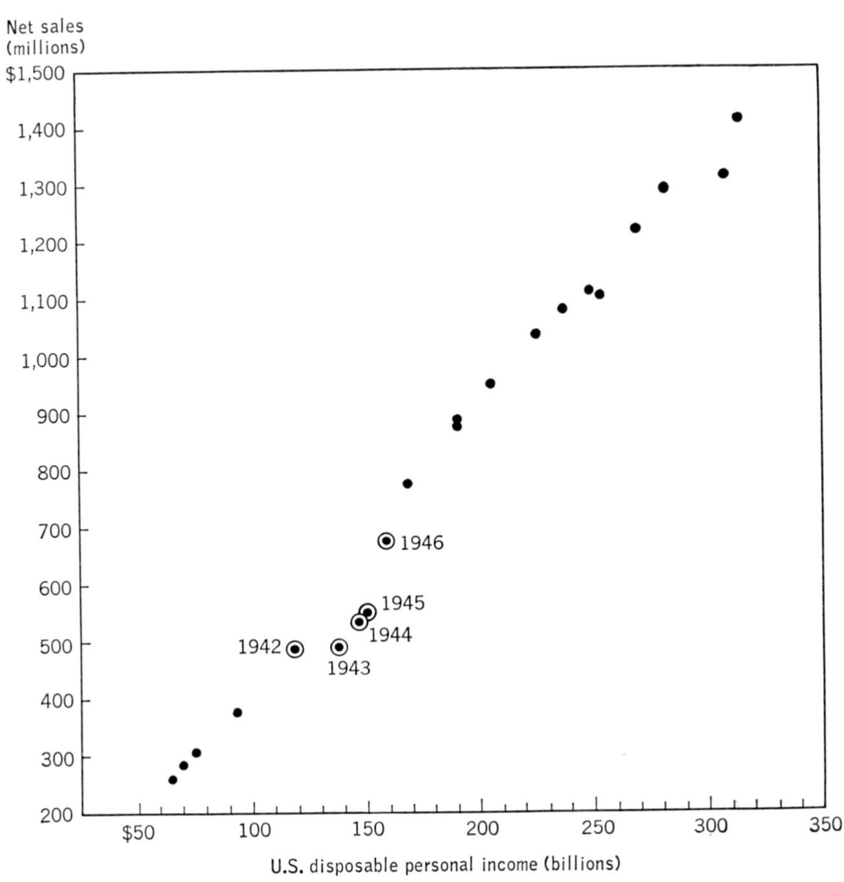

Source: Table 39.

the analysis if significantly distorted. In this analysis, examination of the period in which soft-goods sales were affected by shortages and price controls indicates that data for the five years 1942, 1943, 1944, 1945, and 1946 should be omitted from the analysis.

Based on the relationship indicated in Chart 14, company officials would forecast net sales of about $1,100 million for a year in which disposable income of $250 billion had been forecast; a sales forecast of approximately $1,350 million would follow from a disposable income forecast of $300 billion. A line drawn through the points on a scatter diagram would facilitate forecasting.

THE VALUE OF THE DOLLAR AND CORRELATION ANALYSIS

In the determination of the extent to which series are correlated, it is important to be sure that the observed relationship is not due to the effects of some third factor. Forecasts based on correlation are considered more reliable if it can be demonstrated that the observed relationship is not due to a spurious correlation introduced by some factor such as the changing value of the dollar. Also, in planning future operations it is wise to make separate adjustments for the effects of inflation or deflation in the value of the dollar. Changes in the level of operations are determined by changes in physical activity, not changes in dollar sales.

Examination of the relationship of J. C. Penney Co. sales and disposable personal income after the two series have been adjusted for changing price levels (Chart 15, page 196) indicates that the relationship here is not due to the effects of price level changes. In fact, adjustment for price changes appears to make little difference in the degree of relationship. It appears reasonable, however, to use the deflated series in determining the relationship between the two series.

Computation of correlation measures

For many purposes a scatter diagram and a freehand or ruled line are adequate for sales forecasting. Advanced training in statistics and mathematics is not required for either the application of the technique or the interpretation of the results; hence it may be utilized readily by all firms, large and small alike. However, firms may often benefit from the computation of measures which describe the degree of correlation with more exactness. Fortunately these computations are relatively simple when the relationship between the series of data is linear (straight-line). The three most useful measures are listed in the order in which they normally are computed:

1. An equation describing the line of best fit through the points on a scatter diagram.

2. A measure of the deviation or scatter of the points around the line of best fit (regression line).
3. Some coefficients, or *pure numbers*, which indicate the degree of relationship with a precision which cannot be achieved by graphic means.

Each of these measures will be discussed in the sections which follow.

STRAIGHT-LINE EQUATION

The reader will recall the use of a least-squares straight-line equation in Chapter 7 to describe long-time trend. Its application in correlation analysis is similar. In trend analysis the equation expresses the change in a series of data which tends to occur with each passing year; in correlation analysis the equation expresses the change in one series of data which tends to occur with a given change in another series of data.

The basic equation for a straight line is $Y = a + bX$. The symbol Y is used to denote the variable to be forecast, and the symbol X refers to the related variable. The constant a represents the value of Y when X is zero, and b represents the average amount of change in Y which occurs with each unit change in X.

Unfortunately the short formulas for computation of values of a and b which were used in trend analysis are not applicable in correlation analysis. This is true because it cannot be assumed that the value of sales at the origin (where $X = 0$) is the mean or average value of sales (Y). Also, X values remain in original units, whereas in trend analysis substitute values (for years) of X were used, which canceled out to zero. However, reasonably short formulas for a and b are available. Although these formulas appear formidable at first glance, the computations are neither difficult nor time consuming if a table of squares and a calculator are utilized. These formulas are as follows:

$$a = \frac{\Sigma X^2 \Sigma Y - \Sigma X \Sigma XY}{N \Sigma X^2 - (\Sigma X)^2}$$

$$b = \frac{N \Sigma XY - \Sigma X \Sigma Y}{N \Sigma X^2 - (\Sigma X)^2}$$

It should be noted that the same denominator occurs in each formula.

Computation of the regression equation. Steps required to determine the value of the constants a and b in the regression equation are illustrated in Table 40. Sales, as the variable to be forecast, has been assigned

TABLE 40. Computation of regression equation constants for deflated J. C. Penney Co. net sales and U. S. disposable income

(1938–1958, war years omitted)

Year	(1) Deflated sales (millions) Y	(2) Deflated disposable personal income X	(3) Sales times income XY	(4) Sales squared Y^2	(5) Income squared X^2
1938	483	109	52,647	233,289	11,881
1939	537	118	63,366	288,369	13,924
1940	571	127	72,517	326,041	16,129
1941	680	148	100,640	462,400	21,904
		(1942–1946 omitted)			
1947	799	177	141,423	638,401	31,329
1948	855	183	156,465	731,025	33,489
1949	885	185	163,725	783,225	34,225
1950	968	200	193,600	937,024	40,000
1951	968	204	197,472	937,024	41,616
1952	1,020	209	213,180	1,040,400	43,681
1953	1,059	219	231,921	1,121,481	47,961
1954	1,061	221	234,481	1,125,721	48,841
1955	1,176	236	277,536	1,382,976	55,696
1956	1,225	247	302,575	1,500,625	61,009
1957	1,227	256	314,112	1,505,529	65,536
1958	1,312	255	334,560	1,721,344	65,025
Total:	14,826	3,094	3,050,220	14,734,874	632,246

Source: J. C. Penney Company Net Sales from Table 39 have been deflated by the apparel component from the *Consumer Price Index* (Bureau of Labor Statistics) as taken from *Business Statistics*, U. S. Dept. of Commerce. Disposable Personal Income from Table 39 has been deflated by the Consumer Price Index as given in Table 24, page 133.

$$a = \frac{\Sigma X^2 \Sigma Y - \Sigma X \Sigma XY}{N \Sigma X^2 - (\Sigma X)^2} = \frac{(632{,}246)(14{,}826) - (3{,}094)(3{,}050{,}220)}{(16)(632{,}246) - (3{,}094)^2}$$

$$= \frac{9{,}373{,}679{,}196 - 9{,}437{,}380{,}680}{10{,}115{,}936 - 9{,}572{,}836}$$

$$= \frac{-63{,}701{,}484}{543{,}100} = -117.29, \quad \text{or} \quad \mathbf{-117.3}$$

$$b = \frac{N \Sigma XY - \Sigma X \Sigma Y}{N \Sigma X^2 - (\Sigma X)^2} = \frac{(16)(3{,}050{,}220) - (3{,}094)(14{,}826)}{(16)(632{,}246) - (3{,}094)^2}$$

$$= \frac{48{,}803{,}520 - 45{,}871{,}644}{10{,}115{,}936 - 9{,}572{,}836}$$

$$= \frac{2{,}931{,}876}{543{,}100} = 5.398, \quad \text{or} \quad \mathbf{5.40}$$

the symbol Y, and disposable income, the related variable, has been denoted by X. Column 3 lists the products of X and Y, and Columns 4 and 5 contain the squared values of Y and X, respectively. The totals of the five columns in Table 40 provide all the components required for the formulas for a and b. The symbol N represents the number of paired values, 16 in this illustration. The regression equation for J. C. Penney Co. sales and U. S. disposable personal income can now be written as

$$Y_c = -117.3 + 5.40X$$

Whereas Y represents actual sales, Y_c indicates estimated or forecast sales.

Meaning of a *and* b. The value of a in the above equation, -117.3, is the value of Y_c at the *mathematical origin* of the equation. Interpreted literally, a indicates that estimated J. C. Penney Company net sales would be a minus \$117,300,000, if U. S. disposable personal income (X) were to drop to zero. The reader should ignore this nonsense interpretation and accept a as indicating the height of the regression line above the X-axis.

The constant b can be interpreted in a more meaningful manner. The b value of 5.40 in the above equation indicates that annual net sales in 1947–1949 dollars, increase (or decrease) \$5,400,000, with each increase (or decrease) of \$1 billion dollars in 1947–1949 dollars, in U. S. disposable personal income.

Application in forecasting sales. Computation of estimated sales in 1947–1949 dollars for any given amount of deflated disposable income is an easy step once the regression equation has been determined. Suppose a disposable personal income of \$250 billion has been forecast for a coming year. Substitution of \$250 billion for X in the regression equation permits solution for Y_c, estimated sales.

$$\begin{aligned} Y_c &= -117.3 + 5.40(250) \\ &= -117.3 + 1{,}350.0 = \mathbf{1{,}232.7} \end{aligned}$$

Since sales were listed in millions of dollars, this may be interpreted as a forecast of \$1,232,700,000 of net sales in 1947–1949 dollars.

A regression line may be charted as soon as estimated sales have been determined for two amounts of disposable income. Estimated sales for a disposable income of $250 billion were computed above. Estimated sales for deflated disposable income of $120 billion would be $530,700,000 in constant dollars. These two pairs of points are plotted as in Chart 15 and connected with a straight line. Forecasting may then be done arithmetically with the formula or graphically by reference to the charted regression line.

The reader should not be misled by the mathematical exactness of the above computations. Events may occur which will change the average relationship which prevailed between average store sales and disposable personal income during the period 1938–1958. The likelihood of such events can be estimated, if at all, only by analysis of underlying factors; not all of these latter factors can be reduced to

CHART 15. Line of average relationship between J. C. Penney Co. net sales and U. S. disposable personal income, 1938–1958, war years omitted (1947–1949 dollars)

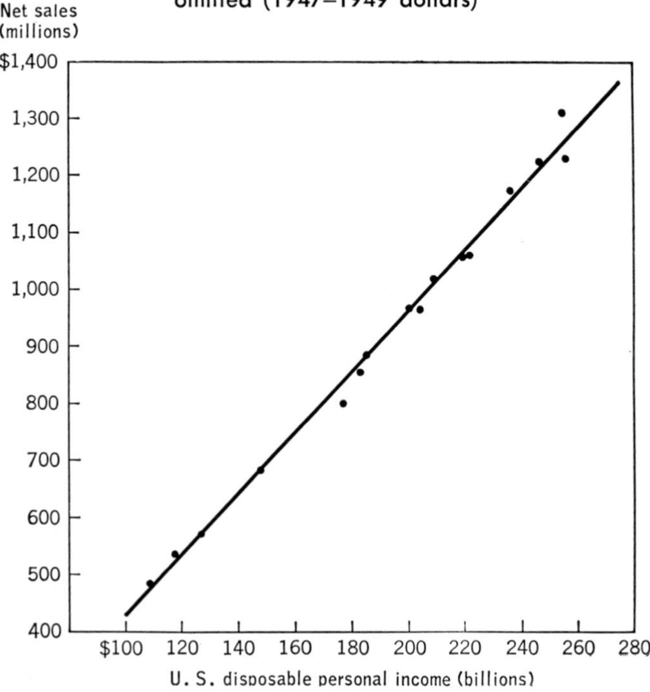

Source: Table 40.

mathematical terms. Even in the absence of any change in the basic relationship, it must be observed that the regression equation expresses an *average* relationship, not an *exact* relationship. Actual sales can be expected to fluctuate above and below the line of average relationship. A measure of the variation or scatter of actual sales around the regression line would be useful. It would then be possible to forecast *average* sales and also the *range* around the average within which sales would be most likely to occur.

Computation of standard error of estimate

SIMILARITY TO STANDARD DEVIATION

The standard error of estimate is a measure of variation which bears the same relationship to the regression line as the standard deviation does to the arithmetic mean. It will be recalled that approximately 68 per cent of the items in a series which tends to be normally distributed are located within the range of the mean plus and minus 1 standard deviation ($\overline{X} \pm 1s$); about 95 per cent of the items are included when the range is increased to plus and minus 2 standard deviations, and almost 100 per cent are within the range of the mean plus and minus 3 standard deviations. The standard error of estimate possesses these same characteristics with respect to the regression line. However, the arithmetic mean is a single value, whereas the regression line is a whole series of values which form a straight line and the standard error of estimate is used to measure the range of variation at any and all points along the regression line. In effect, the regression line plus and minus 1 standard error of estimate represents a zone around the regression line within which 68 per cent of the plotted points occur. This relationship is illustrated graphically in Chart 16.

STEPS IN COMPUTATION

The standard deviation was computed by (1) squaring the deviations between the values of individual items in a series and their mean, (2) taking an average of the squared deviations, and (3) extracting the square root of this average. These same basic steps are required to compute the standard error of estimate.

Table 41 shows the steps required to calculate the squared deviations between actual net sales and net sales estimated on the basis

CHART 16. Line of average relationship plus and minus one standard error of estimate, J. C. Penney Co. net sales and U. S. disposable income, 1938–1958, war years omitted (1947–1949 dollars)

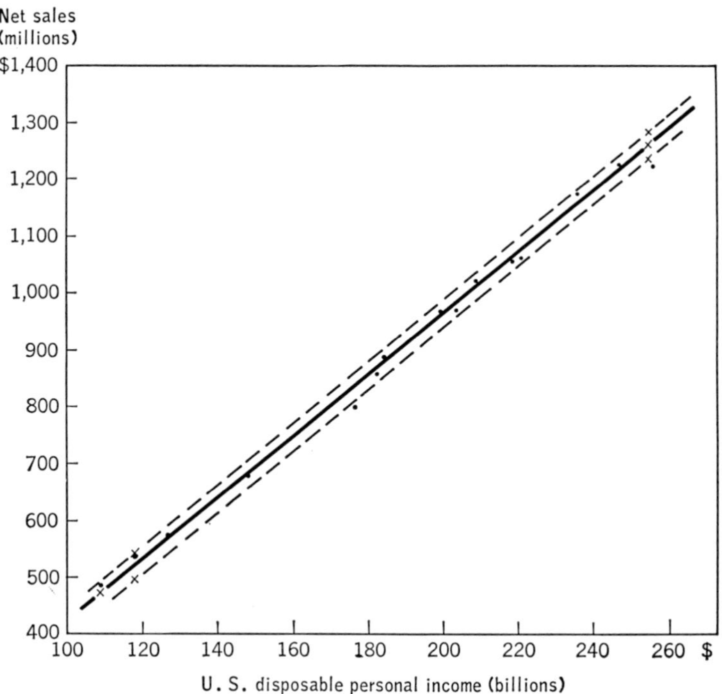

Source: Tables 40 and 41 and related computations.

of disposable personal income. Estimated net sales in column 3 were computed by substituting corresponding disposable personal income amounts from column 1 in the regression equation $Y_c = -117.3 + 5.40X$. Solving for 1938,

$$Y_c = -117.3 + 5.40(109) = 471.3, \quad \text{or} \quad \mathbf{471}$$

The deviation between actual sales (column 2) and estimated sales (column 3) in 1938 was $12 millions, as indicated in column 4. Deviations occurred because sales were dependent in part on factors other than disposable personal income. Column 5 contains the squared deviations and their sum.

Note that the sum of the Y_c (calculated values of Y) in column 3 is almost the same as the sum of net sales (actual values of Y) in column

TABLE 41. Computation of standard error of estimate—J. C. Penney Company net sales and U. S. disposable personal income

Year	(1) Disposable personal income (billions) X	(2) Net sales (millions) Y	(3) Computed sales (millions) Y_c	(4) Deviation of computed from actual sales $(Y - Y_c)$	(5) Deviations squared $(Y - Y_c)^2$
1938	109	483	471	12	144
1939	118	537	520	17	289
1940	127	571	568	3	9
1941	148	680	682	−2	4
		(1942–1946 omitted)			
1947	177	799	838	−39	1,521
1948	183	855	871	−16	256
1949	185	885	882	3	9
1950	200	968	963	5	25
1951	204	968	984	−16	256
1952	209	1,020	1,011	9	81
1953	219	1,059	1,065	−6	36
1954	221	1,061	1,076	−15	225
1955	236	1,176	1,157	19	361
1956	247	1,225	1,216	9	81
1957	256	1,227	1,265	−38	1,444
1958	255	1,312	1,260	52	2,704
Total:	3,094	14,826	14,829	−3	7,445

Source: Table 40 and related computations.

2. The difference (−3) is due to rounding off a and b in the regression equation from which the Y_c were calculated. If a and b had been carried to enough decimals the sum of column 3 would equal the sum of column 2 and the deviations in column 4 would total zero.

The standard error of estimate (S_y) may now be calculated by the formula:

$$\text{standard error of estimate} = \text{square root of } \frac{\text{sum of squared deviations}}{\text{number of paired values} - 2}$$

or, expressed in mathematical symbols,[3]

[3] $N - 2$ is used in the denominator to correct for the "degrees of freedom" lost in estimating Y_c by the regression equation which contains the two constants, a and b. Unless N is small, the correction is minor and is necessary only with small samples (under 30).

$$S_y = \sqrt{\frac{\Sigma\,(Y - Y_c)^2}{N - 2}}$$

Substituting values from Table 41, we may compute the standard error of estimate for J. C. Penney Company sales as follows:

$$S_y = \sqrt{\frac{7{,}445}{16 - 2}} = \sqrt{531.8} = 23.06, \quad \text{or} \quad \mathbf{23.1}$$

The standard error of estimate may be computed in a simpler fashion by utilizing the following formula:

$$S_y = \sqrt{\frac{\Sigma\,Y^2 - a\,\Sigma\,Y - b\,\Sigma\,XY}{N - 2}}$$

The values of the several terms in the above equation are available from Table 40. Substituting,

$$S_y = \sqrt{\frac{14{,}734{,}874 - (-117.29)(14{,}826) - (5.3984)(3{,}050{,}220)}{16 - 2}}$$

$$= \sqrt{\frac{14{,}734{,}874 + 1{,}738{,}942 - 16{,}466{,}308}{14}}$$

$$= \sqrt{\frac{7{,}508}{14}} = \sqrt{536.3}$$

$$= 23.16, \quad \text{or} \quad \mathbf{23.2}$$

Note that the values of a and b used in this short form were not rounded. This is necessary to get the same answer as by the longer method when the sums used in the formula are so large. Even so, S_y obtained by the short-cut method (23.2) differs slightly from S_y obtained by the long method (23.1) due to rounding differences.

Interpretation of standard error of estimate. The regression equation

$$Y_c = -117.3 + 5.40X$$

enabled us to forecast net sales of \$1,233,700,000 when disposable personal income had been estimated at \$250 billion. However, the \$1,233,700,000 merely represents an *average*; that is, *on the average* during years when disposable personal income is \$250 billion, net sales will be \$1,233,700,000.

The standard error of estimate can be used to set up a confidence interval around the estimate of \$1,233,700,000, an interval within which we have a stated degree of confidence of including the actual deflated net sales. For example, within one standard error of estimate (\$23,100,000) there is a 68.3 per cent probability of finding the actual value of net sales (deflated) when disposable income (deflated) equals \$250 billion. This range is

$$\$1,233,700,000 \pm \$23,100,000,$$

or from \$1,210,600,000 to \$1,256,800,000. There is approximately a 95 per cent probability of finding deflated net sales in the range of

$$\$1,233,700,000 \pm (2)(23,100,000)$$

or from \$1,187,500,000 to \$1,279,900,000.

The value of the regression equation as a forecasting tool increases as the *relative* size of the standard error of estimate decreases. If a perfect relationship existed between two series of data, the standard error of estimate would be zero. Under these hypothetical circumstances, every change in the dependent series could be fully accounted for by changes in the independent series. Since such perfect relationships are almost never present in sales forecasting, the standard error of estimate is an important supplement to the regression equation.

There are several coefficients computed as pure numbers independent of the size and type of the units of the original data which measure the relationship—or lack of relationship—between two series of data. These measures are more useful than the standard error of estimate for describing the strength of the relationship between two variables.

STRENGTH OF THE RELATIONSHIP

Variance to be explained. The objective of correlation analysis is to improve our ability to estimate the value of the dependent variable (Y) by basing our estimates (of Y) on values of the independent variable (X). In the absence of any knowledge of the nature of the relationship between X and Y, the *best* estimate of Y, regardless of the value of X, would be the mean value of Y; i.e., using the mean of Y ($\bar{Y}$) as the estimate in all cases would give the smallest *total* error for *all* estimates. If the relationship between X and Y is such that the estimates of Y are better when based on X, then the relationship has made it possible to account for at least a part of the variation of the Y values away from their mean. The variation of the Y values around the mean of Y

is measured by the *variance* of Y, which is defined as the square of the standard deviation of Y (s_y^2). The coefficients below measure the amount of the variance in Y which is accounted for by relating values of Y to values of X. Thus, they indicate the degree to which the ability to estimate Y is improved when estimates of Y are based on values of X.

Coefficient of nondetermination. This coefficient measures the variance in the variable to be forecast (sales) which is *not* explained by variance in the related variable (income). It is computed by expressing a measure of *unexplained* variance as a per cent of a measure of *total* variance. The standard deviation of the variable to be forecast is squared (s_y^2) to obtain a measure of total variance in the dependant variable, as explained above. The *squared* standard error of estimate (S_y^2) measures the *variance* in the variable to be forecast which is *not explained* by variation in the related variable. The squared standard deviation of net sales may be computed by the formula[4]

$$s_y^2 = \frac{\Sigma\, Y^2}{N} - \left(\frac{\Sigma\, Y}{N}\right)^2$$

Substituting from Table 40,

$$s_y^2 = \frac{14{,}734{,}874}{16} - \left(\frac{14{,}826}{16}\right)^2$$

$$= 920{,}930 - 858{,}634 = \mathbf{62{,}296}$$

The square of the standard error of estimate for net sales was 531.8. We may now compute the coefficient of nondetermination as follows:

$$\text{coefficient of nondetermination} = \frac{S_y^2}{s_y^2}$$

$$= \frac{531.8}{62{,}296} = \mathbf{0.0085}$$

This may be interpreted as meaning that only 0.85 per cent of the variance in deflated net sales is not matched by variance in deflated disposable personal income. The coefficient of nondetermination is a negative expression of relationship. A positive and more meaningful measure is provided by the coefficient of determination.

Coefficient of determination. If the coefficient of nondetermination is 0.85 per cent, it would seem logical that the coefficient of determina-

[4] The reader may recognize this formula as the square of a formula for the standard deviation of ungrouped data when the assumed mean has been set equal to zero.

tion must be 100 per cent minus 0.85 per cent, or 99.15 per cent. This is true and the coefficient is calculated as follows:

$$\text{coefficient of determination } (r^2) = 1 - \frac{S_y^2}{s_y^2}$$
$$= 1 - 0.0085$$
$$= 0.9915, \quad \text{or} \quad \mathbf{99.15} \text{ per cent}$$

A coefficient of determination of 99.15 per cent suggests that 99.15 per cent of the variance in deflated net sales is associated with variance in deflated disposable personal income. The reader must realize, of course, that this requires an assumption of "other things remaining equal or constant," with "other things" including such important factors as the operating and merchandising policies of the J. C. Penney Company and its competitors. Nevertheless, the coefficient of determination is an important and useful measure.

Coefficient of correlation. This measure is the square root of the coefficient of determination. Hence the coefficient of correlation, r, for J. C. Penney Company net sales and U. S. disposable personal income (both in 1947–1949 dollars) may be computed as follows:

$$r = \sqrt{1 - \frac{S_y^2}{s_y^2}} = \sqrt{1 - 0.0085} = \sqrt{0.9915} = \mathbf{+0.9957}$$

The meaning of this coefficient may be better understood after a reconsideration of S_y^2 and s_y^2. The S_y^2 for the above relationship was small in relation to the s_y^2, the total variance. If the relationship between sales and disposable personal income had been perfect, the S_y and the S_y^2 would have been zero. When zero is substituted for S_y^2 in the correlation formula, the coefficient becomes 1.

$$r = \sqrt{1 - \frac{0}{62{,}296}} = \sqrt{1 - 0} = \sqrt{1} = \mathbf{1}$$

Hence a coefficient of 1 denotes *perfect correlation.*

On the other hand if no relationship had existed between sales and disposable personal income, the S_y^2 would have been as large as the s_y^2. The coefficient of correlation would then have been as follows:

$$r = \sqrt{1 - \frac{62{,}296}{62{,}296}} = \sqrt{1 - 1} = \sqrt{0} = \mathbf{0}$$

Hence, a coefficient of 0 denotes *no correlation.*

We now can see that the correlation coefficient of +0.9957 between

J. C. Penney Company sales and U. S. disposable income indicates a high degree of direct or positive relationship. We know the relationship is positive (direct) because the b value in the regression equation was positive.

Mention should also be made of negative, or inverse, correlation. If increases in one series are accompanied by decreases in the other series, the correlation is said to be negative. This can be determined by referring to the scatter diagram or to the sign of b in the regression equation; a negative b indicates negative correlation. In such cases a minus sign is placed before the correlation coefficient. Consequently, correlation coefficients may range from -1 to $+1$.

Significance of the coefficient of correlation. It is impossible to state arbitrarily how large a correlation coefficient must be to have significance. Much is dependent upon the nature of the series being analyzed and upon the number of paired values. A coefficient of a given size becomes more significant as the number of paired values from which it was computed increases. For some investigations a correlation coefficient of 0.25 or even below may be significant.

Inference tests of hypotheses concerning the true value of r are possible. The correlation coefficient is not a normally distributed statistic except under some unusual special conditions, but r can be transformed into a variable which is normally distributed. This variable (z_r), often called *Fisher's z* after its discoverer, is related to r by the formula

$$z_r = 1.1513[\log_{10}(1 + r) - \log_{10}(1 - r)]$$

The standard error of Fisher's z depends only on the size of the sample.[5]

$$\sigma_z = \frac{1}{\sqrt{N - 3}}$$

The value of r obtained as the correlation between J. C. Penney net sales and disposable personal income is obviously significantly different from zero. Suppose, however, that we have $r = 0.75$ for $N = 39$, and we wish to test the hypothesis that the true (population)

[5] The $N - 3$ in the denominator is a shorter way of writing $N - m - 1$, where N is the total number of observations (size of sample) and m is the number of constants in the regression equation (2 in this case). Thus the denominator is the square root of one less than the degrees of freedom in the problem, a necessary condition in order to obtain a proper measure of sampling error in this case.

value of r is at least 0.80 with a five per cent level of significance, $\alpha = 0.05$. Then,

$$
\begin{aligned}
z\,(0.75) &= 1.1503\,[\log_{10}(1 + 0.75) - \log_{10}(1 - 0.75)] \\
&= 1.1503\,(\log_{10} 1.75 - \log_{10} .25) \\
&= 1.1503\,(10.24304 - 10) - (9.39794 - 10) \\
&= 1.1503\,(0.84510) = \mathbf{0.9721}
\end{aligned}
$$

If $r = 0.80$, by the same formula

$$z\,(0.80) = \mathbf{1.0977}.$$

$$\sigma_z = \frac{1}{\sqrt{N - 3}} = \frac{1}{\sqrt{39 - 3}} = \frac{1}{\sqrt{36}} = \frac{1}{6}, \quad \text{or} \quad \mathbf{0.1667}$$

We now have sufficient information to test whether or not the difference between the sample r of 0.75 and the assumed population value of 0.80 is significant, that is, not just due to sampling error. These two values have been converted into normally distributed deviates ($z.75 = 0.9721$ and $z.80 = 1.0977$) and the standard error of the sample statistic computed ($\sigma_z = \frac{1}{6}$). We can use our standard formula to compute Z, the difference expressed in standard error units.

$$
\begin{aligned}
Z &= \frac{0.9721 - 1.0977}{\frac{1}{6}} = 6(0.9721 - 1.0977) \\
&= 6(-0.1256) = \mathbf{-0.7536}
\end{aligned}
$$

As this is a one-sided test, we read from the area under the normal curve (Table II, Appendix B) that a Z of 0.7536 is less than the value of Z associated with the five per cent level of significance (1.645). Therefore, we conclude that it is possible that the population value or r is at least equal to 0.80.

Tables for transforming r into z exist and obviate the necessity of most of the above computations.[6] Utilizing such a table we could test whether the coefficient of correlation between J. C. Penney sales and disposable income is significantly above 0.95.

$$z0.9957 = 3.14, \qquad z0.95 = 1.84$$

$$\sigma_z = \frac{1}{\sqrt{16 - 3}} = \frac{1}{\sqrt{13}} = \frac{1}{\mathbf{3.606}}$$

[6] See for example: R. A. Fisher, *Statistical Methods for Research Workers*, Oliver & Boyd, Ltd., Edinburgh, 1936 (Table VB). This table is also available in R. Ferber, *Statistical Techniques in Market Research*, New York, McGraw-Hill Book Co., Inc., 1949 (Table 15, Appendix D).

Computing the number of standard error units in the difference:

$$Z = \frac{3.14 - 1.84}{\dfrac{1}{3.606}} = (3.14 - 1.84)3.606$$

$$= 1.30(3.606) = 4.6878, \quad \text{or} \quad \mathbf{4.69}$$

A Z value of 4.69 indicates that there is only a very slight possibility that the observed difference between the computed r of 0.9957 and the hypothetical r of 0.95 could be due to chance errors of sampling. The probability of being so far away from the mean of a normal distribution is between 34/100,000 and 3/100,000 if only sampling error is considered. The obvious conclusion is that the population r is almost certain to exceed 0.95.

Other methods of computing correlation coefficients

The above method, sometimes referred to as the *least-squares* method, was described at some length because (1) it is easily adaptable to forecasting and (2) the reader had been previously introduced to the least-squares method of fitting a straight line. Other methods are available which obtain the value of the correlation coefficient without first computing the regression equation and the standard error of estimate. These latter measures, in this writer's opinion, are of equal or greater importance than the correlation coefficient in so far as sales forecasting is concerned.

However, the reader should be aware that other methods are available. Correlation coefficients for data which have been classified in frequency distributions can best be computed by using a cross-classified table. Special formulas have been developed for correlation of data which cannot be measured with exactness but which can be arranged in order of rank. Discussion of these methods is reserved for subsequent courses in statistics.

Other applications of correlation analysis

Correlation analysis is widely used in fields other than business administration. Within business administration it has many applications other than in sales forecasting. For example, it is used extensively in personnel testing. Training new personnel is costly. Appreciable savings can be realized by using tests to eliminate those applicants whose scores indicate their performance would be unsatisfactory. Such tests may be constructed by experts who analyze responses to test questions by employees of known performance.

Correlation analysis may be used as a means of testing quality of products, thereby possibly avoiding the necessity of tests which would result in destruction of items to be tested. Numerous applications may be made in the field of finance where the relationships among stock prices, dividends, earnings, money rates, and other items are of much interest.

Correlation may be applied in market analysis to estimate the sales potential in new areas. Knowledge of the relationship of pertinent factors to sales enables a company to expand operations to areas of likely high sales and to avoid expansion to areas which have low sales potentials.

Although correlation analysis has many varied applications, the basic objective is always the same: prediction of the value of one variable based on the value of another variable.

SUMMARY

Correlation analysis is utilized to measure the relationship which exists between two or more series of data. Determination of the relationship of sales to other factors facilitates sales forecasting; for example, if fluctuations in sales bear a close relationship to income, forecasts of income by government or private economists may be used as a basis for forecasting sales.

This chapter has been limited to a description of the correlation of but two series of data whose graphic relationship approximates a straight line; this is known as *simple linear correlation.* Analyses of curvilinear relationships and of relationships among more than two series of data (multiple and partial correlation) have been reserved for advanced courses in statistics.

Correlation for sales forecasting involves four basic steps:

1. Preparation of a scatter diagram,
2. Computation of the equation for the regression line,
3. Computation of the standard error of estimate,
4. Computation of significant coefficients of relationship.

The scatter diagram provides a rough approximation of the pattern of relationship and the amount of deviation from this pattern. If no pattern of relationship is apparent, the analysis should be discontinued at this point. If the pattern is clearly evident and the amount of deviation is slight, it is possible that a firm may achieve satisfactory forecasting results by reference to a freehand smooth line drawn through the points in the scatter diagram. However, in many cases accuracy of forecasting may be improved by computation of additional measures.

Computation of a least-squares equation permits a *line of best fit* to be drawn through the points in a scatter diagram. The constant b in the straight-line equation $Y_c = a + bX$ represents the average amount of change in Y_c (sales) which may be anticipated with each unit change in X, the series with which sales have been correlated. Forecasts of values of X can be substituted in the equation to determine probable future sales.

The standard error of estimate is a measure of the variation of sales around the regression line. It bears the same relationship to the regression line as the standard deviation does to the arithmetic mean. Hence it enables the forecaster to determine a range within which forecast sales are likely to occur.

The squared error of estimate (S_y^2) represents variance in sales unassociated with variance in the related series; the squared standard deviation of sales (s_y^2) represents total variance in sales. The expression of S_y^2 as a per cent of s_y^2 (that is, S_y^2/s_y^2) measures the percent of variance in sales which is not associated with changes in the related series; this measure is known as the coefficient of nondetermination.

The coefficient of determination, $1 - (S_y^2/s_y^2)$, is a positive expression of the coefficient of nondetermination. It measures the per cent of variance in sales which is associated with changes in the related series. The coefficient of determination is of obvious significance in sales forecasting.

The coefficient of correlation is merely the square root of the coefficient of determination. It is the most widely known coefficient of relationship, principally because other methods of correlation analysis proceed directly to its computation without first computing (1) the regression equation, (2) the standard error of estimate, or (3) coefficients of nondetermination and determination. The easily understood meaning of the coefficient of determination makes it a more useful measure than the coefficient of correlation for sales forecasting and many other business applications. The correlation coefficient varies from -1 to $+1$; a value of -1 denotes perfect *negative* correlation,

+1 denotes perfect *positive* correlation, and 0 indicates *no* correlation.

The occurrence of a high coefficient of determination or correlation is not in itself evidence of a meaningful relationship between series. Cases of *spurious* or *nonsense* correlation are not uncommon. Therefore it is of utmost importance that the logic of relationship between series of data be determined by sound subjective analysis.

Questions and Exercises

1. Explain what is meant by the term "correlation." Distinguish between positive and negative correlation.
2. Prepare a scatter diagram of sales for the same company selected in exercise 5, Chapter 7, and U. S. disposable personal income as published by the U. S. Department of Commerce in *Business Statistics* and *Survey of Current Business.* Discuss the degree of relationship suggested by your chart. Discuss the meaning of any relationship which is revealed.
3. Draw a freehand line through the scatter diagram prepared in exercise 2.
4. Compute the regression equation for your company's sales and U. S. disposable personal income. (Refer to Table 40.)
5. Explain the meaning of all symbols in the regression equation. Interpret the values in the regression equation computed in exercise 4.
6. Using the regression equation computed in exercise 4, compute two points for the regression line. Plot these points on the scatter diagram prepared in exercise 2 and connect with a straight line. Compare this line with your freehand line drawn in exercise 3. Does a straight line appear to be reasonably appropriate?
7. Compute the standard error of estimate for the relationship of your company's sales to U. S. disposable personal income. (Refer to Table 41.)
8. Plot the range of one standard error of estimate around the regression line which you plotted in exercise 6.
9. Interpret the significance of the standard error of estimate.
10. Using the above regression equation and standard error of estimate (computed in exercises 4 and 7), make a forecast of company sales

for a selected future year. What qualifications should be attached to your forecast?

11. Compare the forecast computed in exercise 10 with a similar forecast based on the trend equation of exercise 5, Chapter 7.

12. Define the following coefficients:
(a) Coefficient of nondetermination,
(b) Coefficient of determination,
(c) Coefficient of correlation.

13. Compute the above coefficients for your company's sales and U. S. disposable personal income. Interpret your results.

14. Discuss the comparative advantages and disadvantages of trend analysis and correlation analysis as alternative forecasting techniques.

15. The ABC Company has analyzed its sales experience by counties and has related this experience to disposable personal income in these same counties. The regression equation expressing the relationship between sales and income was found to be $Y_c = \$7{,}000 + 3{,}000X$, where X represents millions of dollars of disposable income. The firm is considering expansion of sales to County Z, which has a disposable personal income of \$8 million. What sales may the firm expect on the basis of past experience as reflected by the regression equation?

16. The ABC Company in the above exercise has determined the standard error of estimate for sales to income to be \$4,000. In the light of this information, refine the forecast which you made in exercise 15.

17. (a) The ABC Company in the above exercises has estimated that county sales of \$35,000 are required to recover costs. Do you believe the ABC Company should expand sales operations to County Z? Explain fully, citing any additional information which should be considered.
(b) How would your recommendation change if ABC could expect to recover costs if sales amounted to \$33,000? \$31,000? Explain fully.

9 *Statistical reports for management: statistical tables*

Importance of reports for management

Reports are essential to modern business administration. Executives of all but the smallest firms are dependent upon reports for information necessary to plan and control business operations. Stockholders and owners not active in management require reports to evaluate their investments and their executives. Creditors and various regulatory bodies often require reports. Management employs reports as one means of communication with employees, labor unions, and the general public.

A report is not a mere listing of data. Rather, it is a presentation of pertinent data in such a manner that recipients of the report may readily determine their significance. This is not an easy task. Statisticians, accountants, and analysts who prepare the reports are familiar with the data and the records from which they are drawn and consequently may be able to interpret them with relative ease. However, this is not the case with most users of reports. Therefore it becomes highly important that persons preparing reports view the reports from the standpoint of the recipients. Information must be *effectively communicated* if it is to be of any value. All too frequently important findings of staff assistants have been lost or obscured because reports have failed to communicate their significance to persons responsible for making decisions.

Effective communication may be achieved only if persons responsible for preparation of reports possess the following information:

1. Knowledge of the purpose for which a report is to be prepared
2. Knowledge of different types of reports and their advantages and limitations
3. Knowledge of problems of interpretation encountered by users of the reports

It is, of course, highly desirable that users of reports be familiar with different types of reports and develop skill in their interpretation. Nevertheless, initial responsibility for effective communication rests with those persons who prepare the reports.

Although reports may be either oral or written, this text is concerned only with written reports. Many executives are of the firm belief that all important reports should be written; information in oral reports is easily forgotten and is more subject to misinterpretation than is information in written reports.

Quantitative data to be included in reports may be presented in a variety of ways. A limited amount of data may be interwoven with the written narrative as was done in the following excerpt from the annual report of the American Iron and Steel Institute:

> "Steel output for 1958 totalled 85.3 million net tons of ingots, representing 101.8 per cent of the annual average for 1947–49."[1]

This method of reporting is useful in highlighting significant data but is not so effective in communicating masses of quantitative data as are the two principal methods of presenting quantitative data, namely, tables and charts. Properly constructed tables and charts are useful and effective means not only for communicating but also for analysis of quantitative data. The remainder of this chapter will

[1] American Iron and Steel Institute, *Charting Steel's Progress*, 1959, New York, p. 23.

be devoted to a discussion of statistical tables; graphic presentation methods will be described in Chapter 10.

The statistical table

PURPOSE OF TABLES IN REPORTS FOR MANAGEMENT

There are several different objectives in presenting statistical information. The research worker wishes to present all of his material with his interpretations of its meaning so that others may study it, agree or disagree with his conclusions, and use it as a basis for further research. A statistical agency such as the Bureau of the Census primarily presents information for the use of others. Reports to management are designed to present specific information which will be used as the basis for decisions. Management reports to the stockholder are designed to present information that will help them in evaluating the operations and the current status of the organization. All of these people are interested in presenting information forcefully and convincingly.

A table is merely one way of presenting information clearly and accurately. It usually involves some classification or cross-classification of the data to give them a logical order and meaning. Any person designing a table should be aware of the basic purpose of the table and the characteristics of a well-constructed table.

TYPES OF TABLES

Tables may be classified by two major types, *reference* and *summary* tables. *Reference tables*, sometimes referred to as general purpose tables, contain large quantities of data which are presented for general information. Census tables are illustrations of this type, as is also Table 42 which presents life insurance in force in the United States by states in 1958, as published in the *Life Insurance Fact Book 1959*, p. 12. Reference tables are designed as sources of data; summary tables are frequently derived from reference tables. When included in a business report, reference tables are usually placed in the appendix; in this position they do not distract the reader who desires a rapid preview of the main theme of the report, but are available to those readers who may wish more detailed information.

Summary tables are employed to present relatively few data in a

TABLE 42

LIFE INSURANCE IN FORCE IN THE U. S. BY STATES 1958

	ORDINARY		GROUP		INDUSTRIAL		CREDIT		TOTAL	
STATE	No. (000 Omitted)	Amount (000,000 Omitted)	Certifs. (000 Omitted)	Amount (000,000 Omitted)	No. (000 Omitted)	Amount (000,000 Omitted)	No.* (000 Omitted)	Amount (000,000 Omitted)	No. (000 Omitted)	Amount (000,000 Omitted)
Ala.	832	$ 3,150	525	$ 1,801	5,462	$ 1,349	817	$ 434	7,636	$ 6,734
Ariz.	423	1,602	199	590	194	80	286	218	1,102	2,490
Ark.	434	1,556	159	534	676	238	186	139	1,455	2,467
Calif.	6,093	24,049	4,323	15,947	4,170	1,799	1,966	1,983	16,552	43,778
Colo.	900	2,980	390	1,173	466	226	412	285	2,168	4,664
Conn.	1,742	5,736	891	2,870	1,347	624	580	323	4,560	9,553
Del.	259	921	110	533	368	151	135	97	872	1,702
D. C.	404	1,589	564	1,584	745	256	243	135	1,956	3,564
Fla.	1,728	6,384	594	2,077	4,483	1,612	1,220	765	8,025	10,838
Ga.	1,304	4,621	715	2,590	5,487	1,766	1,298	683	8,804	9,660
Idaho	280	850	98	284	44	17	96	80	518	1,231
Ill.	6,828	20,527	2,831	10,259	5,959	2,411	1,167	800	16,785	33,997
Ind.	2,581	7,318	990	4,232	2,836	1,126	1,290	699	7,697	13,375
Iowa	1,688	4,825	424	1,249	582	207	384	264	3,078	6,545
Kans.	1,256	3,574	339	1,143	673	270	375	273	2,643	5,260
Ky.	1,067	3,114	388	1,452	2,320	826	602	281	4,377	5,673
La.	818	3,445	505	1,915	3,840	1,164	1,101	519	6,264	7,043
Maine	455	1,392	170	407	356	158	218	122	1,199	2,079
Md.	1,470	4,984	598	2,526	2,781	974	719	303	5,568	8,787
Mass.	2,976	9,349	1,156	4,367	3,476	1,488	1,069	497	8,677	15,701
Mich.	3,885	12,086	2,259	7,991	3,652	1,486	1,454	988	11,250	22,551
Minn.	1,692	5,368	724	2,306	667	252	494	381	3,577	8,307
Miss.	399	1,529	191	633	847	243	375	255	1,812	2,660
Mo.	2,467	6,960	1,019	3,204	2,576	1,023	956	582	7,018	11,769
Mont.	306	1,030	101	334	55	19	125	99	587	1,482
Nebr.	856	2,474	205	658	275	103	236	176	1,572	3,411
Nev.	95	373	67	169	21	5	25	18	208	565
N. H.	350	1,085	104	311	318	138	183	132	955	1,666
N. J.	4,176	13,771	1,550	6,911	3,774	1,682	527	338	10,027	22,702
N. Mex.	274	1,071	142	555	170	83	123	92	709	1,801
N. Y.	11,296	36,949	4,269	19,393	7,050	3,047	3,005	2,000	25,620	61,389
N. C.	1,608	4,930	665	2,262	3,690	1,300	1,371	583	7,334	9,075
N. Dak.	296	829	73	176	8	2	91	71	468	1,078
Ohio	5,555	17,124	2,167	9,371	6,470	2,664	1,255	927	15,447	30,086
Okla.	990	3,136	359	1,481	652	278	467	300	2,468	5,195
Oreg.	715	2,610	379	1,089	182	68	326	289	1,602	4,056
Pa.	7,719	21,498	2,724	10,252	9,514	3,769	3,020	1,256	22,977	36,775
R. I.	550	1,674	206	482	696	300	181	111	1,633	2,567
S. C.	732	2,153	321	1,041	3,334	1,217	560	291	4,947	4,702
S. Dak.	335	922	74	213	10	3	78	61	497	1,199
Tenn.	1,058	3,716	630	2,202	3,371	1,150	855	512	5,914	7,580
Texas	4,013	14,023	1,748	6,577	4,569	1,852	2,356	1,427	12,686	23,879
Utah	456	1,338	195	593	185	64	273	184	1,109	2,179
Vt.	220	646	50	138	137	60	94	57	501	901
Va.	1,470	5,097	650	2,520	3,353	1,160	1,076	536	6,549	9,313
Wash.	1,162	4,186	657	2,246	388	141	337	212	2,544	6,785
W. Va.	662	1,950	300	1,262	921	368	448	229	2,331	3,809
Wis.	2,234	6,845	869	2,502	1,082	422	492	419	4,677	10,188
Wyo.	151	495	49	202	14	5	57	48	271	750
Total U.S.	89,260	$287,834	38,716	$144,607	104,246	$39,646	35,004	$21,474	267,226	$493,561

*Includes group credit certificates.

Source: Institute of Life Insurance. Total life insurance in force in 1958 in Alaska was $0.3 billion and in Hawaii $2.1 billion, as presented in *Life Insurance Fact Book, 1959*, p. 12.

manner which facilitates their analysis. Occasionally informal summary tables are effectively incorporated with narrative, as in the following excerpt from page 1 of the McGraw Electric Company *1952 Annual Report:*

> *A Noteworthy Trend*
>
> It is interesting to observe that our recent acquisitions are bringing about a redistribution of our sales as between utilities, consumer outlets, and others. A marked change took place in 1952, as the following figures show:
>
> | | *1950* | *1951* | *1952* |
> |---|---|---|---|
> | Utilities.............. | 50% | 55% | 65% |
> | Consumer goods...... | 35% | 30% | 18% |
> | Industrial, Government and miscellaneous... | 15% | 15% | 17% |
>
> We believe that our present sales pattern has definitely contributed to the stability of our earning power and the consistency of our dividend payments. It is important in this connection to recognize the potential of the electrical industry, with which all divisions of our company are associated, because the business of producing electric power and light is one of America's outstanding "growth" industries and its further rapid expansion can be safely forecast.

A more common format for presentation of summary tables is illustrated by Table 43. Most tables in business reports are summary rather than reference tables. Consequently, the following sections are devoted principally to the description and illustration of various forms of summary tables. Many guides for table construction apply to both summary and reference tables.

PARTS OF A TABLE

Formal tables consist of several parts as illustrated in the sketch below. Some tables require but a few parts, whereas other tables require all parts. Every table, however, has a title, column headings, stub, and body. The terms *heading* and *caption* are often used interchangeably. Table 43 has all parts except a sub-title and footnotes; Table 42 has a footnote but no subtitle or prefatory note. It will be noted that the ages in the stub of Table 43 are headings for the horizontal rows arranged in outline form; the race and sex designations, white and non-white, male and female, are column headings. Hence, each amount in the body of the table is *cross-classified* by age and by race and sex; the space which an amount occupies is called a *cell.*

The prefatory note (years) applies to data in all the columns; if it did not apply to all columns, it would have been placed as a note under each appropriate column heading.

TABLE 43

EXPECTATION OF LIFE AT VARIOUS AGES IN THE UNITED STATES 1957

(Years)

AGE	WHITE		NON-WHITE		ALL RACES
	Male	Female	Male	Female	
0	67.1	73.5	60.3	65.2	69.3
20	49.9	55.7	44.7	48.9	52.0
40	31.4	36.6	27.8	31.3	33.4
45	27.0	32.0	24.0	27.3	29.0
50	22.9	27.5	20.4	23.6	24.8
55	19.1	23.3	17.2	20.3	20.9
60	15.7	19.2	14.5	17.4	17.3
65	12.7	15.4	12.4	14.8	14.0
70	10.1	12.1	11.1	13.2	11.2

Source: *Life Insurance Fact Book, 1959*, p. 109.

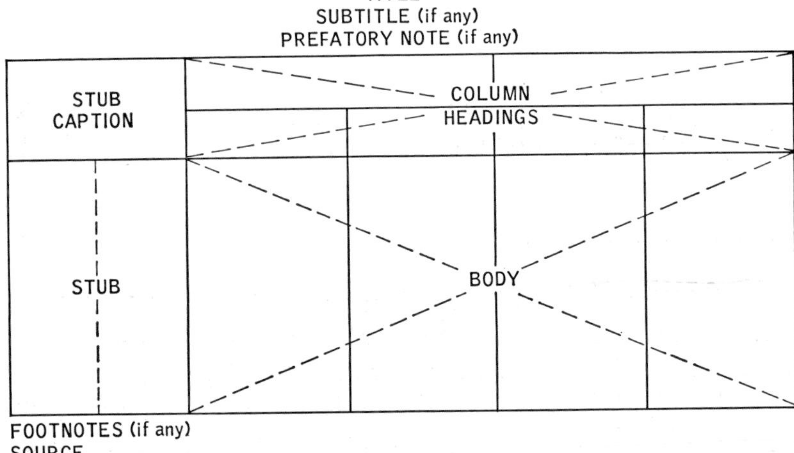

CHARACTERISTICS OF GOOD TABLES

Simplicity and clarity. These attributes are essential if summary tables are to be effective. Titles, column headings, and stub designations must be concise and lucid. It frequently has been stated that a title should specify *what*, *where*, *how classified*, and *when*. However, literal interpretation of this rule may lead to an extremely long and unwieldy title in some cases. This is usually unnecessary because stub and column headings conveniently provide answers to some of the basic questions. Also, a short, eye-catching title may be supplemented by a subtitle in smaller and less conspicuous type. A title for Table 43 which would provide answers to all four basic questions could be stated as follows: "Expectation of Life in Years at Various Ages in the United States in 1957 Classified by Race and Sex." This cumbersome title is obviously less desirable than the one which appears on Table 43.

Another illustration of the trend toward less formal titles appears in Table 44. The reader will note several innovations in this table which are somewhat unorthodox but which effectively present the data. The title has been stated in the form of a question and has been placed off center toward the outer edge of the page on which it appeared. The stub headings have been merged with the data in the first column. Note the ease with which the rows of data may be read. For example, "6 officers and wives representing 0.2% of the total number of shareholders, hold 114,641 shares representing 20.8% of the total number of shares outstanding." The omission of a date in

TABLE 44

WHO OWNS MASTER COMMON SHARES ?

SHAREHOLDERS AND WHO THEY ARE	PERCENT OF TOTAL NUMBER OF SHAREHOLDERS	NUMBER OF SHARES HELD	PERCENT OF TOTAL NUMBER OF SHARES
2,759 INDIVIDUALS	92.9%	297,356	54.1%
6 OFFICERS AND WIVES	.2%	114,641	20.8%
205 INSTITUTIONS, INVESTMENT TRUSTS, FIDUCIARIES AND BROKERS	6.9%	137,810	25.1%
TOTAL 2,970	100%	549,807	100%

Source: The Master Electric Company, *Annual Report, 1952*, p. 21.

Table 44 was questionable procedure, even though the table appeared in an annual report for the year ending December 31, 1952.

Use of *rounding* and *percentages* often make data more readable. Rounding was used in Table 42 and percentages appear in Table 44. Abbreviations must be used with caution since their meanings are not always clear; this is particularly true in the case of abbreviations which may represent several terms. Ditto marks are not considered good form. The word "none" or the symbol 0 should be used to indicate a zero value; dashes (- - -) or dots (. . .) may be used to indicate that a particular cell in a table is not applicable for the data recorded. If a cell is applicable but data are not available, the abbreviation "n.a." may be inserted in the cell and explained in a footnote.

Emphasis. Since people are accustomed to reading from left to right and from top to bottom, the upper left corner of the table is considered to be the most prominent and the lower right corner the least prominent. When totals are to be emphasized, they may be placed at the top and to the left as in Table 47. Totals are normally placed at the bottom and in the right-hand columns, as in Table 42, when individual items are of equal or greater significance.

Comparisons are emphasized by placing the data to be compared in adjacent columns rather than in adjacent rows; this is true because the eye can make horizontal comparisons more readily than vertical

TABLE 45

LIFE INSURANCE PERSONNEL IN THE UNITED STATES

	Home Office	Agency Cashiers & Clerks	Agency Managers & Assistants	Full-Time Agents	Total Personnel
1945					
Men	26,700	3,200	21,900	121,600	173,400
Women	53,800	26,800	100	7,100	87,800
Total	80,500	30,000	22,000	128,700	261,200
1955					
Men	44,000	4,400	38,000	184,100	270,500
Women	83,800	38,000	500	5,500	127,800
Total	127,800	42,400	38,500	189,600	398,300
1956					
Men	46,600	4,200	40,600	189,900	281,300
Women	86,600	40,300	400	5,900	133,200
Total	133,200	44,500	41,000	195,800	414,500

Sources: Institute of Life Insurance and Life Insurance Agency Management Association, as presented in *Life Insurance Fact Book, 1959*, p. 99.

comparisons. This may be illustrated by reference to Tables 45 and 46; comparison of the number of men with the number of women employed in various insurance offices during each year is made most easily by reference to Table 46.

Logical arrangement. Items in the column headings and in the stub should be arranged in some systematic order. Items in reference tables should be arranged in a manner which facilitates their location; items in summary tables should be arranged to facilitate comparisons and

TABLE 46. Life insurance personnel in the United States

	1955			1956		
Office or agency	Men	Women	Total	Men	Women	Total
Home office........	44,000	83,800	127,800	46,600	86,600	133,200
Agency cashier and clerks...........	4,400	38,000	42,400	4,200	40,300	44,500
Agency managers and assistants....	38,000	500	38,500	40,600	400	41,000
Full-time agents....	184,100	5,500	189,600	189,900	5,900	195,800
Total personnel:	270,500	127,800	398,300	281,300	133,200	414,500

Source: Adapted from Table 45.

TABLE 47. Life insurance personnel in the United States

	Total		Men		Women	
Office or agency	1955	1956	1955	1956	1955	1956
Total personnel:	398,300	414,500	270,500	281,300	127,800	133,200
Home office......	127,800	133,200	44,000	46,600	83,800	86,600
Agency cashier and clerks	42,400	44,500	4,400	4,200	38,000	40,300
Agency managers and assistants...	38,500	41,000	38,000	40,600	500	400
Full-time agents...	189,600	195,800	184,100	189,900	5,500	5,900

Source: Adapted from Table 45.

to place the most significant items in the most prominent positions.

Some common bases for arrangement of data are alphabetical, magnitude, geographical, customary, chronological, and progressive. The *alphabetical* arrangement is frequently used in reference tables, such as Table 42. The classification in Table 42 is also *geographical*, by state. The stub arrangement in Table 43 was by magnitude of age within the race and sex categories; items arranged by magnitude may progress either from low to high or from high to low. Column arrangements are in part chronological in both Tables 46 and 47. A *customary* arrangement is illustrated in Table 45 where "Men" precedes "Women" in the stub and the "Home Office" is given precedence in the column order. The *progressive* arrangement is used in financial statements where each succeeding figure contributes toward the amount of some intermediate or end item such as cost of goods sold, current assets, or net profit.

Space considerations frequently cause more items to be placed in the stub than in the column headings; it is easier to expand the number of rows than to increase the number of columns. If space is not a factor, stub and column arrangements should be determined on the basis of desired comparisons and emphasis. Three different classifications of the same data are illustrated in Tables 45, 46, and 47. Table 45 emphasizes employment by type of office or agency; comparison may also be made of the numbers of men and women employed by type of office during each year. However, this latter comparison is made more easily under the arrangement in Table 46. Total employment receives primary emphasis in Table 47, and the numbers of men and women employed by years in the various offices are more easily compared than in either Table 45 or Table 46. To illustrate, comparison of male employment in 1955 and 1956 in Table 46 requires the eyes to travel from the first to the fourth column; in Table 47 this comparison is made in the adjacent third and fourth columns.

Footnotes and source designations. Footnotes should be employed whenever additional explanation is required for titles, column headings, stub designations, or data appearing in the body of the table. Often data in chronological series are not wholly comparable, because of changes in recording or collection procedures. Items and their respective footnotes should be cross-referenced by symbols (*, †, ‡, etc.) or letters of the alphabet; numbers should not be used as footnote references, since there is danger of confusion with numbers in the body of the table.

The source from which data in a table were obtained should always be acknowledged unless the data were originally collected or recorded by the person or firm which prepared the table. This procedure is both a matter of courtesy to the author and publisher of the source material and an aid to readers who may desire to locate the source material for further investigation. A source note should include the author, title, publisher, volume, date or dates of publication, and page, *if appropriate*. In actual practice no hard rule can be made concerning the exact content of source notes, but the source note should be adequate to facilitate location of the source by the reader. If complete source notes would be lengthy and of little concern to most readers, it may suffice to give a brief source note, such as "U. S. Department of Commerce." However, it is imperative for the person who has prepared the table to keep a file record of the complete source for future personal reference and also for replies to requests for source identification from others.

PROCEDURE FOR CONSTRUCTION OF TABLES

Initial planning for tables should be commenced during the early phases of investigation and report preparation. Sketches of final table forms are useful in planning survey questionnaires and worksheets for recording data from questionnaires, internal records, or published sources. Lack of integrated planning is likely to result (1) in failure to collect significant data and (2) in the collection of data not essential to the investigation. Both of these results may prove costly and damaging to the value of the final report.

Worksheets should be planned to facilitate required computations of totals, averages, and percentages; this entails leaving an ample number of columns and rows vacant when recording the basic data. When data in a column of a worksheet or summary table have been derived from data in other columns, the method of derivation should be indicated in the column heading. An illustration of this may be seen in Table 34, page 170. Columns and rows in worksheets should be arranged to facilitate the copying of pertinent data to final summary tables.

As in all statistical and accounting work, *accuracy* is important. All recordings and computations should be checked, preferably by someone other than the person who did the original work. Written procedures specifying the order in which computations are to be made and checked are highly desirable.

Finally, the finished summary table must be presented in the most effective manner possible, keeping in mind the characteristics of a good table. Special attention should be given to table size and shape, rulings, spacings, and general eye appeal. Variety in table construction is desirable. Tables which effectively communicate their data usually reflect the imagination and originality of their designer.

Illustrations of tables useful to management

ACCOUNTING REPORTS

The old saying that "one picture is worth a thousand words" expresses the reason why tables and charts are the most effective means of communicating quantitative data. This saying also suggests that the best way to demonstrate this point is by ample use of illustrations. Accordingly, a number of tables will be shown in the pages which follow. However, these illustrations are by no means exhaustive of either table styles or applications. The reader is encouraged to supplement these illustrations from other readily available sources.

Operating summaries. These statements contain a wide variety of significant financial and nonfinancial data. Table 48 is an operating summary for the Chesapeake and Ohio Railway for 1958 and 1959. Note that data for the year 1959 are placed in the left column—the most prominent position. The placement of 1958 data in the adjacent column facilitates comparison of the highlighted information.

Table 49 is an informal tabular design. This intermixture of narrative and data is most effective when limited to actual data for only one year; percentage and net changes from the previous year can be effectively included.

Table 50 illustrates the use of bold headings, bold lines, and differences in shading of the background to focus attention on separate sections of the table. The reader is urged to compare Tables 48, 49, and 50 and consider their relative merits. Table 48 is more concise; Table 49 is more informal and has appeal for that reason; Table 50 is longer and more detailed than either of the others, but makes greater use of technical aids for attracting and holding attention.

TABLE 48

HIGHLIGHTS	1959	1958
Dividend Paid per Common Share	$4.00	$4.00
Earned per Common Share	5.60	6.36
Operating Revenues (millions)		
Coal and Coke	162	177
Merchandise	161	151
Other	25	28
Total Operating Revenues	348	356
Expenses, Taxes, etc. - Net	302	304
Net Income (millions)	46	52
Working Capital at Year End (millions)	61	55

Source: Chesapeake and Ohio Railway, *1959 Annual Report*, p. 2.

Income statements. Table 51 is a summary statement of income and retained earnings designed for stockholders. Like other tables in this section, it is designed for the information of stockholders. Each item in the income section of the statement would be supported by detailed schedules or tables designed for the various management levels. For example, the sales department would receive a detailed breakdown on sales cross-classified by products and territories as well as reports on individual salesmen and possible reports on sales to various classes of customers. Likewise the production department would receive detailed reports on the material, labor, and overhead expense items which constituted the manufacturing cost of goods sold. However, the general format of these tables could be similar to that of Table 51.

Source and disposition of funds statements. This type of statement, illustrated in Table 52, has gained wide acceptance in recent years. As indicated in Table 52, net earnings as determined in the income statement are adjusted for book charges (depreciation, depletion, etc.) and for receipt and disposition of funds; the resulting figure is the decrease in net working capital.

Financial position statements. These statements are also referred to as balance sheets and statements of financial condition. Whereas income

TABLE 49

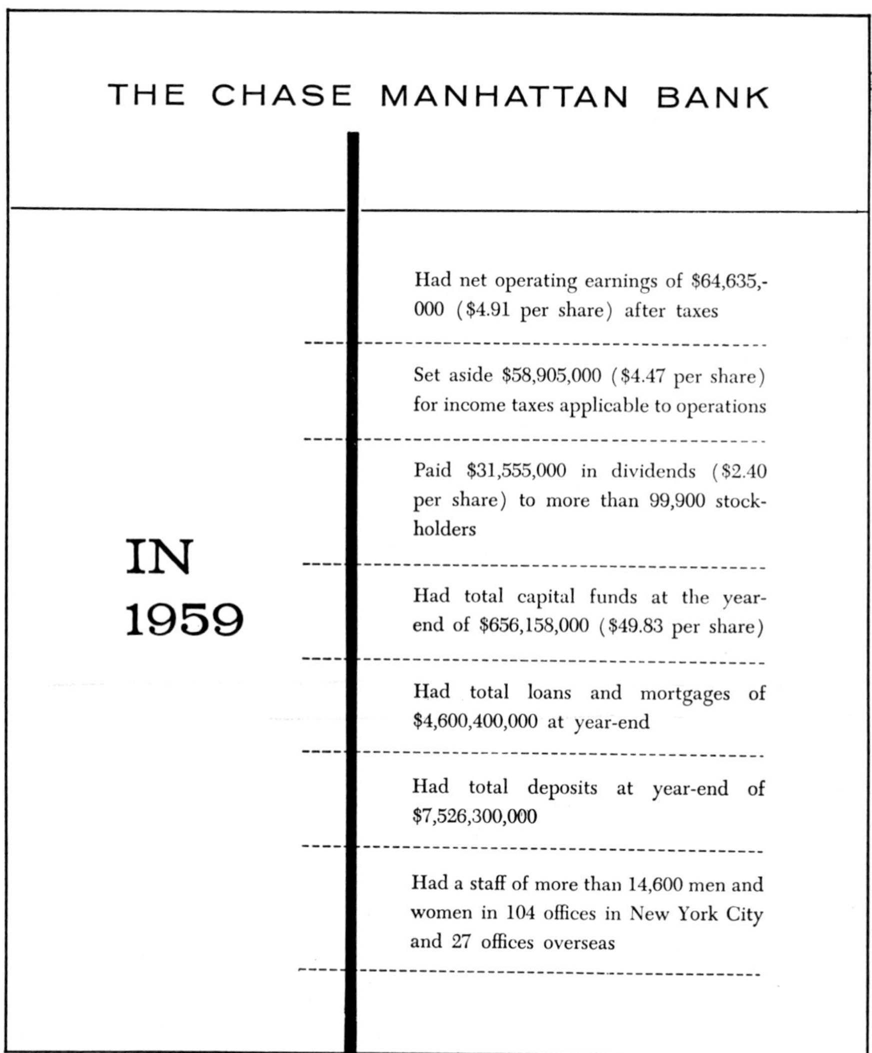

THE CHASE MANHATTAN BANK

IN 1959

IN 1959	Had net operating earnings of $64,635,000 ($4.91 per share) after taxes
	Set aside $58,905,000 ($4.47 per share) for income taxes applicable to operations
	Paid $31,555,000 in dividends ($2.40 per share) to more than 99,900 stockholders
	Had total capital funds at the year-end of $656,158,000 ($49.83 per share)
	Had total loans and mortgages of $4,600,400,000 at year-end
	Had total deposits at year-end of $7,526,300,000
	Had a staff of more than 14,600 men and women in 104 offices in New York City and 27 offices overseas

Source: The Chase Manhattan Bank, *Annual Report, 1959*, p. 2.

TABLE 50

THE STORY IN BRIEF

		Fiscal Years Ended January 31	
		1960	1959
SALES	Net sales	$679,488,000	$643,778,000
	Sales % increase — company	5.5%	1.7%
	Sales % increase (decrease) — comparable stores	4.2%	(1.3%)
EARNINGS	Before federal income taxes	$ 28,087,000	$ 24,204,000
	After federal income taxes	14,637,000	12,004,000
	Earnings per share	$5.17	$4.18
TAXES	Taxes — federal, state and local	$ 28,206,000	$ 24,990,000
	Taxes per share	$10.64	$9.44
DEPRECIATION	Depreciation	$ 6,761,000	$ 6,512,000
WAGES	Wages and salaries	$118,386,000	$110,612,000
	Average number of employees	31,000	30,500
DISPOSITION OF AFTER-TAX EARNINGS	Dividends paid		
	— Total	$ 8,887,000	$ 8,860,000
	— 4% Preferred	937,000	950,000
	— Common	7,950,000	7,910,000
	— Common per share	$3.00	$3.00
	Retained earnings	$ 5,750,000	$ 3,144,000
WORKING ASSETS	Working capital	$145,965,000	$138,985,000
	Current asset ratio	3.4 to 1	3.4 to 1
	Merchandise on order	$ 29,700,000	$ 27,200,000
	Inventories	98,466,000	90,569,000
	Lifo reduction — cumulative	6,906,000	6,777,000
CAPITAL STOCK	Preferred Stock outstanding	231,897 shares	234,517 shares
	Common Stock outstanding	2,650,284 shares	2,646,034 shares
	Common Stock equity	$162,526,000	$156,557,000
	Common Stock equity per share	$61.32	$59.17
NUMBER OF STORES	Department stores	35	35
	Major branch stores	14	14
	Junior department stores	34	35
	Specialty stores	2	2

Source: Allied Stores Corporation, *1959 Annual Report*, p. 4.

TABLE 51

DIEBOLD, INCORPORATED AND SUBSIDIARIES
Statements of Income and Earnings Retained in the Business

STATEMENT OF INCOME	Year Ended DECEMBER 31, 1959	Year Ended DECEMBER 31, 1958
Gross profit from products and services sold	$11,851,523	$10,299,367
Selling, advertising, administrative and general expenses	8,438,536	7,131,152
	3,412,987	3,168,215
Other income	279,058	63,312
	3,692,045	3,231,527
Other deductions:		
Interest charges	117,047	72,118
Miscellaneous	45,641	56,175
	162,688	128,293
Income before Federal taxes on income	3,529,357	3,103,234
Federal taxes on income—estimated	1,750,000	1,536,138
NET INCOME	$ 1,779,357	$ 1,567,096
EARNINGS RETAINED IN THE BUSINESS		
Unappropriated:		
Balance at January 1	$ 4,790,139	$ 3,875,200
Add:		
Net income for the period	1,779,357	1,567,096
Other additions	2,350	—0—
	6,571,846	5,442,296
Deduct:		
Cash dividends paid or provided for:		
Common—four dividends at 15¢ a share paid on shares outstanding at the respective dividend dates	384,948	368,468
Less 1957 declaration paid in 1958	—0—	90,694
	384,948	277,774
Dividends paid in common stock at par (plus $23,225 paid in 1958 in lieu of fractional shares)	—0—	313,970
Other deductions	—0—	60,413
	384,948	652,157
EARNINGS RETAINED IN THE BUSINESS AT DECEMBER 31	$ 6,186,898	$ 4,790,139

Source: Diebold Incorporated, *Annual Report to Shareholders for 1959*, p. 9.

TABLE 52

SUMMARY OF CHANGE IN WORKING CAPITAL		1959
SOURCE OF FUNDS:		
Income for the year	$ 40,890,769	
Depreciation and depletion — wear and exhaustion of facilities	34,778,058	
Plant facilities — sold or scrapped	5,023,882	
Decrease in miscellaneous investments	1,148,960	
Common stock sold to employees — stock option plan	1,591,223	
Increase in reserve for deferred income taxes	5,100,000	
Decrease in deferred accounts and bills receivable	164,164	
Decrease in deferred charges to future operations	740,984	$89,438,040
DISPOSITION OF FUNDS:		
Capital expenditures for plant, equipment and timberlands	52,710,962	
Dividends on common and preferred stock	34,311,524	
Long-term indebtedness payable within one year	3,000,000	
Increase in investments in and receivables from non-consolidated subsidiaries	1,150,965	91,173,451
Decrease in working capital		$ 1,735,411
Working Capital — December 31, 1959	$231,936,838	
December 31, 1958	233,672,249	

Source: American Can Company, *Annual Report to Stockholders, 1959*, p. 23.

TABLE 53

CONSOLIDATED STATEMENT OF FINANCIAL POSITION

DECEMBER 31, 1959-1958

	1959	1958
CURRENT ASSETS		
Cash	$ 229,980,921	$ 225,782,208
Marketable securities, at lower of cost or market	1,155,234,300	1,072,932,364
Notes and accounts receivable, less estimated doubtful amounts	1,010,633,669	946,615,000
Inventories:		
Crude oil and petroleum products	640,211,015	584,292,710
Other merchandise	40,017,198	35,376,828
Materials and supplies	233,563,987	255,422,447
Total current assets	3,309,641,090	3,120,421,557
LESS—CURRENT LIABILITIES		
Notes and loans payable	236,420,420	257,561,469
Accounts payable and accrued liabilities	870,459,152	831,431,866
Income taxes payable	498,322,272	443,573,024
Total current liabilities	1,605,201,844	1,532,566,359
WORKING CAPITAL	1,704,439,246	1,587,855,198
INVESTMENTS AND LONG-TERM RECEIVABLES, at cost or less	456,326,810	435,824,819
PROPERTY, PLANT, AND EQUIPMENT, less depreciation and depletion	5,960,086,505	5,739,614,027
PREPAID CHARGES AND OTHER ASSETS	168,600,538	182,833,066
TOTAL ASSETS LESS CURRENT LIABILITIES	8,289,453,099	7,946,127,110
DEDUCTIONS		
Long-term debt	791,641,979	699,149,057
Deferred credits	109,032,431	94,946,060
Annuity, insurance, and other reserves	409,811,948	382,564,346
Equity of minority shareholders in affiliated companies	291,274,425	312,263,214
NET ASSETS	$6,687,692,316	$6,457,204,433
SHAREHOLDERS' EQUITY		
Capital:		
Stock issued—(see page 10)	$1,515,728,627	$1,504,227,844
Amount in excess of par value	859,928,833	789,281,166
Earnings reinvested and employed in business	4,312,034,856	4,163,695,423
	$6,687,692,316	$6,457,204,433

Source: Standard Oil Company (New Jersey), *1959 Annual Report*, p. 28.

statements reflect the results of operations over a *period of time*, financial position statements reflect the financial condition of a firm at a given *point in time*. Table 53 provides a comparison of the financial conditions at year's end in 1958 and 1959. Worthy of note is the manner in which the results progress toward the final equality between net assets and shareholders' equity. Also worthy of note in Table 53 is the immediate deduction of current liabilities from current assets prior to the presentation of other assets.

Financial and operating trend statements. Tables 54, 55, and 56 are illustrations of trend statements which are gaining in favor. Such statements enable the reader to make rough applications of times series and correlation analysis. For example, the long-time trend and the cyclical fluctuations of sales, earnings, stockholders, employees, and other data can be approximated. The availability of data makes it possible for readers to apply more refined techniques of trend and cyclical measurement if they wish. Similarly, visual correlation analysis may be applied to such series as earnings per share and dividends per share. The reader should note the different series included in the statements and also the effective use of rulings and the greater spacings in Tables 55 and 56.

RESEARCH AND OTHER REPORTS

Many styles of tabular presentation may be applied to an endless variety of quantitative data. It would be impossible to illustrate all potential styles and applications. However, the wide variety of tables presented in this and other texts should provide the reader with some inkling of the broad scope of tabular presentation techniques and applications.

Two final and different illustrations of tabular presentation are shown in Tables 57 and 58. Table 58 is a somewhat complicated table; in reality it is four tables, all indicating how family characteristics were related to life insurance ownership in 1956. If there is a logical reason for expecting these relationships to continue to prevail during the immediate future, forecasts of changing family characteristics could form the basis for forecasts of premium income. Alternatively, the figures indicate that some types of families might provide a market for increased sales of life insurance.

TABLE 54

U. S. Steel's OPERATING and FINANCIAL STORY 1940-1959

Operating Story (net tons in thousands)

Year of oper.	Total ores mined	Total fluxes produced	Total coal mined	Total coke produced	Total iron produced	Ingots & castings: Total production	Ingots & castings: % Capacity operated	Steel products shipped	Employment statistics: No. of employes	Employment statistics: Weekly hours	Employment statistics: Hourly earnings	Employment statistics: Weekly earnings
1940	34,047	15,730	29,528	16,144	18,367	22,934	82.5	15,014	254,393	36.7	$ .898	$32.97
1941	43,318	19,176	29,076	18,563	22,321	28,963	96.8	20,417	304,248	38.1	.994	37.91
1942	52,012	20,864	32,317	19,275	23,496	30,030	98.1	20,615	335,866	38.8	1.086	42.17
1943	51,649	19,478	29,046	19,028	23,660	30,540	97.8	20,148	340,498	42.2	1.159	48.94
1944	49,842	19,208	30,709	20,503	23,445	30,815	94.7	21,052	314,888	44.2	1.257	55.53
1945	47,655	19,030	27,622	18,341	19,648	26,479	82.0	18,410	279,274	42.0	1.287	54.03
1946	37,972	20,874	24,463	15,242	15,853	21,287	72.9	15,182	266,835	35.0	1.426	49.91
1947	47,434	24,827	29,639	20,806	21,511	28,570	96.7	20,242	286,316	38.5	1.550	59.64
1948	48,926	26,870	26,795	21,237	22,228	29,292	93.8	20,655	296,785	38.2	1.680	64.21
1949	41,543	23,746	19,181	17,688	19,546	25,807	82.5	18,212	291,163	34.3	1.775	60.94
1950	46,334	26,985	22,280	20,078	23,574	31,457	98.2	22,635	288,265	37.8	1.828	69.10
1951	57,457	29,224	24,460	21,504	25,821	34,323	101.3	24,626	301,328	38.7	2.046	79.24
1952	45,660	26,571	19,241	18,023	22,022	29,436	85.0	21,133	294,263	34.7	2.265	78.53
1953	58,682	30,270	26,048	21,582	27,167	35,827	98.4	25,091	301,560	37.9	2.394	90.66
1954	37,891	25,232	22,678	18,724	20,904	28,355	73.2	20,239	268,142	35.6	2.488	88.47
1955	52,137	29,490	25,159	21,575	26,028	35,309	90.8	25,506	272,646	37.5	2.698	101.28
1956	47,439	28,586	22,991	20,615	24,633	33,402	85.2	23,911	260,646	37.1	2.926	108.47
1957	57,895	27,648	23,478	22,293	26,378	33,738	85.2	23,414	271,037	36.3	3.186	115.75
1958	39,824	20,919	16,765	15,052	18,094	23,819	59.2	16,992	223,490	34.2	3.497	119.70
1959	36,382	23,352	15,047	14,849	18,553	24,445	58.3	18,094	200,329	35.1	3.776	132.61

Production data, which are grouped in broad product classifications, include all production of the materials by the operating divisions and subsidiaries and exclude all materials purchased. The average weekly hours and average weekly earnings shown are based on the average monthly number of employes receiving pay. Hourly and weekly earnings exclude social security taxes, pensions, insurance and other employe benefit costs.

Financial Story (dollars in millions)

Year of oper.	Products & services sold	Employ-ment costs	Products & services bought	Wear and exhaustion	Interest & other costs on debt	Income & other taxes	Income	Preferred stock dividend	Common stock dividend	Reinvested in business	% Income of sales
1940	1,079.1	464.3	358.3	72.6	13.6	68.1	102.2	25.2	34.8	42.2	9.5
1941	1,622.3	628.3	604.6	98.6	6.0	168.6	116.2	25.2	34.8	56.2	7.2
1942	1,863.0	782.7	673.4	128.2	6.2	201.3	71.2	25.2	34.8	11.2	3.8
1943	1,972.3	912.9	730.6	134.0	6.3	125.9	62.6	25.2	34.8	2.6	3.2
1944	2,082.2	957.2	814.4	139.0	5.0	105.8	60.8	25.2	34.8	.8	2.9
1945	1,747.3	825.5	670.1	123.4	3.5	66.8	58.0	25.2	34.8	2.0[d]	3.3
1946	1,496.1	704.5	560.4	68.7	4.8	69.1	88.6	25.2	34.8	28.6	5.9
1947	2,122.8	903.6	839.4	114.0	2.5	136.2	127.1	25.2	45.7	56.2	6.0
1948	2,481.5	1,035.7	1,008.9	146.0	2.4	158.9	129.6	25.2	52.2	52.2	5.2
1949	2,301.7	945.9	885.7	119.7	2.3	182.2	165.9	25.2	56.1	84.6	7.2
1950	2,956.4	1,179.4	1,118.8	143.9	2.2	296.6	215.5	25.2	92.7	97.6	7.3
1951	3,524.1	1,374.5	1,327.9	162.1	2.0	473.3	184.3	25.2	78.3	80.8	5.2
1952	3,137.4	1,322.1	1,307.6	176.9	1.9	185.3	143.6	25.2	78.3	40.1	4.6
1953	3,861.0	1,569.2	1,418.7	236.6	2.1	412.3	222.1	25.2	78.3	118.6	5.8
1954	3,250.4	1,387.0	1,134.3	261.8	5.2	266.7	195.4	25.2	85.5	84.7	6.0
1955	4,097.7	1,614.9	1,355.2	285.2	9.1	463.2	370.1	25.2	122.9	222.0	9.0
1956	4,228.9	1,681.0	1,487.5	277.6	7.7	427.0	348.1	25.2	144.9	178.0	8.2
1957	4,413.8	1,862.0	1,324.2	276.0	7.0	525.2	419.4	25.2	161.3	232.9	9.5
1958	3,472.1	1,488.5	1,085.6	204.9	11.5	380.1	301.5	25.2	161.4	114.9	8.7
1959	3,643.0	1,576.2	1,278.2	189.9	17.6	326.6	254.5	25.2	161.8	67.5	7.0

The data are in some respects necessarily approximate, and are based on the yearly earnings reported annually to stockholders without adjustment for surplus charges and credits except that the years 1942 and 1943 reflect renegotiation settlements made in the succeeding years. For example, taxes are as accrued before adjustments. Employment costs include pensions and social security taxes and, beginning with 1949, also include payments for insurance and other employe benefits.

[d] denotes deficit.

Source: United States Steel Corporation, *Annual Report, 1959*, p. 37.

TABLE 55

TEN YEAR FINANCIAL POSITION

	1960	1959	1958
ALLIED STORES CORPORATION AND SUBSIDIARIES CONSOLIDATED			
Current assets	$207,536	$196,806	$203,320
Current liabilities	61,571	57,821	58,731
Working capital	145,965	138,985	144,589
Investment in and advances to Alstores Realty Corporation (not consolidated)	16,358	20,775	15,486
Property and equipment (net)	62,908	61,230	61,343
Other assets	3,285	4,488	3,240
Working capital and other assets	228,516	225,478	224,658
Long-term debt	42,800	45,400	47,850
Minority interest	—	69	124
Net assets	185,716	180,009	176,684
Represented by:			
Preferred Stock — $100 per share	23,190	23,452	24,164
Common Stock — stated at $1 per share	2,650	2,646	2,626
Surplus	159,876	153,911	149,894
ALSTORES REALTY CORPORATION AND SUBSIDIARIES			
Property and equipment (net)	155,095	157,191	147,059
Other assets	2,989	2,820	2,292
Total assets	158,084	160,011	149,351
Long-term debt	135,890	133,980	126,923
Other liabilities	2,012	1,867	3,780
Advances from Allied Stores Corporation	15,267	19,706	14,442
Total liabilities	153,169	155,553	145,145
Stockholder's equity	4,915	4,458	4,206

TABLE 55 (cont.)

—FISCAL YEARS ENDED JANUARY 31

(in thousands of dollars)

1957	*1956*	*1955*	*1954*	*1953*	*1952*	*1951*
$208,137	$210,174	$183,760	$172,733	$173,900	$160,874	$152,573
59,358	60,716	53,165	49,763	51,507	45,354	48,678
148,779	149,458	130,595	122,970	122,393	115,520	103,895
9,719	2,294	4,945	7,745	5,353	8,918	6,644
62,096	51,353	44,406	43,603	39,317	40,931	40,438
3,398	3,346	2,846	2,517	2,240	2,197	1,489
223,992	206,451	182,792	176,835	169,303	167,566	152,466
50,300	37,750	39,950	39,900	37,600	39,800	29,750
130	127	122	128	126	128	—
173,562	168,574	142,720	136,807	131,577	127,638	122,716
24,806	25,685	25,596	26,096	25,123	25,743	25,607
2,622	2,612	2,217	2,196	2,196	2,196	2,108
146,134	140,277	114,907	108,515	104,258	99,699	95,001
105,157	95,671	88,705	80,897	78,008	69,279	46,690
1,424	1,310	1,116	986	1,036	879	1,055
106,581	96,981	89,821	81,883	79,044	70,158	47,745
92,331	91,592	81,652	71,320	71,606	59,573	39,704
1,847	767	1,142	1,322	943	784	719
8,477	1,070	4,444	7,262	4,889	8,473	6,218
102,655	93,429	87,238	79,904	77,438	68,830	46,641
3,926	3,552	2,583	1,979	1,606	1,328	1,104

Source: Allied Stores Corporation, *1959 Annual Report*, pp. 26–27.

TABLE 56

TEN YEAR OPERATING RESULTS

RESULTS FOR YEAR	*1960*	*1959*	*1958*
Net sales	$679,488	$643,778	$632,814
Gross margin	234,719	217,703	213,191
Operating expenses	205,695	192,404	186,880
Earnings before federal income taxes	28,087	24,204	25,151
Consolidated net earnings	14,637	12,004	12,351
Earnings of Alstores Realty Corporation not included above	457	252	281
Wages and salaries	118,386	110,612	108,017
Taxes — federal, state and local	28,206	24,990	25,361
Rent	16,604	15,945	14,850
Depreciation	6,761	6,512	6,096
Interest	1,903	1,939	1,882
Dividends — Preferred Stock	937	950	986
— Common Stock	7,950	7,910	7,875
Retained earnings	5,750	3,144	3,490
PER SHARE OF COMMON STOCK			
Earnings	5.17	4.18	4.33
Dividends	3.00	3.00	3.00
Common stockholders' equity	61.32	59.17	58.08
OTHER STATISTICS			
Number of stores	85	86	87
Number of employees	31,000	30,500	31,000

TABLE 56 (cont.)

— FISCAL YEARS ENDED JANUARY 31

(in thousands of dollars)

1957	1956	1955	1954	1953	1952	1951
$615,773	$581,901	$543,984	$515,830	$501,841	$476,693	$439,909
208,329	197,508	183,825	172,217	166,593	152,671	146,869
178,388	167,038	154,815	146,426	140,338	134,864	119,609
28,462	29,172	27,331	24,259	25,337	16,858	26,669
14,262	13,972	13,231	11,809	12,137	8,258	14,944
374	266	250	373	278	224	61
103,832	96,231	89,228	83,906	80,044	76,099	68,958
25,023	25,348	23,647	21,404	21,837	16,661	19,020
14,096	12,887	12,271	11,971	11,355	10,401	9,636
5,507	4,883	4,466	4,209	4,079	3,775	3,358
1,588	1,380	1,544	1,370	1,390	1,491	1,114
1,017	1,015	1,035	996	1,024	1,021	836
7,861	7,649	6,605	6,588	6,588	6,521	6,323
5,384	5,308	5,591	4,225	4,525	716	7,785
(in dollars)						
5.05	5.09	5.50	4.92	5.06	3.31	6.69
3.00	3.00	3.00	3.00	3.00	3.00	3.00
56.72	54.70	52.84	50.42	48.48	46.40	46.07
84	79	75	73	72	71	73
31,000	29,600	28,900	27,800	27,100	27,200	25,500

Source: Allied Stores Corporation, *1959 Annual Report*, pp. 28–29.

TABLE 57

SOURCES OF GROSS INCOME OF SAVINGS AND LOAN ASSOCIATIONS

Year	Interest on Mortgage Loans	Interest on Other Investments	Premiums, Commissions and Fees	Other Income	Total
1941	89.7%	1.0%	3.2%	6.1%	100.0%
1942	91.0	1.1	2.3	5.6	100.0
1943	88.6	3.2	2.6	5.6	100.0
1944	84.9	7.2	2.6	5.3	100.0
1945	77.9	11.0	2.5	8.6	100.0
1946	76.5	12.0	2.7	8.8	100.0
1947	82.8	9.2	2.9	5.1	100.0
1948	86.2	7.1	3.2	3.5	100.0
1949	86.1	6.1	4.0	3.8	100.0
1950	85.1	5.3	5.9	3.7	100.0
1951	86.1	5.0	4.9	4.0	100.0
1952	85.4	4.9	5.4	4.3	100.0
1953	84.6	4.8	6.1	4.5	100.0
1954	84.3	4.5	6.6	4.6	100.0
1955	84.3	4.1	7.4	4.2	100.0
1956	84.7	4.3	7.1	3.9	100.0
1957	83.9	4.6	7.5	4.0	100.0
1958*	83.6	4.8	7.6	4.0	100.0

* Estimated
Source: U. S. Savings and Loan League, based on date of Federal Home Loan Bank Board as reported in *Savings and Loan Fact Book*, 1959, Table 46, p. 89.

TABLE 58

FAMILY CHARACTERISTICS AND LIFE INSURANCE OWNERSHIP 1956

Income of Family	% of Families Insured	Average Premium Payment*
Under $1,000	43	$ 60
$1,000-$1,999	53	60
$2,000-$2,999	67	85
$3,000-$3,999	81	105
$4,000-$4,999	91	120
$5,000-$7,499	93	185
$7,500 or over	96	440
All Families	79	190

Occupation of Family Head	% of Families Insured	Average Premium Payment*
Professional	90	$290
Managerial, Self-Employed	92	415
Clerical, Sales	89	185
Skilled, Semi-Skilled	88	140
Unskilled	72	95
Farm Operator	57	130
Other	60	105
All Families	79	190

Age of Family Head	% of Families Insured	Average Premium Payment*
18-24	69	$ 80
25-34	88	160
35-44	89	275
45-54	85	230
55-64	80	190
65 or over	56	90
All Families	79	190

Liquid Assets of Family	% of Families Insured	Average Premium Payment*
None	62	$ 80
$1-$199	82	135
$200-$499	85	165
$500-$999	87	190
$1,000-$1,999	85	205
$2,000-$4,999	87	215
$5,000 or over	85	475
All Families	79	190

* For insured families only.
Source: Survey of Consumer Finances conducted for the Federal Reserve Board by the Survey Research Center of the University of Michigan. This survey, conducted in early 1957, covered all types of life insurance, including National Service and fraternal. "Family" in the above table means spending unit, which is defined as a group of persons living in the same dwelling and related by blood, marriage or an option, who pool their incomes for their major items of expense. In some instances a spending unit consists of only one person. As reported in *Life Insurance Fact Book, 1959*, p. 17.

Advantages and limitations of tabular presentation

Quantitative data can be communicated more effectively by means of tabular presentation than by direct inclusion of data in narrative reports. It is extremely difficult to read intelligently and grasp the significance of considerable quantities of data included in a written paragraph. Tables, to be effective, must be designed to facilitate understanding by the persons for whom they are prepared. Simplicity and clarity are essential in table preparation.

Tables may be useful analytical tools. Visual trend and correlation analysis are facilitated by properly constructed tables. Significant facts can be placed in positions of emphasis where the attention of the reader is most likely to be attracted.

Relative to graphic presentation, tabular presentation is superior in that it can communicate a greater quantity of detailed data, but it is inferior in its ability to highlight rapidly and dramatically a few significant data. These points will be illustrated at some length in the following chapter on graphic presentation.

Questions and Exercises

1. Discuss the importance of reports for management.
2. What knowledge is a prerequisite to preparation of a report which effectively communicates pertinent information?
3. Distinguish between *reference* and *summary* tables, clearly denoting their respective functions and characteristics.
4. Describe the characteristics of good tables.
5. Outline the procedure for construction of tables.
6. Draw a sketch of a table format, identifying each of the parts.
7. The sales manager of your company has requested you to prepare a table illustrating sales for the past year classified by (1) territories, (2) product lines, and (3) products. There are three territories (A, B, C), three product lines (I, II, III), and three products (1, 2, 3) in each product line. Prepare several table outlines, experimenting with the different possible arrangements of territories, product lines, and products. Data in which position of a triple cross-classified table receive the most emphasis? The least emphasis? Which of your table

outlines do you believe would best serve the needs of the sales manager? Why?

8. Discuss the advantages and limitations of tabular presentation.

9. Prepare tables required for your term research project.

10 *Statistical reports for management: graphic presentation*

The statistical chart

The statement that "one picture is worth a thousand words" applies to charts even more than it does to tables. No means has yet been devised which can communicate statistical data as rapidly and with as lasting an impression as is possible with charts.

Presentation of business and economic data in graphic form is largely a development of the twentieth century—particularly of the past few decades. Graphic presentation takes many forms and has a wide variety of uses. All readers will recall seeing charts in advertisements and in various government and civic reports and news releases. Public speakers sometimes use charts to illustrate quantitative data.

PURPOSE OF CHARTS IN REPORTS FOR MANAGEMENT

Management has found charts to be useful at all levels of administration. Charts may be used to highlight significant daily, weekly, or monthly operating data; although these data may be found in company records and summary tables, charts serve to alert the busy executive to points which otherwise might pass unnoticed.

Frequently charts and tables are used in conjunction with each other. Charts attract the immediate attention of the reader to the most important items or relationships, and accompanying tables provide data in more exact detail for reference purposes. Many executives use statistical books which contain up-to-date charts and tables on key operating data. Such books enable executives to make rapid reference to important trends and to comparative performances of various departmental and field units.

The growth of the conference method in business management has contributed much to the increased use of graphic methods. Charts are decidedly superior to tables for purposes of presentation of data to a group of persons. Large display charts are becoming increasingly common fixtures in conference rooms. Some organizations provide elaborate exhibits for their executives and directors. Special equipment may include beautiful frames for large wall charts, projectors and screens for chart slides, and various types of chart easels. However, these embellishments are of value only when they contribute to the effective communication of the data.

PARTS OF A CHART

Charts and tables are very similar in design; both have five major parts. The corresponding parts of the two forms of data presentation are compared on page 241.

CHARACTERISTICS OF A GOOD CHART

Simplicity and clarity. As with tables, simplicity and clarity are essential characteristics of good charts. Rather complex charts may be designed in cases where presentation is to be restricted to persons already well informed in a subject area. However, a series of simple charts is usually superior to a few complex charts.

Visual balance. A chart is intended to present information in such a way as to dramatically demonstrate an idea—a relationship. Care must be taken that the desire for dramatic impact does not lead to a distortion of the facts. The visual interpretation of a chart is influenced in part by its size and placement on the page and the relationship of its total dimensions. Charts 17A, 17B, 17C, and 17D all present

COMPARISON OF PARTS OF TABLES AND CHARTS

	Part of Table	*Part of Chart*	*Purpose*
I	Title Sub-title (if any) Prefatory note (if any)	Title Sub-title (if any) Prefatory note (if any)	Indicates what, when, where, how classified for data presented.
II	Stub captions	Vertical scale captions	*Table:* Indicates the basis of classification in horizontal rows. *Chart:* Indicates the scale units and basis of classification of horizontal grid lines.
III	Column headings	Horizontal scale captions	*Table:* Indicates the basis of classification in vertical columns. *Chart:* Indicates the scale units and basis of classification of vertical grid lines.
IV	Body	Body	Contains the information presented.
V	Footnotes and source notes	Footnotes and source notes	*Footnotes* explain any interruptions or discontinuities and clarify obscure terms, etc. *Source Notes* normally give author, title, publication, publisher, volume, date or dates of publication, and page or table number.

exactly the same data, but each gives the viewer a different impression of the manner in which mortgage debt on nonfarm homes has changed since the end of World War II. Charts 17A and 17C indicate that there has been a substantial increase in the debt, with 17C giving the greater emphasis to that increase. Charts 17B and 17D, on the other hand, tend to minimize the extent of the increase in mortgage debt. The reader is urged to study these charts carefully before concluding which is most appropriate.

Footnotes and source designations. The same general rules which apply for tables also apply to charts. Footnotes should be used to explain obscure terms, interruptions or discontinuities, and any other unusual

CHART 17. Total mortgage debt on nonfarm homes at year end 1945–1958 (presented on four scales)

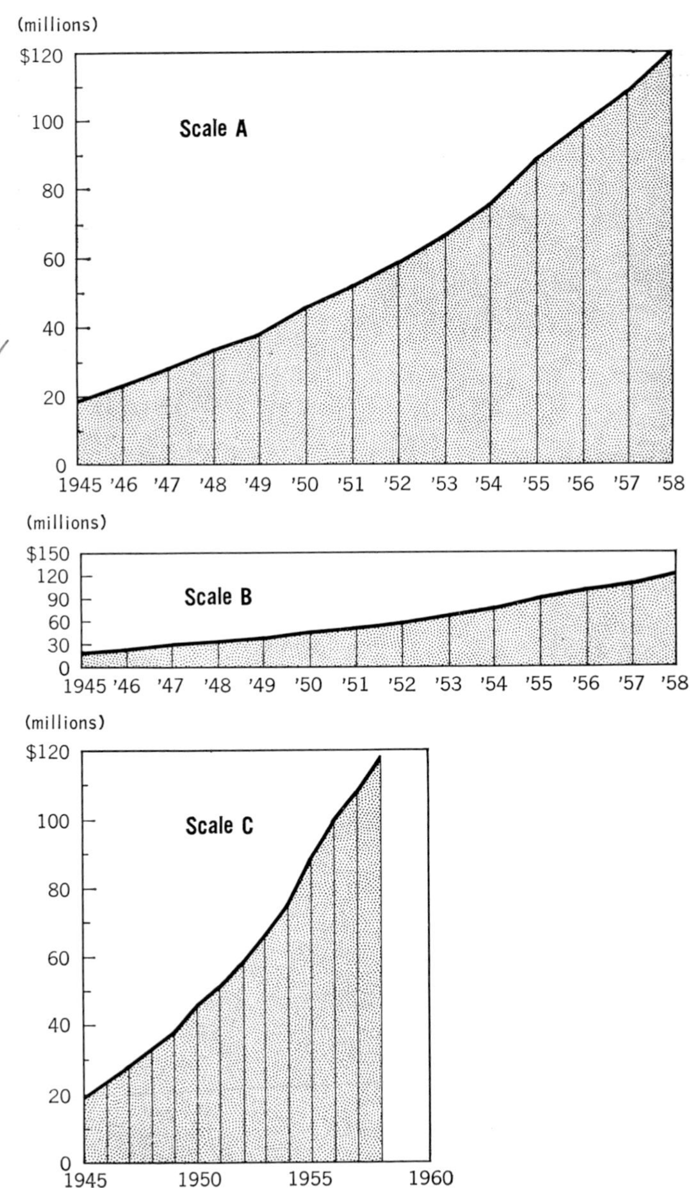

CHART 17. (cont.)

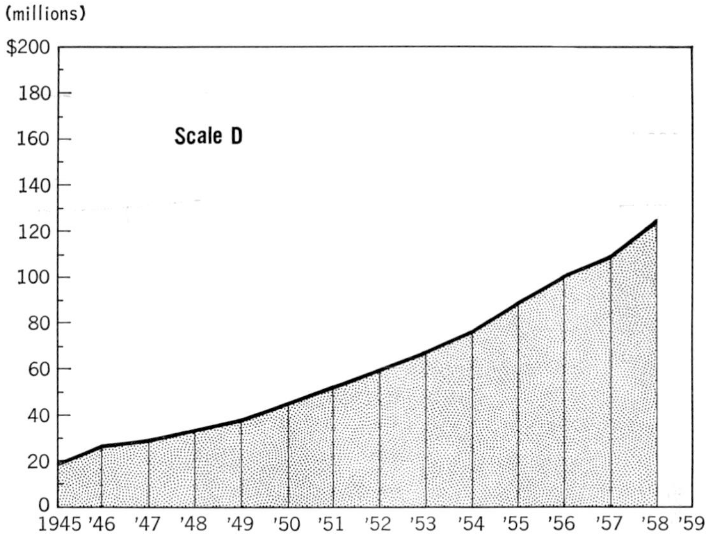

Source: Data from Home Loan Bank Board as reported in *Savings and Loan Fact Book*, 1959, Table 31, p. 58.

circumstances which might confuse or mislead the reader. Source notes should provide as much of the following as is appropriate to the source used: author, title, publication, publisher, volume, date or dates of publication, and page or table numbers.

GENERAL PROCEDURE FOR CONSTRUCTION OF CHARTS

Types of charts. Graphic presentation is much more flexible than tabular presentation. Among the more common types of charts are (1) arithmetic scale line charts, (2) semilogarithmic scale line charts, (3) vertical-bar charts, (4) horizontal-bar charts, (5) statistical maps, (6) pie charts, and (7) pictograms. Each type has many variations and also may be used in combination with other major types. The use of color, crosshatching, and shading further increases the range of possible variation in graphic presentation. Illustrations of each major type of chart will be presented in this chapter.

It is important that a type of chart be selected which will effectively communicate the message to the intended audience. Each type of chart has certain advantages; some highlight trends, others emphasize comparisons among items at specific points in time, and still others point up significant relationships. The same set of data may be portrayed in a multitude of ways. The designer must select a chart type appropriate to the purpose of the presentation. In case of doubt, final selection of chart type should be made only after preliminary experimentation with several types.

Selection of chart type should not be placed solely in the hands of a draftsman unless that individual possesses thorough knowledge of the data, the purpose of the presentation, and the ability of the intended recipients to make interpretations. The executive, statistician, analyst, or accountant who requests preparation of a chart should discuss the selection of chart type with the draftsman. Frequently the draftsman can make valuable suggestions, but usually he does not possess adequate knowledge to make an independent selection of chart type.

It is highly desirable that the individual who plans the chart and the draftsman who prepares it both possess a high degree of imagination and ingenuity. Just as "variety is the spice of life," so "variety is the spice of graphic presentation." This does not mean that key operating data should be presented in a different chart form each week or month. On the contrary, continuation of the same chart form for a particular set of data facilitates periodic analysis by executives. However, the same chart form need not be used to portray all series of operating data. Further, much variety may be introduced in charts reflecting results of special investigations which supplement the recurring reports on operations.

Title and scale designations. Titles may be placed either above or below the charts, although in this writer's opinion the top is the most effective position. Titles for large display charts are almost always placed above the body of the chart.

The vertical and horizontal scale designations for line, column, and bar charts are the counterparts of column headings and stub designations in tables. Captions and units for vertical scales should be placed at the top of the scale line rather than in a centered vertical position parallel to the scale line; scale designations are difficult to read in this latter position.

Scales and grid lines. Equal distances on an arithmetic scale should always represent equal values. For example, it would be inappropriate to mark points denoting equal scale distances as follows: 0, 10, 25, 50,

100, etc. Scale value markings should be limited to those which are necessary to communicate the approximate amounts, trends, or relationships. Most charts are not designed to present data with exactness; this is a function of tables.

Grid lines are lines in the body of a chart perpendicular to the bordering scale lines from which they originate. Grid lines customarily are restricted to scale points where values have been indicated. Their purpose is to facilitate reading the approximate value of a line or column at a distance from the scale lines. Grid lines are drawn more lightly than scale lines. Line charts ordinarily have both vertical and horizontal grid lines; vertical-bar charts require only horizontal grid lines, and horizontal bar-charts require only vertical grid lines; occasionally grid lines are completely omitted on all or a part of a chart.

Emphasis. Color, crosshatching, and different kinds of lines are the principal means of securing emphasis in graphic presentation. Color is very effective; the line or segment of a bar which is to be emphasized most may be colored red.

If color is not used, crosshatching or shading may be employed to denote emphasis. In general, the darker the shading the greater the emphasis. Occasionally, crosshatching and color are combined.

Multiple lines on the same chart may be distinguished either by different colors, by using solid and broken lines, or by varying the widths of the lines. Solid lines provide more emphasis than broken lines; wide, heavy lines attract more attention than narrow, light lines.

Illustrations of charts useful to management

The illustrations which follow provide some indication of the tremendous scope of graphic presentation. Variation of chart designs and applications are virtually unlimited. The reader is encouraged to supplement illustrations in this text by reference to other texts on graphic presentation, to annual reports of business firms, and to government publications such as the *Survey of Current Business*, *Monthly Labor Review*, and the monthly and annual *Federal Reserve Charts on Bank Credit, Money Rates and Business*.[1]

[1] Two texts on graphic presentation are: R. R. Lutz, *Graphic Presentation Simplified*, New York, Funk & Wagnalls Company, 1949; and Mary Eleanor Spear, *Charting Statistics*, New York, McGraw-Hill Book Company, Inc., 1952.

ARITHMETIC LINE CHARTS

Several illustrations of line charts have appeared in earlier chapters of this text. Some of these charts contained but a single line and others contained two or more lines. A third variety of line chart is obtained by coloring, shading, or crosshatching the areas between and below the lines. This latter type was illustrated in Chart 17. Each of these types will be discussed below.

Single-line charts. Chart 18 reflects changes in the number of General Electric Share-Owners over almost three decades. Horizontal grid lines aid the reader in approximating the number of shareholders in any period. However, it is difficult to determine location of the value for any specific year due to the lack of vertical grid lines.

Multiple-line charts. The two lines in Chart 19 indicate that the rate of turnover of the money supply has increased substantially, while the size of the money supply has increased relatively little. However, the use of different scales for each series should cause the reader to question the true state of affairs. Actually, the analysis of the values indicates that the turnover rate has increased almost 30 per cent while the money supply has increased only about 11 per cent.

CHART 18

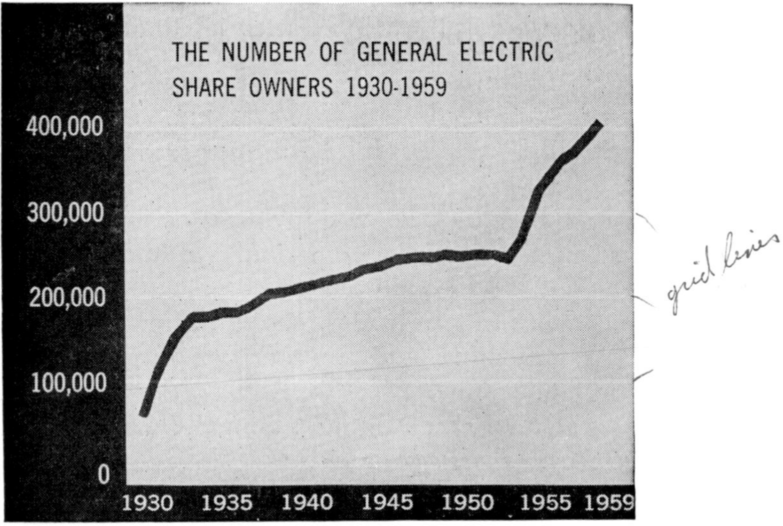

Source: General Electric Company, *1959 Annual Report,* p. 6.

CHART 19

MONEY SUPPLY AND RATE OF TURNOVER

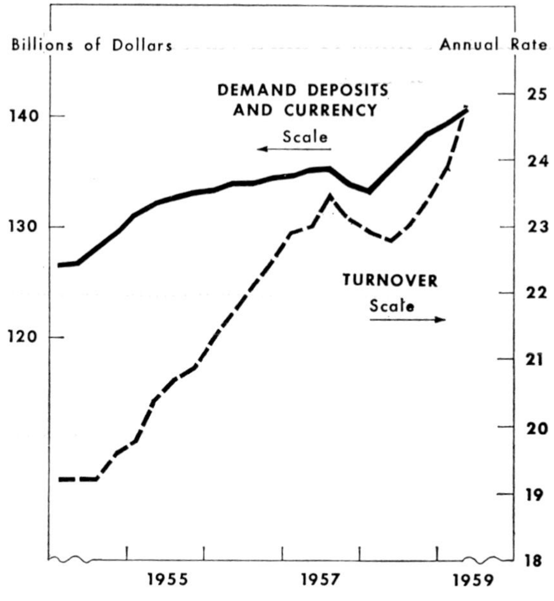

Note. Figures for deposits and currency are quarterly averages of seasonally adjusted data for last Wednesday of month and are partly estimated. Demand deposits are for all banks in the United States and exclude U. S. Government and interbank deposits and items in process of collection. Currency excludes bank vault cash. Figures for turnover are quarterly averages of monthly figures for 337 leading centers outside New York and 6 other financial centers. All data for second quarter of 1959 are preliminary.
Source: Board of Governors, Federal Reserve System, *Federal Reserve Bulletin*, July 1959, p. 697.

A type of multiple-line chart which is useful in analysis is illustrated in the several charts of Chart 20. These charts are called *tier charts* and are particularly useful in comparing movements of variables over time in different periods of time. The interpretive commentaries used in place of titles on the individual charts give greater meaning to the charts.

Chart 21 indicates another use for multiple-line charts and also illustrates one method of differentiating the lines. Note that the solid middle line is a weighted average of the interest rates indicated by the two broken lines.

Index numbers are utilized in Chart 22 to show the relative movements of freight traffic revenue from different types of cargo. By

CHART 20

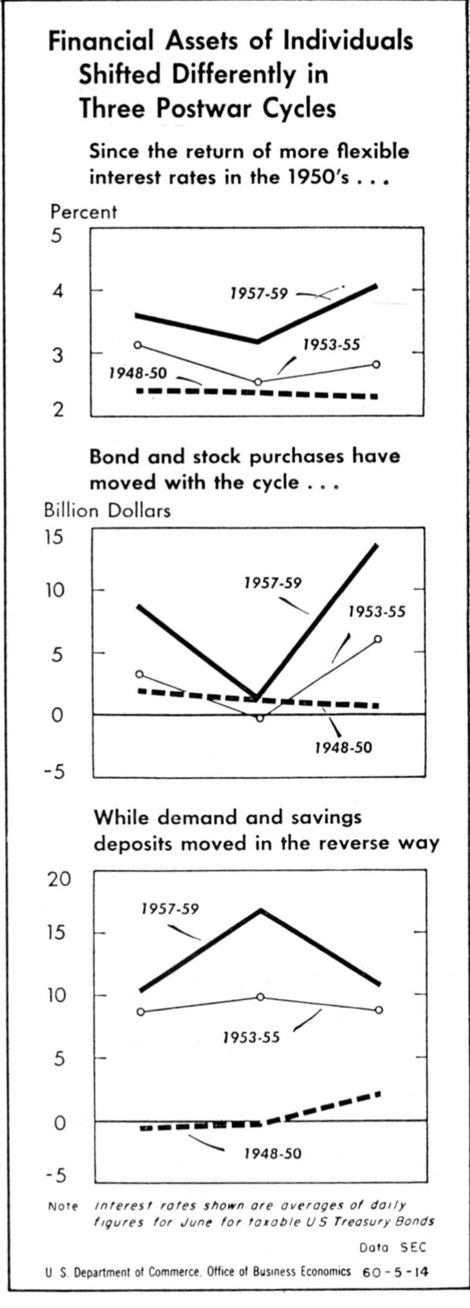

Source: *Survey of Current Business,* May 1960, p. 21.

CHART 21

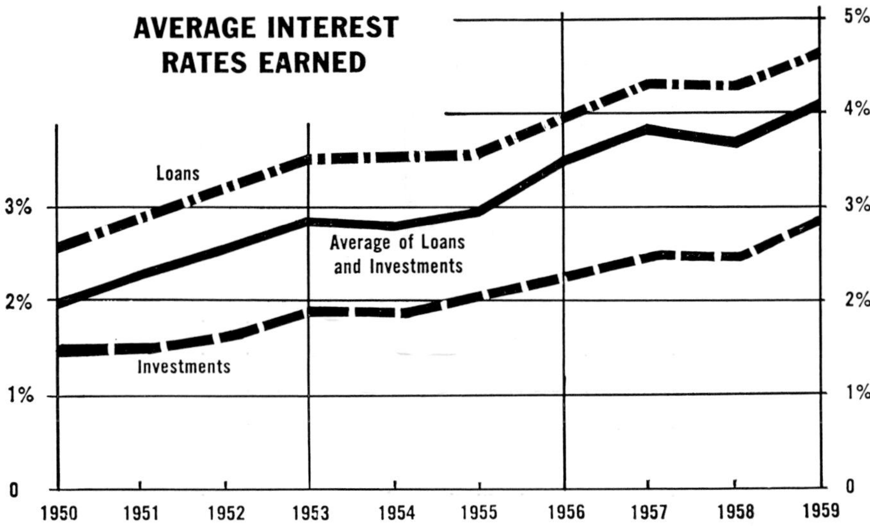

Source: The Chase Manhattan Bank, *Annual Report, 1959*, p. 9.

CHART 22

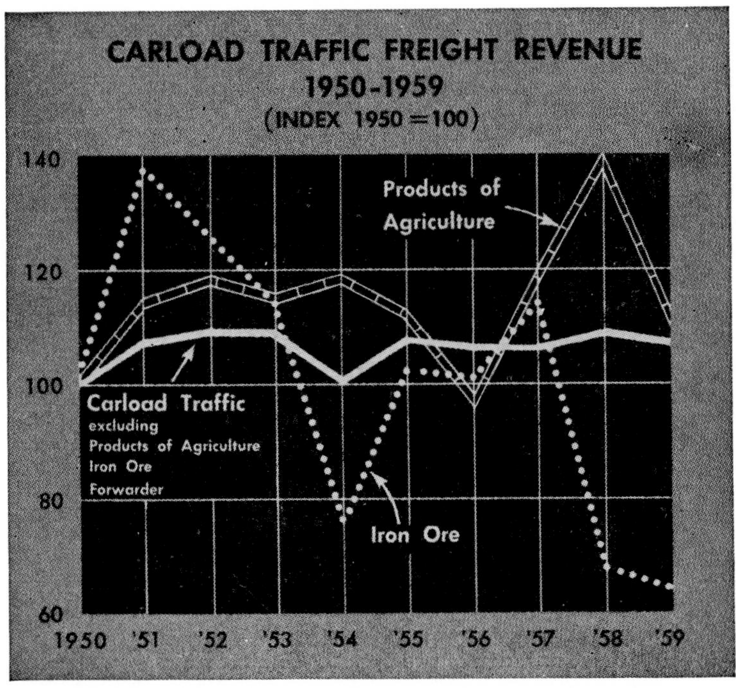

Source: Chicago and North Western Railway Company, *Annual Report, 1959*, p. 5.

expressing each value as a relative of its individual value in 1950, comparison of gains or losses in relation to one another are discernible.

SEMILOGARITHMIC CHARTS

The logarithmic scale. The three scales below are known as two-cycle logarithmic scales. The first or A scale best illustrates why they are called two-cycle. It will be noted that the scale begins with 1, 2, 3, . . . , 9 and then the sequence is repeated. The series is run through twice, thus, two cycles.

The scales can be recognized as logarithmic because of the unusual spacing of the numbers 1, 2, 3, etc. Constant distances (one inch) measure constant *ratios*. On this scale, a distance of one inch measures

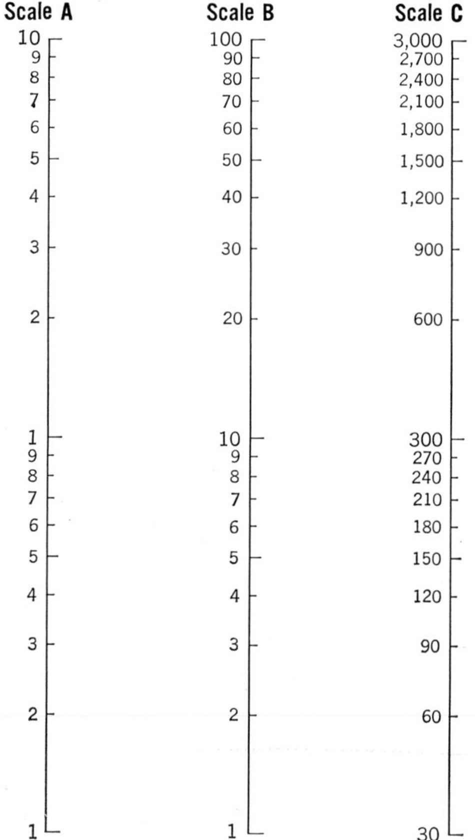

Illustration of two-cycle logarithmic scales.

a ratio of about 3.2 to one. With a different scale, that is, one with different distances between the numbers, one inch would measure a different constant ratio.

It should also be noted that there is no zero line on the logarithmic scale. This is because the logarithm zero corresponds to the value (antilogarithm) one in natural numbers. (Any number raised to the zero power is one.)

On scale A is shown the type of scaling found on purchased ratio or semilogarithmic paper. Such paper can be purchased with from one to five cycles per page.

Scale B illustrates the result when it is desired to carry out the full scale with the base line equal to 1. It will be noted that moving through one cycle increases the base line value to ten times its original value. In the second cycle and each subsequent cycle the new base value is also increased to ten times its original value. In other words, the original value will be increased ten times in the first cycle, then to 100 times its original value in the second cycle, then to 1000 times its original value, etc.

Scale B indicates what happens in the general case by starting with a base value of one. Scale C illustrates the particular case when the original base value was not one but 30. The original base value can be any value: 1, 10, 13, 25, 6,000,000, etc. The base value is the unit of counting for the first cycle; ten times the base value becomes the unit of counting for the second cycle; one hundred times the base value becomes the unit of counting for the third cycle; etc.

The semilogarithmic chart. The logarithmic scale illustrated in the previous section is often used as the vertical scale with an ordinary arithmetic horizontal scale. The result is called a *semilogarithmic* or *ratio* chart. This type of chart has two basic uses: (1) to show relative or per cent changes—the *rate* of change—and (2) to compare rates of change in series stated in different units (tons vs. dollars, bushels vs. board feet, etc.) or series of widely different magnitudes (hundreds vs. billions, units vs. hundreds, etc.). A semilogarithmic chart is valid *only* for comparing rates of change. Values along the vertical axis are plotted at the point where their logarithms would occur on an arithmetic scale. Thus, constant distances indicate constant ratios. Note that on Scale B, above, the distances from 1 to 2, 2 to 4, 4 to 8, 3 to 6, 5 to 10, and 10 to 20 are all equal and all these numbers involve ratios of 2 to 1.

The data presented in Chart 19, page 247 has been redrawn on a semilogarithmic scale in Chart 23. On the arithmetic scale, the casual reader was left with the impression that turnover rate had increased several times over, and money supply had remained relatively constant. On the ratio chart it is revealed that turnover rate has grown at a more rapid rate (the line for turnover rate has a greater slope), but not to the extent indicated in Chart 19.

The reader should note the vertical scaling used in Chart 23; the scale for money supply runs from 15 to 150 in units of 15; the scale for turnover rate runs from 4 to 40 in units of 4. The horizontal scale is arithmetic.

Interpreting the semilogarithmic chart. The slope of a line on a ratio chart indicates the percentage change between the two points of time. A continuing line of the same slope indicates a constant rate of change over the period and two parallel lines represent the same rate of change; the steeper the slope the greater the per cent rate of change. It is particularly important to remember that a given absolute vertical

CHART 23. Semilogarithmic chart—money supply and rate of turnover (1954–1959)

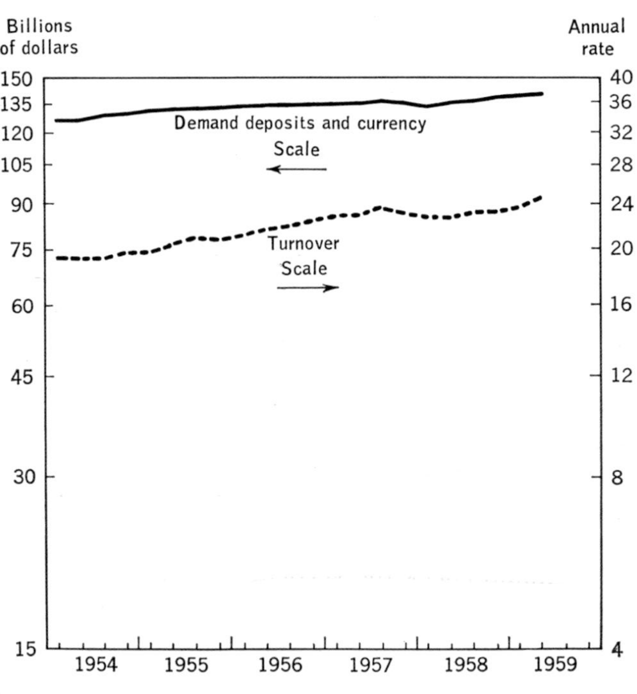

Source: Federal Reserve Board (see Chart 19).

distance indicates the same percentage difference *anywhere* on the chart.

Any series changing at a constant rate (percentage) each time period will plot as a straight line on a ratio chart. Series changing by other than constant rates (by constant amounts, for example) will plot as curved lines on a ratio chart. A series increasing by a constant amount per period would form a curve moving upward to the right with decreasing slope (would be concave to the base line of the chart).

Ratio charts should not be used as a visual picture of absolute amounts nor merely for the purpose of compressing data into a narrower range. Because there are no logarithms for zero or negative values, ratio charts can be used to show positive values only.

BAR CHARTS

Vertical-bar charts. Vertical-bar charts, also called column charts, more clearly identify the value for each year (or other horizontal scale designation) than do line charts. This is illustrated in Chart 24. Note the spacing arrangement and compare it to the spacing of the bars in Chart 25, which has a more customary spacing arrangement. Spaces between bars ordinarily range in width from about one-half to a full bar width. Omission of the spacing in Chart 24 tends to emphasize the trend. The only space between bars in Chart 24 indicates the omission of information for the war years of 1941–1945.

Chart 25 is, in reality, two charts, a ratio chart and a vertical-bar chart indicating percentage rates of growth for five year periods, 1900 to 1959. The ratio chart indicates that the rate of growth has been relatively constant over this entire period, except for the decade of the 1930's. The decline in the rate of growth during the 1930's is illustrated dramatically in the vertical-bar chart; the maximum percentage growth rates in the first decade of this century were apparently about three times the percentage growth rates in the 1930's. However, the scale shows that the maximum growth rate did not quite reach two per cent.

The reader should check the vertical scale on the ratio chart carefully. Note that only part of a cycle has been reproduced. The grid lines are somewhat misleading; on the bottom half of the chart, they measure distances of 10,000,000; on the top half the lines occur at intervals of 20,000,000.

CHART 24

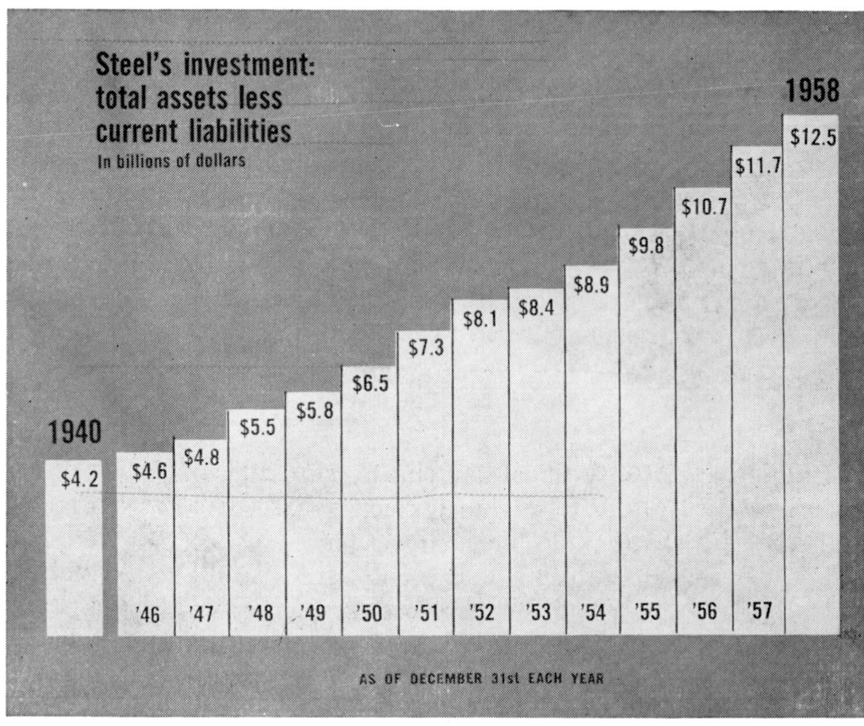

Source: American Iron and Steel Institute, *Charting Steel's Progress, 1959*, p. 67.

Horizontal-bar charts. Chart 26 is an illustration of a horizontal-bar chart. Note that the only difference between this chart and a vertical-bar chart is that the bars run horizontally instead of vertically. The two types of charts may be used in much the same way, although time series data are more often plotted in vertical bars.

In those cases where years are not involved, arranging bars in either ascending or descending magnitude facilitates comparisons among bars. Bars are arranged in descending order in Chart 27.

The *Gantt Chart* is an application of the bar chart for purposes of production control. Chart 28 is an illustration of a man record chart designed to reflect each man's performance in relation to a predetermined quota or standard of performance. In Chart 28, days of the week have been separated by vertical double lines and the space under each day has been subdivided into five equal columns; each subdivision represents 20 per cent of the quota or standard perform-

CHART 25

POPULATION AND ITS GROWTH

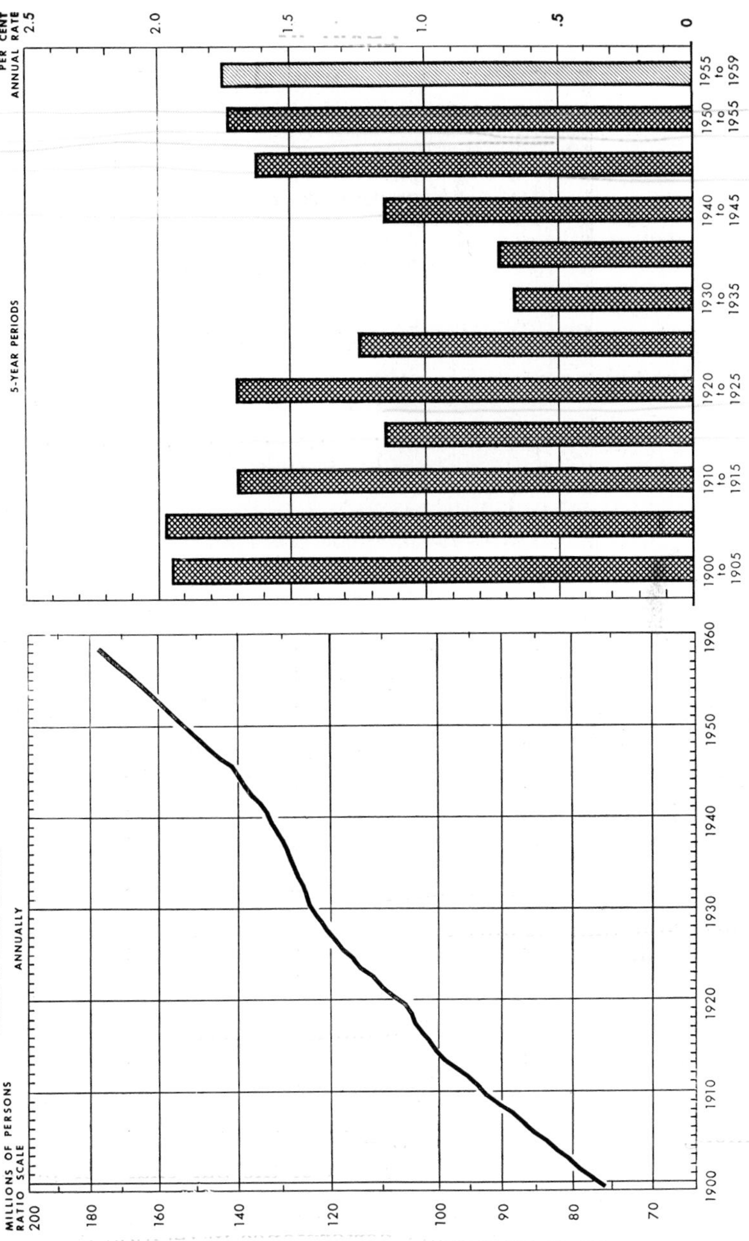

Source: Board of Governors of the Federal Reserve System, *Historical Supplement to Federal Reserve Chart Book on Financial and Business Statistics*, September, 1959, p. 84.

CHART 26

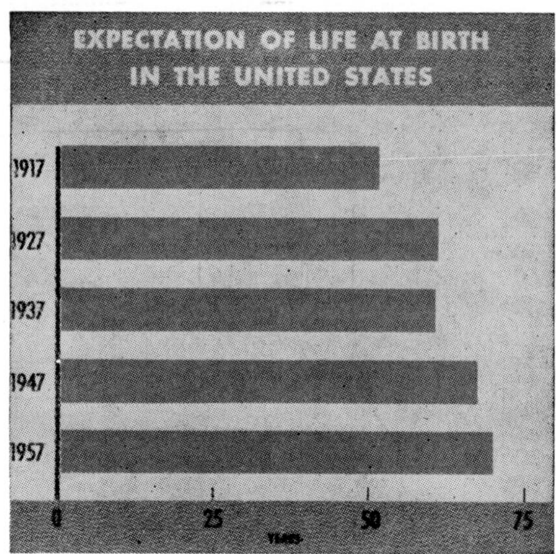

Source: *Life Insurance Fact Book*, 1959, p. 109.

ance per day. The narrow horizontal line or bar opposite each worker's name represents the per cent of standard output actually achieved. On Monday, June 21, Adams met the standard and Jones exceeded it by 20 per cent, as shown by the second narrow line drawn opposite his name. Berg and Lund failed to achieve standard for reasons indicated by the symbols. A worker who consistently failed to meet standards without justifiable cause probably would be released or shifted to some other department where he could perform satisfactorily.

The wide bar represents the cumulative per cent of standard achieved to date. Although Chart 28 has been posted only through Thursday, Jones's higher than standard performance on Monday, Tuesday, and Thursday has caused his cumulative bar to extend into the space for Friday. If Jones's performance on Friday were to be over 40 per cent of standard, his cumulative bar would have to be doubled back toward the left.

The Gantt Chart has many applications for management planning and control purposes. Major types of Gantt Charts are (1) man and machine record charts, (2) layout and load charts, and (3) progress charts. Machine record charts are similar to the man record chart illustrated above. The layout chart is used to schedule advance work for individual employees, against which their actual performance is

CHART 27. Percentage of total home mortgage recordings originated by savings and loan associations, 1958

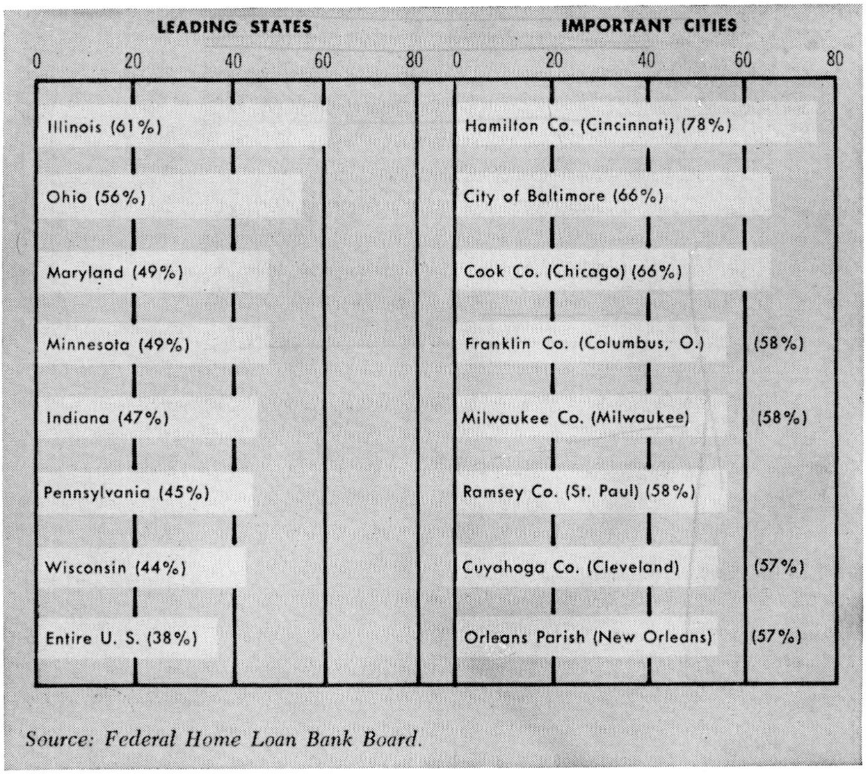

Source: Federal Home Loan Bank Board, as reported in *Savings and Loan Fact Book*, p. 38, (chart 14).

plotted. Load charts are used to reflect the amount of scheduled work ahead in a plant or department. Progress charts are used to reflect actual performance.

Multiple-bar charts. This type of chart is illustrated in Chart 29 where revenue from different commodities for the years 1957, 1958, and 1959 are compared. Individual bars in each group of three bars refer to different years—note how bars are differentiated by shading.

A multiple-bar chart with horizontal bars is shown in Chart 30. Note that the titles on each bar would have been difficult to use with vertical bars. With the horizontal bars, it is possible to have quite lengthy titles at the bases of the bars.

CHART 28. Man record chart

EMPLOYEE	June 21 Monday	22 Tuesday	23 Wednesday	24 Thursday	25 Friday
Adams, J.S.		W	P	R	
Berg, D.M.	T		A		
Jones, F.C.					
Lund, O.P.	W	M	P	R	

‖ ‖ Space between double lines represents standard amount of work per day.

—— Per cent of standard actually achieved.

| Cumulative per cent of standard achieved to date.

V Denotes date to which chart has been posted.

A - Absent
M - Material trouble
P - Power trouble
R - Repairs
T - Tool trouble
W - Waiting for set-up

Combined bar and line charts. This is a device employed as a substitute for a multi column chart. In Chart 31 the capital structure of Allied Stores is indicated. Long term debt is shown as a line rather than as a third bar.

COMPONENT-PART CHARTS

Component-part line charts. In this type of chart, color, crosshatching, or shading are employed to differentiate the different components of a total. Emphasis is also possible; brighter colors or darker shading can draw attention to particular components. Often, the darker shadings are used for the component at the bottom and successively lighter shading for other components. This was done in Chart 32 which pictures the changing components of the United States labor force, 1929–1958.

Component-part bar charts. The component-part vertical-bar chart illustrated by Chart 33 is also called a subdivided-bar (or column)

CHART 29

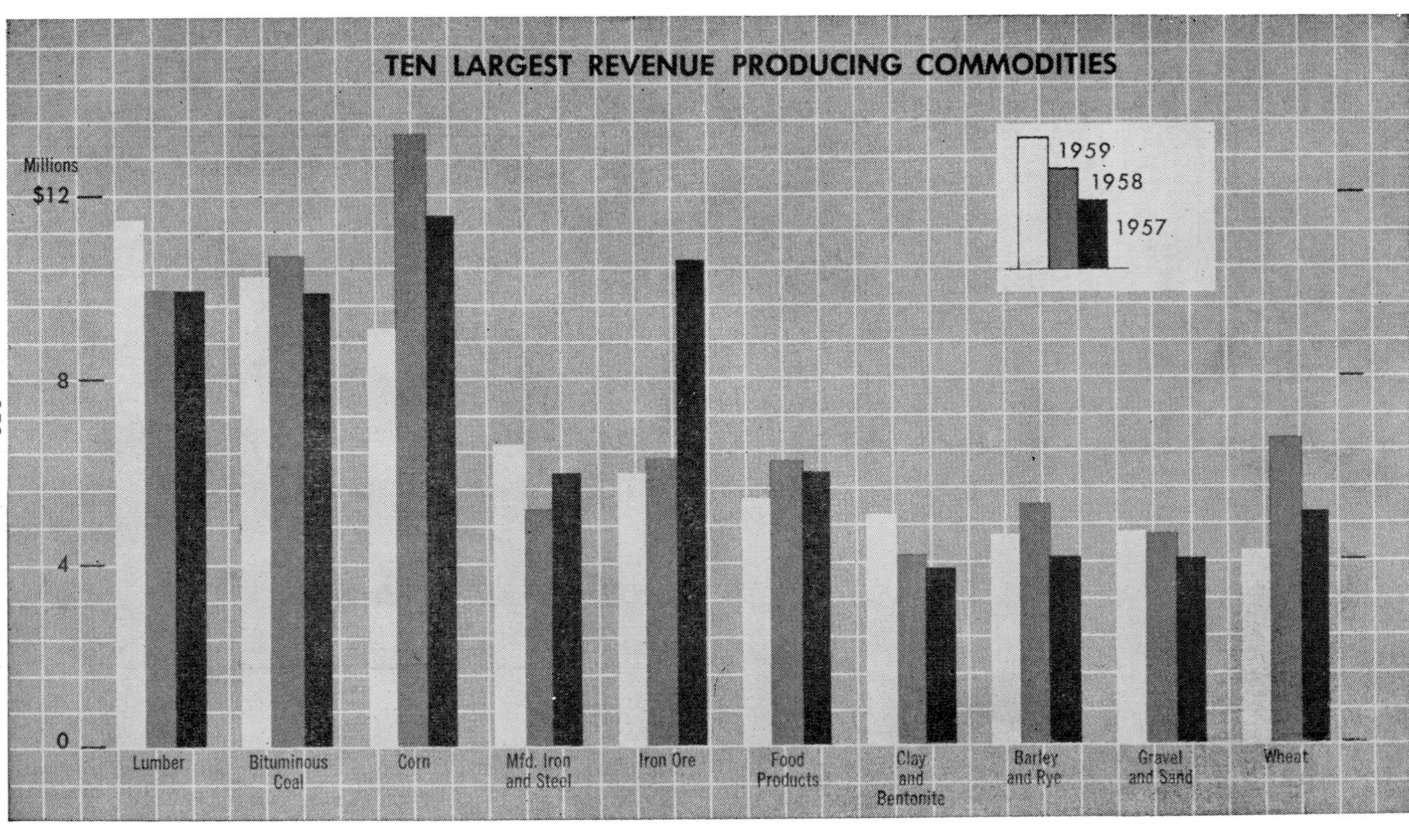

Source: North Western Railway Company, *Annual Report, 1959*, p. 7.

CHART 30

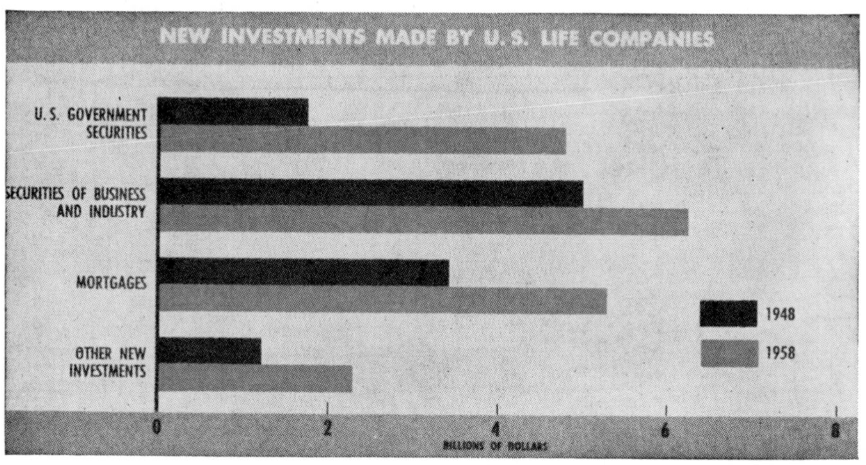

Source: Institute of Life Insurance, *Life Insurance Fact Book,* 1959, p. 90.

CHART 31

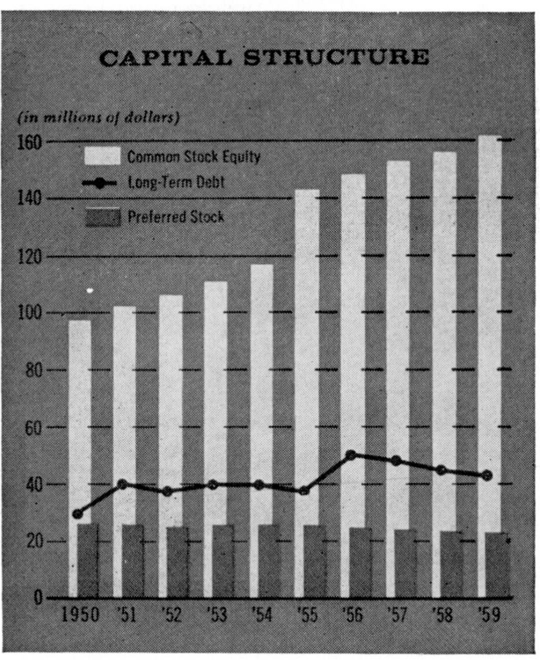

Source: Allied Stores Corporation, *1959 Annual Report,* p. 13.

CHART 32

LABOR FORCE, EMPLOYMENT, AND UNEMPLOYMENT

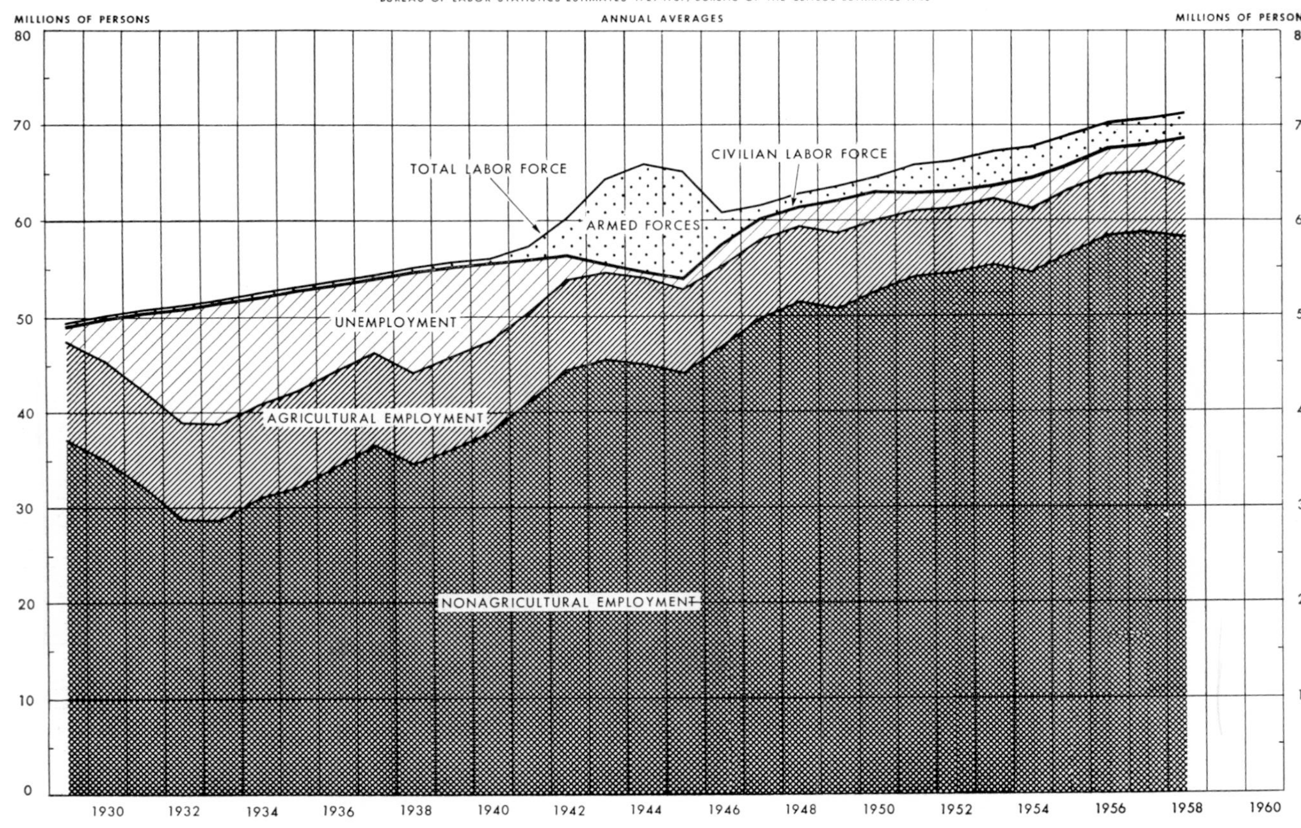

Source: Board of Governors of the Federal Reserve System, *Historical Supplement to Federal Reserve Chart Book on Financial and Business Statistics*, September, 1959, p. 89.

CHART 33

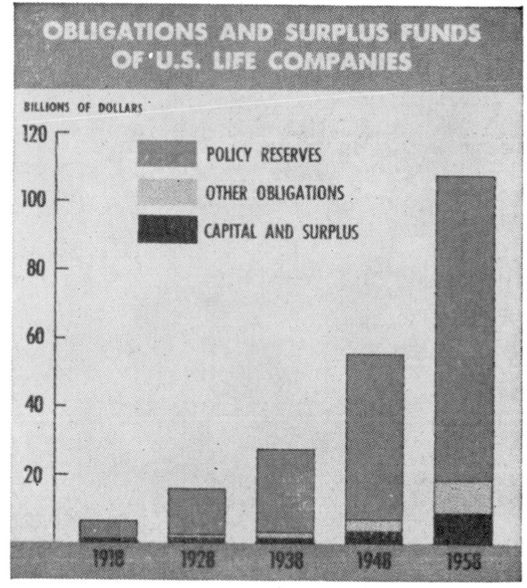

Source: *Life Insurance Fact Book*, 1959, p. 61.

CHART 34

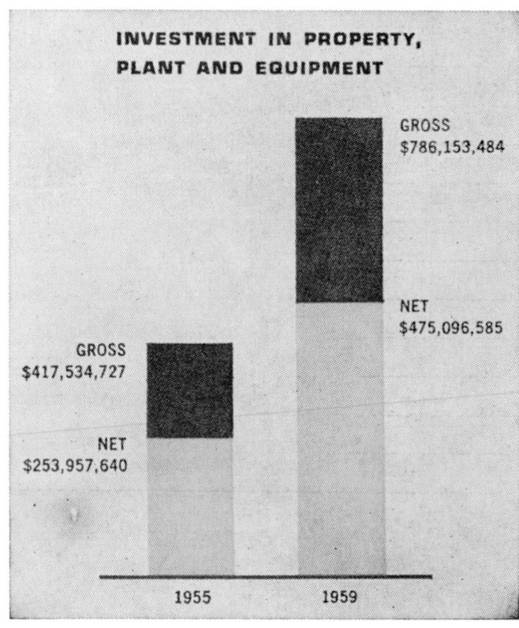

Source: American Can Company, *Annual Report to Stockholders, 1959*, p. 16.

chart. Comparisons are easily made among bars as a whole and among components adjacent to the base; however, some difficulty may be encountered in making comparisons among components which are not adjacent to the base line. (Chart 35 is a better illustration of this latter point; it is difficult to determine whether dividends paid have or have not changed since 1956.) The exact value of the bars and their components can be given the reader by printing these amounts either within the column or at the side of the column as is done in Chart 34. When this procedure is followed, the size of the printed amounts must be kept small in relation to the size of the bars if they are not to distract from or distort the apparent size of the bars.

CHART 35

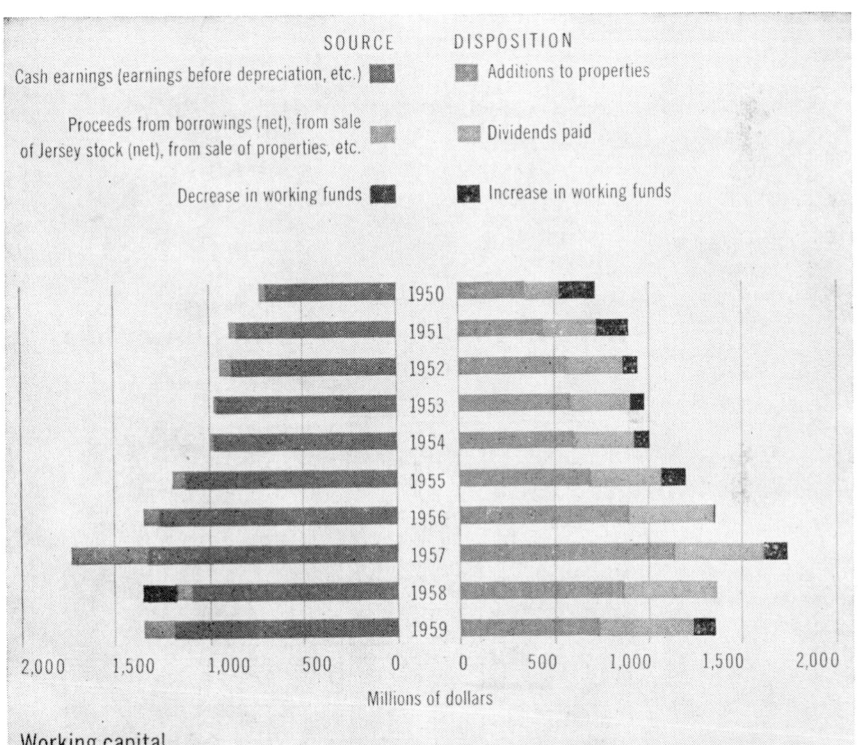

Working capital

In 1959 additions to plant facilities for Jersey's worldwide operations were again substantial, although lower than in any of the three years preceding. Improved cash earnings, supplemented by borrowings of some affiliates, resulted in an increase in working funds after making expenditures for additions to properties and meeting dividend requirements.

Source: Standard Oil Company (New Jersey), *1959 Annual Report*, p. 10.

Chart 35 is not only a composite bar chart but is also referred to as a *paired-* or *bilateral*-bar chart. In this case, the length of opposing bars are equal. The bars on the left indicate the source of funds, those on the right indicate the disposition of the funds.

CHART 36

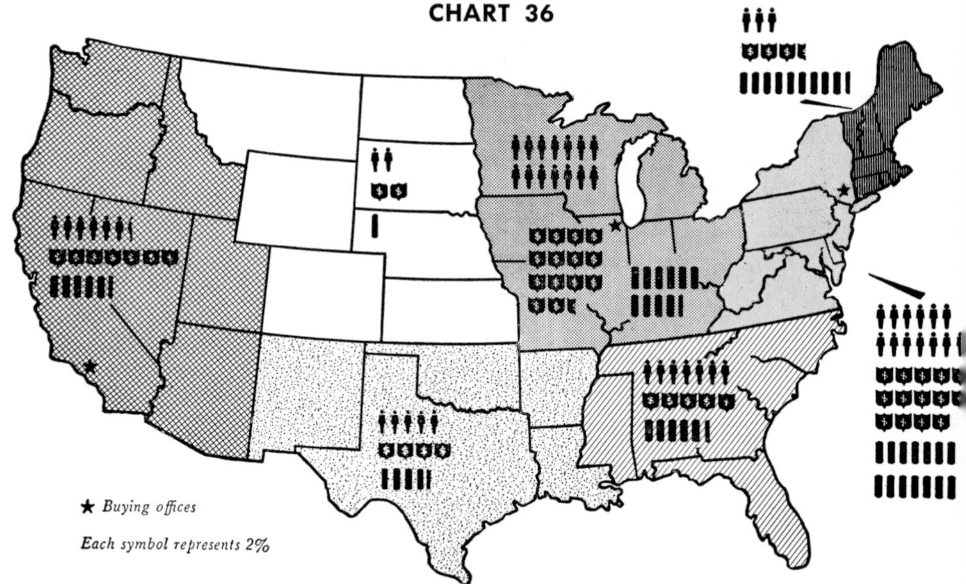

National Distribution of Allied Stores' Sales

Compared with U. S. Population and Income

AREA	U. S. POPULATION % TO TOTAL	U. S. INCOME % TO TOTAL	ALLIED SALES % TO TOTAL
New England	6	7	19
Middle East	25	28	28
Southeast	14	10	11
Central	28	29	21
Southwest	10	8	9
West	4	4	1
Far West	13	14	11
TOTAL	100%	100%	100%

Source: Allied Stores Corporation, *1959 Annual Report*, p. 15.

STATISTICAL MAPS

This type of chart is used to indicate the geographical distribution of data. There are a great many possible variations of this chart form. In Chart 36, shading indicates the area distribution of Allied Stores' sales. The symbols and shading on the map are a picture of the data presented in the table below. The title has been placed below the chart rather than in the more customary position above the chart because it also applies to the accompanying table.

Individual regions have been identified by their physical separation from adjacent regions in Chart 37. Percentage increases for each region are shown exactly in the superimposed ovals. Chart 38 illustrates the use of shading and cross-hatching. The darker and more solid areas denote a greater amount of assets, as indicated in the legend at the bottom of the chart.

CHART 37. Percentage increase in savings and loan assets by regions, 1953–1958

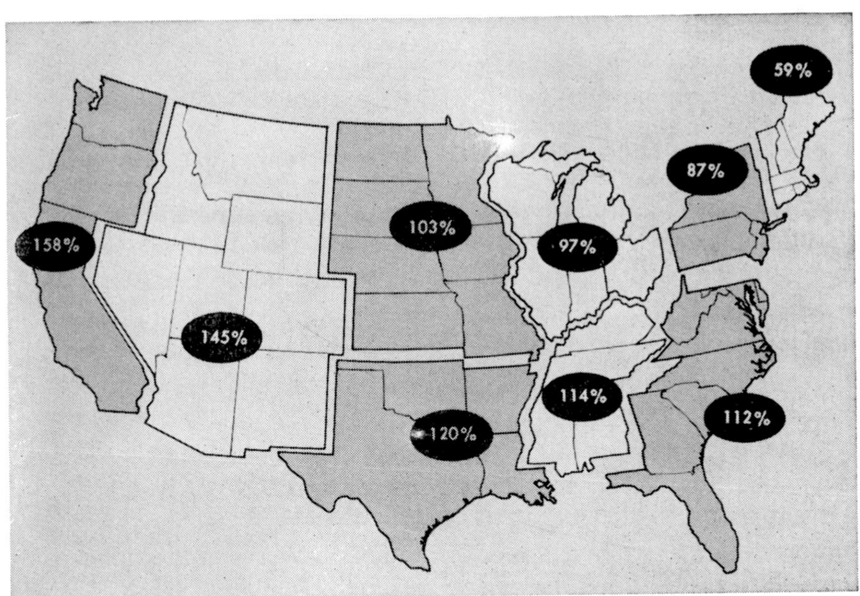

Note: Regional divisions are those used by the U. S. Bureau of the Census.
Source: United States Savings and Loan League, as reported in *Savings and Loan Fact Book*, 1959, p. 76.

CHART 38. Savings and loan assets, by states, as of December 31, 1958

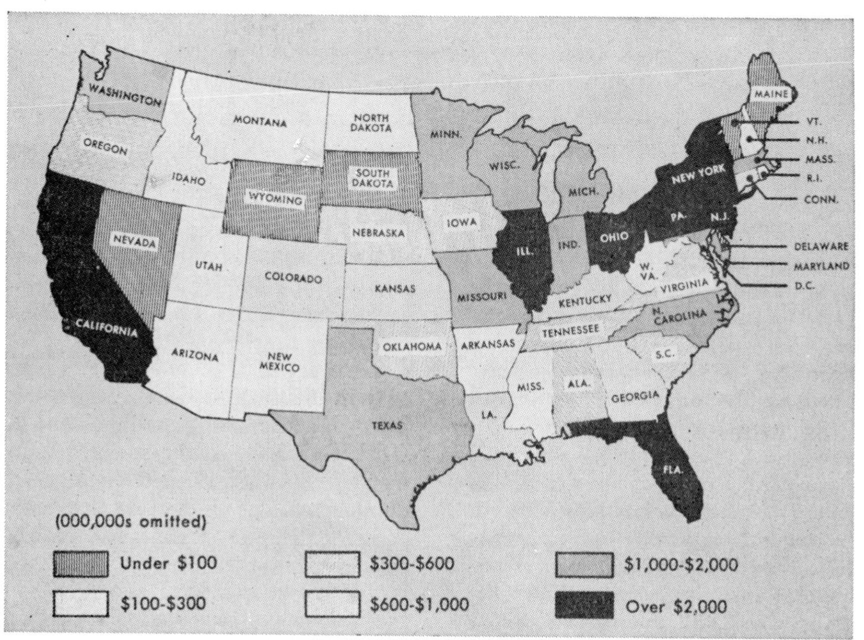

Source: United States Savings and Loan League, as reported in *Savings and Loan Fact Book, 1959*, p. 74.

PIE CHARTS

This type of chart is eye-catching but its usefulness is limited by the difficulty encountered in making comparisons among sectors of the pie or circle. Presentation of several pies of varying sizes on the same chart is questionable procedure; even approximate determinations of the actual amounts represented by several pies are virtually impossible. However, single pies which have relatively few sectors may be employed to good advantage.

General rules sometimes stated for construction of pie charts are (1) to arrange the sectors in order of magnitude and (2) to commence the largest sector at the 12 o'clock position, proceeding clockwise thereafter. This writer sees merit in the first rule for most applications but sees merit in the second rule only when comparison is to be made among sectors of several pies—a doubtful procedure in itself.

In Chart 39 the sectors of the pie have been separated to facilitate

CHART 39

how the average U.S. family divided its dollars for consumer goods and services in 1956

THE AVERAGE HOUSEHOLD: **TOTAL EXPENDITURE $4,106**

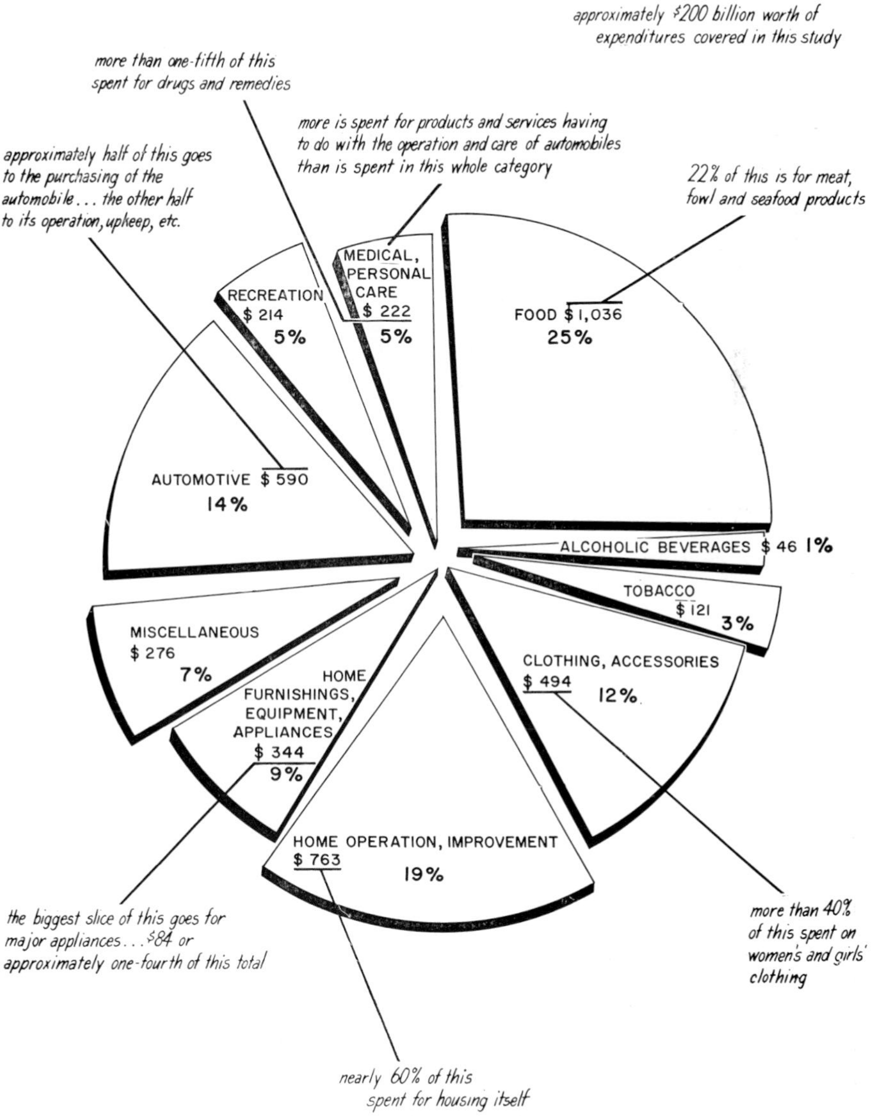

approximately $200 billion worth of expenditures covered in this study

more than one-fifth of this spent for drugs and remedies

more is spent for products and services having to do with the operation and care of automobiles than is spent in this whole category

approximately half of this goes to the purchasing of the automobile . . . the other half to its operation, upkeep, etc.

22% of this is for meat, fowl and seafood products

MEDICAL, PERSONAL CARE $ 222 5%

RECREATION $ 214 5%

FOOD $ 1,036 25%

AUTOMOTIVE $ 590 14%

ALCOHOLIC BEVERAGES $ 46 1%

TOBACCO $ 121 3%

MISCELLANEOUS $ 276 7%

HOME FURNISHINGS, EQUIPMENT, APPLIANCES $ 344 9%

CLOTHING, ACCESSORIES $ 494 12%

HOME OPERATION, IMPROVEMENT $ 763 19%

the biggest slice of this goes for major appliances . . . $84 or approximately one-fourth of this total

more than 40% of this spent on women's and girls' clothing

nearly 60% of this spent for housing itself

Source: *The Life Study of Consumer Expenditures*, Time, Inc. 1957.

comparison. Even so, only a general impression may be obtained of the values of individual sectors until reference is made to the percentages in each sector.

Two pies are presented in Chart 40, which is another graphic presentation of the source and disposition of funds. The pies, however, do not show total amounts but only percentages. Note that the two pies are not being compared, but each stands alone.

CHART 40

THE CHASE MANHATTAN DOLLAR

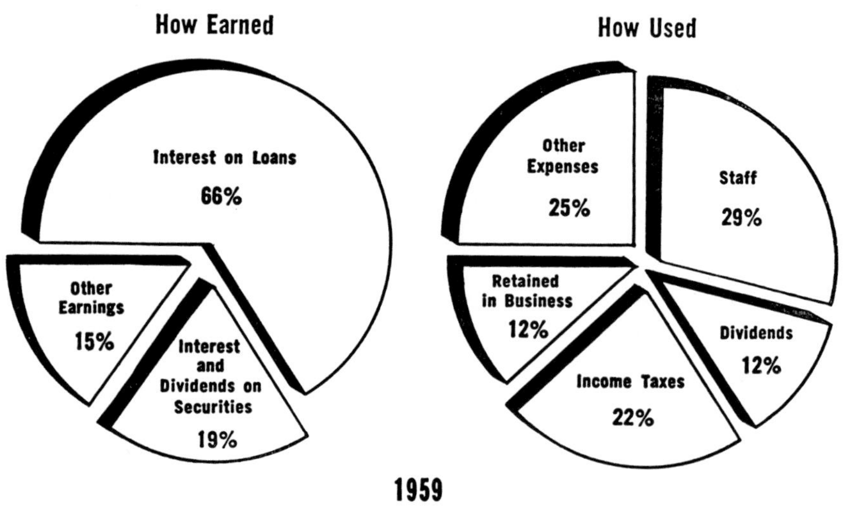

Source: Chase Manhattan Bank, *Annual Report, 1959,* p. 12.

PICTOGRAMS

Variety and a great deal of eye appeal may be achieved by careful use of pictograms. However, care must be used to avoid distortion of the statistics presented and also to avoid distraction from the data.

Chart 41 combines a pictogram, a picture, and a vertical bar chart quite effectively. Note that actual population figures are given at the end of each column of figures. Note also that the percentages of farmers are indicated by different and darker figures and the exact figures are given as well.

Pictures, columns, actual data, and a curve were effectively combined in Chart 42. Gaps in school enrollment data are reflected graphically by gaps between the columns. The reader may have been disturbed by the apparent lack of coordination between the dates for births shown on the curved line and dates for enrollment as indicated by the columns. However, birth data were posted six years earlier than school enrollment for an obvious reason.

Drafting and reproduction of charts

DRAFTING

There is a common misunderstanding that presentable charts can be prepared only by draftsmen who have become skilled as a result of long years of training. Although this may have been true at one time, the development of equipment and supplies has made it possible for clerical personnel to become virtually self-trained in a few months. Skilled statistical draftsmen are, of course, to be preferred, but relatively few are available and many small and medium-sized businesses cannot justify employment of a full-time draftsman.

Mechanical lettering guides enable persons with little, if any, freehand skill to make uniform letters of varying sizes. These guides solve a troublesome problem for beginners and more experienced personnel as well, since lettering of titles, scales, and legends is often the most time-consuming part of chart preparation. Specialized typewriters in which plates of several sizes of type can be used are also available.

Occasionally a firm has the good fortune of employing a person who can do fine freehand work. A freehand artist can usually do somewhat faster work than is possible with a lettering guide. This is an important asset in the drafting of large display charts which often require lettering of sizes larger than can be provided by mechanical lettering guides. Minor imperfections in lettering are of no real consequence; also, these imperfections will be considerably obscured if the charts are photographically reduced for reproduction purposes.

Another important aid for chart preparation is the availability of both colored and crosshatched adhesive paper which can be easily applied; it can also be removed with ease—in case of error—and reapplied if desired. This paper is available in sheets of varying sizes and also may be obtained in rolls of varying narrow widths which are ideal for line charts. Preprinted symbols for pictograms may also be procured in sheet form.

CHART 41

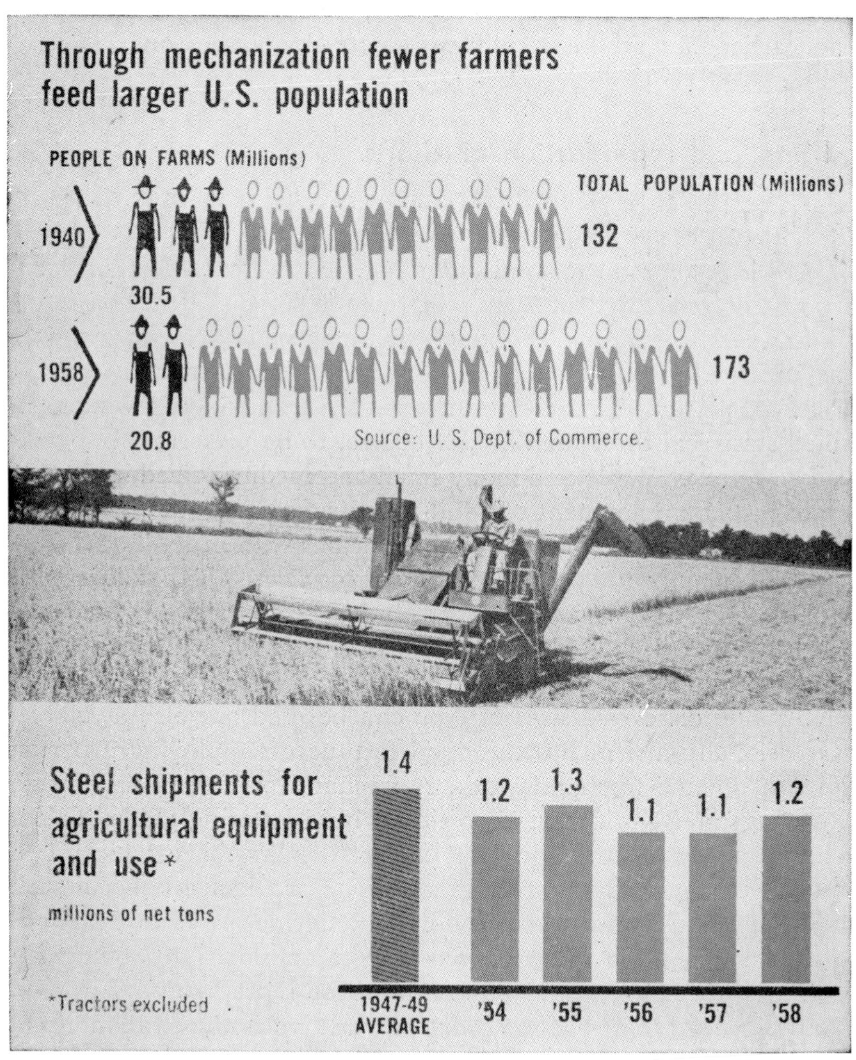

Source: American Iron and Steel Institute, *Charting Steel's Progress*, 1959 edition, p. 40.

CHART 42

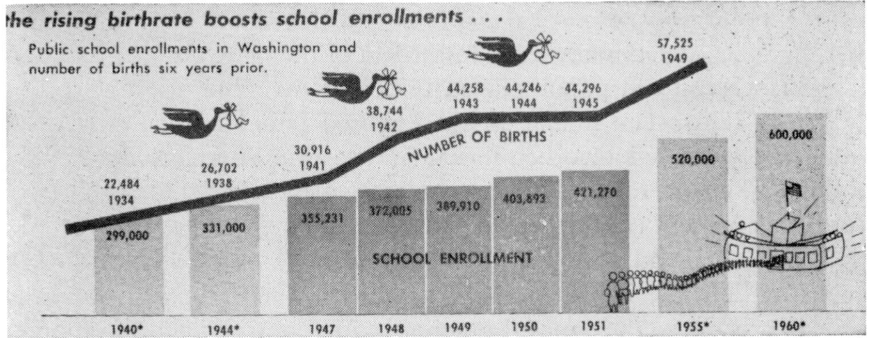

* Includes group credit certificates.
Source: Superintendent of Public Instruction. From *Your Dollar's Worth of State Government*, 1952, p. 19.

REPRODUCTION

Several methods are available for chart reproduction. The photostat process is excellent if fewer than fifty copies are required. Photostating provides black-on-white copies; color may be reproduced but only at a high cost. When color is desired on the original chart for display purposes, colored lines should be broken in various patterns in order that they may be differentiated in the photostated reproductions. Red, orange, brown, green, and violet appear gray-black in reproductions. When confronted with this problem it is wise to consult with experienced photostat technicians *before* preparation of the original chart.

The *photo-offset* method of reproduction will provide up to about 25,000 copies. This method consists of preparation of a sensitized aluminum plate from a photographic negative of the chart. In the reproduction process, ink adheres only to the image of the chart, with the result that the inked image is transferred to a rubber roller and thence to the paper.

The *multilith* process is a popular method which provides over 5,000 copies. This method involves drafting the chart directly on a thin aluminum plate, which then is used in the same manner as plates in the photo-offset process. Reproductions are not quite as clear as printing done from photo-offset plates, but they are much less costly.

The *xerography* process will provide up to 25,000 copies. In this method, either a paper or a metal master is sensitized, exposed and developed. This master is used in much the same manner as the multilith and photo-offset plates to print copies.

A number of methods are available which provide a limited number of copies at relatively little cost. Most of these are contact methods in which sensitized paper placed under or over the original is subjected to light. The image on the exposed paper is then developed and/or transferred to other sheets by use of a chemical developing fluid. The resulting copies are usually less sharply detailed than the original and will fade if exposed to sunlight.

Mimeograph and *ditto* processes may also be employed. Although reproductions are inferior in appearance to charts reproduced by the above processes, they may be suitable for control and information reports.

Advantages and limitations of charts

Graphic presentation communicates statistical data more rapidly and with a more lasting impression than is possible by any other means. This is a tremendous advantage. Display charts, although moderately expensive, are invaluable aids for management planning and control purposes.

Oft-cited limitations of charts are, first, that only a few sets of data can be included in a single chart, and second, that exact amounts cannot be determined. In the author's opinion, these are not serious limitations. The first limitation may be overcome by using a series of simple charts rather than a single complex one. The second limitation can be met by inserting exact amounts in charts when necessary, and by supplementing charts with tables, which perform a valuable independent function.

Questions and Exercises

1. Discuss the major types of charts, indicating the strengths and weaknesses of each.
2. State the general rules for good chart design.
3. In what ways may emphasis be achieved in graphic presentation? Prepare specific examples to illustrate your listing.
4. Prepare a series of at least six charts, each different from the others. Obtain data from available sources, such as (1) publications of

Standard & Poor's Corporation and *Moody's Investors Service*, (2) company annual reports, (3) *Survey of Current Business*, (4) *Monthly Labor Review*, (5) *Statistical Abstract of the United States*, (6) U. S. census volumes. State why you selected each chart type. State the significant facts revealed in each chart.

5. Discuss the advantages and limitations of graphic presentation. Compare graphic and tabular presentation as alternative methods of presenting numerical information.

6. Prepare charts required for your term research project.

7. Refer to the sections on bar charts and develop a comparison of the relative advantages and limitations of using horizontal bars instead of vertical bars.

8. Refer to Table 56, pp. 234-5, and prepare a ratio chart comparing total net sales, total net earnings, and dividend per share. Interpret the results.

9. Compare the advantages and limitations of arithmetic line charts and semilogarithmic line charts as alternative methods of presenting numerical information.

11 *Internal administrative control*

The technology of business management is changing rapidly. The scientific method slowly pushed its way into the factory, and is now making significant contributions in the areas of managerial decision making and administrative control. Techniques of statistical inference are coming to be applied frequently in making day-to-day decisions. Systematic techniques for making inferences, testing them, and controlling the degree of their uncertainty have been discussed in previous chapters. Statistical techniques of forecasting also have been discussed. This chapter indicates how these techniques may be utilized for purposes of administrative control. Administrative control refers to the executive control which is required to insure efficient performance in carrying out *predetermined* programs of operations.

Statistical measures useful in administrative control

Most of the statistical techniques described in the preceding chapters may be adapted by management for administrative control purposes.

In order to achieve forecast levels of activity, it is customary to establish various goals, budgets, quotas, and standards of cost and performance. Many of these quotas and standards are in the nature of *averages*. Within certain specified limits, *variances* from these averages may be ignored; however, the occurrence of significant variances or "exceptions" is a warning that immediate investigation is required.

Ratios and *percentages* are widely used in business administration. Among illustrations of these are ratios of (1) current assets to current liabilities, (2) inventory to average daily sales, and (3) earnings to capital investment. Expression of large physical quantities and dollar amounts as percentages facilitates comparisons and highlights shifts in various distributions of assets, liabilities, incomes, expenses, and profits.

Index numbers, which normally are percentage expressions of averages or totals, are receiving increased attention from administrators and accountants as a means of adjusting original cost valuations to reflect the impact of periods of sharp inflation and deflation. This becomes important where provision for plant and equipment replacement reserves on an original cost basis is grossly inadequate because of highly inflated costs.

Sampling techniques, long recognized as important tools in market and consumer research, have recently gained increased recognition as tools of administrative control. Statistical quality control of factory production and office clerical work has been growing by leaps and bounds. Measures of central tendency, variation, and methods of sampling are all utilized in statistical quality control. Scientific auditing also is based on sampling theory and techniques.

Trend analysis, discussed in Chapter 7 in relation to forecasting, may also be employed in analyzing the trends of incomes and expenses on a company basis and by company departments, territories, products, and other meaningful classifications. *Correlation analysis*, another forecasting device, may be used to discover significant cost-volume relationships. Many such relationships are of a straight-line nature and therefore require a minimum of mathematical treatment. Knowledge of cost-volume relationships on a departmental basis is most important for the administration of a flexible budget program. Awareness of these relationships aids executives to maximize profits while changing operations to meet unforeseen developments.

Statistical tables and charts are important parts of those reports which executives require for planning and controlling business operations. Without these reports executives would be unable to function effectively.

PROBABILITY AND STATISTICAL CONTROL

The concept of probability or relative frequency of occurrence over the long run was introduced in Chapter 5 as a foundation for the understanding of statistical inference. Inference of the same kind is involved in many administrative control techniques. Often, however, it is impossible to rely only on the conceptual probabilities (sampling distributions) described in Chapter 5. The inference technique also can be applied to probabilities derived from experience (empirical probabilities). This is the kind of probability upon which insurance rates are based. Birth and death records provide the basis for computing the average life span for persons in the various age groups. Businessmen can use past experience to establish probabilities in the same manner. Such probabilities can be useful in guiding management decisions.

CONTROL CHARTS

Control charts were originally developed by Dr. Walter A. Shewhart of the Bell Telephone laboratories as a tool for controlling the quality of a process. Essentially, they represent a continuous application of statistical hypothesis testing of the type discussed in Chapter 5.

Any physical process is subject to unavoidable variation. This unavoidable variation follows a stable pattern. The first step in setting up a control chart is to obtain information about the average and unavoidable variation inherent in the quality characteristic as produced by the given process. Once the average and the inherent variation (standard deviation) of the process become known, it is possible to compute the expected sampling error associated with periodic control samples. Whenever the average of a control sample varies too far from the process average, the process is said to be "out of control." It is then necessary to stop the process and look for the assignable cause associated with such extreme variation.

Suppose we are manufacturing a gear box. One part in the gear box is a gear hub which is finished on an automatic milling machine. The diameter of the hub is a critical factor in determining the operating characteristics (quality) of the gear box. The design engineers have specified that the diameter of the hub is to be 0.3430 inch with allowable variation of 0.0030 inch either way. The production engineers have set up a process designed to produce within these tolerances.

The quality control statistician draws 20 samples of 5 hubs each from the line during a controlled run of several hundred pieces. The averages of the 20 sample means and of the 20 sample standard deviations are:

$$\overline{\overline{X}} = 0.3430 \qquad \bar{s} = 0.0007$$

Using $\bar{s}$ as equivalent to the process (population) standard deviation (σ), the standard error of the mean of samples of five items each would be:

$$\sigma_{\overline{X}} = \frac{0.0007}{\sqrt{5}} = \frac{0.0007}{2.236} = \mathbf{0.00031}$$

The automatic milling machine is a rather complicated machine and adjustments during a run are time consuming and costly. The quality control statistician and the production engineer decide that the machine should not be stopped to be readjusted unless it seems relatively certain that the process is actually "out of control," that is, that the process is being influenced by identifiable causes in such a fashion as to produce defective hubs. The control limits for the sample average are therefore set at $3\sigma_{\overline{X}}$ from the average of the sample means (process average).

$$\text{LCL} = \overline{\overline{X}} - 3\sigma_{\overline{X}} = 0.3430 - 3(0.00031) = \mathbf{0.34207}$$

$$\text{UCL} = \overline{\overline{X}} + 3\sigma_{\overline{X}} = 0.3430 + 3(0.00031) = \mathbf{0.34393}$$

These limits are shown on the control chart below (Chart 43). The probability of a mean from a random sample of 5 gear hubs falling outside these limits because of chance alone is only 0.0027.

Controlling the mean does not insure that all items are of acceptable quality. It is also necessary to control the variability about the

CHART 43. Quality control chart

Date 6/16/60
Part Gear Hub #1702 Machine M-7 Operator DCM

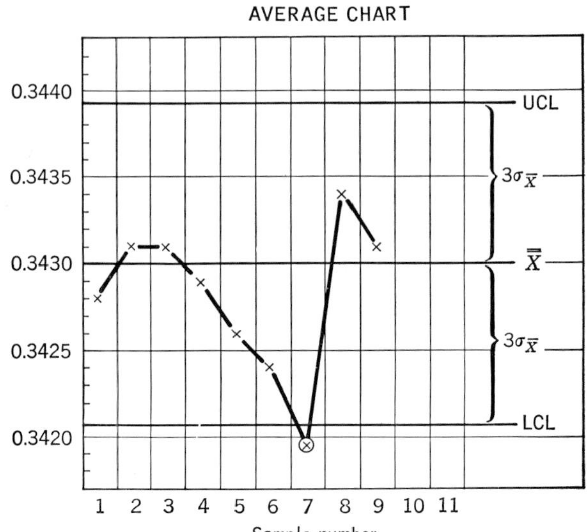

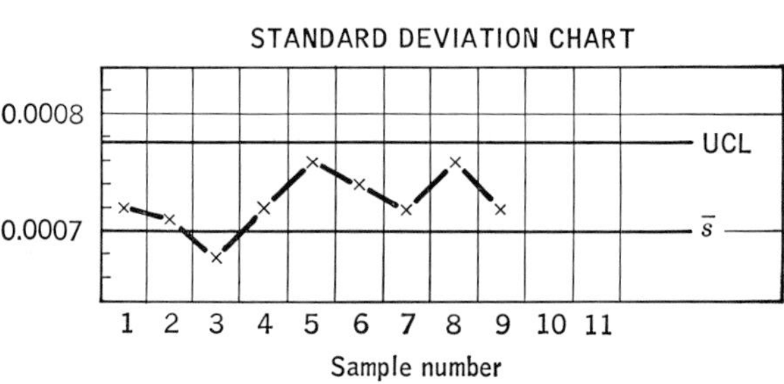

Source: Hypothetical

mean, i.e., the standard deviation.[1] The lower part of Chart 43 is a standard deviation control chart. Note that there is no lower control limit, only an upper control limit. Less-than-average variability is no cause for concern, but excessively large deviations of individual items could lead to defective production even though the sample means

[1] In actual practice, control of variability is more often controlled by control of the average range ($\bar{R}$) of the samples because of the greater ease in computing ranges. Methods for computing control limits for the average range are explained in any standard text on statistical quality control.

remain within the control limits. Excessively large deviations would be reflected in higher values for the standard deviation.

It can be seen that such a control process involves two risks. The first is the risk that a good lot may be incorrectly rejected as being below acceptable quality standards. The probability of such a Type I error is called the *producer's risk*. The second risk is that, by chance, a good sample will be chosen from an unacceptable lot. This would result in acceptance of a bad lot, a Type II error. The risk of Type II error is called the *consumer's risk*. The acceptance limits must be chosen in such a way that these two risks are properly balanced.

Work measurement programs are gaining increased acceptance as a tool for measuring performance and controlling expenses. Under these programs certain *work units*, such as tons received or vouchers issued, are selected as being representative of workloads within organizational units; in effect, this is a judgment sampling procedure. Standards, in terms of man hours, are established for each work unit and regular comparisons are made between actual and standard performance. Standards are of necessity quite subjective; usually they are determined by an analysis of past performance adjusted for increased skill of employees and improved machines, layouts, and procedures. A control chart for performance in processing vouchers is illustrated in Chart 44. Current standard performance is 0.45 man hours per invoice, a reduction of 0.15 man hours from the average of 0.60 for the preceding year. The zone of satisfactory performance is from 0.30 to 0.60 man hours per invoice. Additional zones are established by using the difference between the average and standard performance (0.15). Thus the zone from 0.60 to 0.75 indicates danger and the zone above 0.75 reflects poor performance. Processing vouchers at a rate of 0.30 man hours or less indicates that a new standard perhaps should be established. Of course, care should be exercised to prevent faulty recording or processing of data which could easily cause the appearance of either highly satisfactory or unsatisfactory performances.

There are other types of control charts which can be useful in making routine decisions; e.g., upper and lower control limits can be established to guide management use of forecasts based on time series analysis or correlation analysis. A hypothetical example has been developed from the J. C. Penney data analyzed in Chapter 7. It is supposed that in 1953 management decided that the trend of J. C.

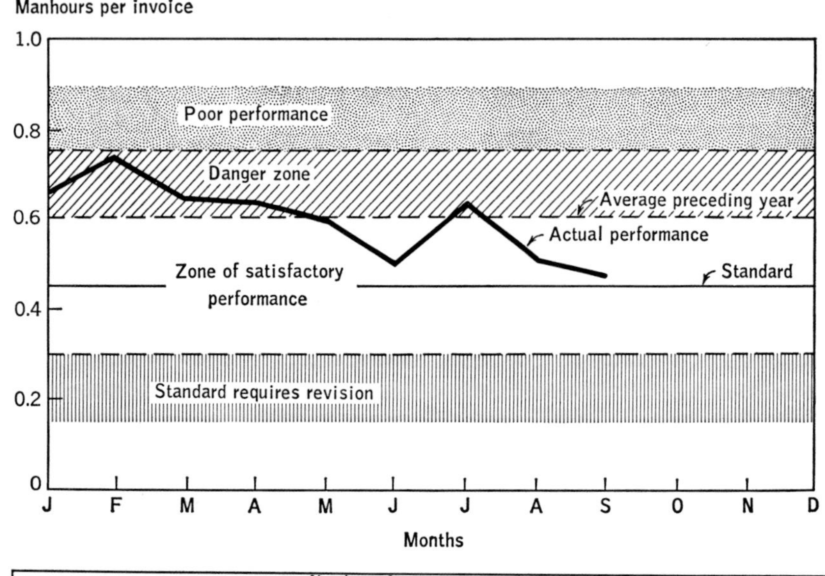

Number of invoices processed											
1,194	904	1,256	1,138	1,241	1,352	1,081	1,359	1,319			

Source: *Management Statistics for Field Installations*, Department of the Army, Office of the Quartermaster, p. 14.

Penney sales had changed and a new trend had developed after World War II. Accordingly, the trend line shown in Chart 45 was computed for the period 1945–1952. The variance of the deviations away from trend during this period was computed and the control limits set at 1.65 standard deviations away from the extrapolated trend line.[2] Actual net sales in every year since 1952 fall below the 90 per cent lower control limit. It is obvious that management would have found it desirable to revise their trend forecast at least by 1954. Control

[2] The variance was computed as

$$\frac{\Sigma\,(Y - T)^2}{N - 2}$$

and the standard deviation as the square root of the variance. The control limits were set at 1.65σ away from the trend line to include a 90 per cent confidence interval on the assumption that the deviations of actual sales from the straight-line trend are normally distributed. From Table II, Appendix B, it can be seen that the interval of 1.65σ on both sides of the mean of a normal distribution includes 90 per cent of the total area under the curve.

limits of this type could be established to include 80, 95, or some other appropriate percentage of past experience. A clerk could be given the responsibility for plotting current experience on the chart and calling management's attention to the situation whenever current experience goes "out of control." Management can then re-evaluate the forecast.

CHART 45. Forecast control, J. C. Penney Company net sales forecast; least-squares trend, 1945–1952. Control limits at 90 per cent of variability, 1945–1952

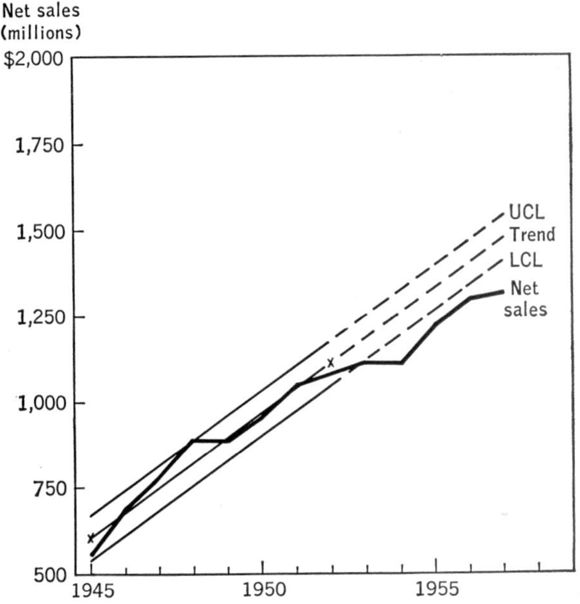

Source: Table 28 and author's computations.

The scatter diagram has recently been adapted for use in forecast control. In this process, illustrated in Chart 46, forecast or budgeted performance is plotted along the X-axis and actual performance is plotted along the Y-axis. Equality of budgeted performance and actual performance is indicated when the scatter of points follows a 45 degree line from the origin (Case 1). Control limits may be established in terms of absolute amounts as in Case 2 or in percentage deviations as in Case 3.

CHART 46. Scatter diagram control charts

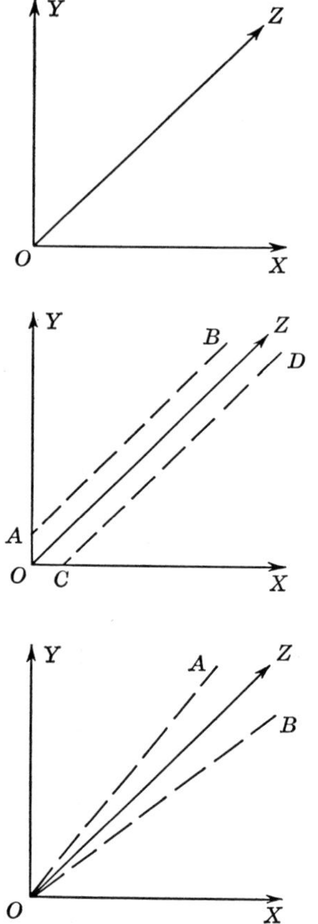

CASE 1. Perfect control.

Y = Actual performance

X = Forecast or budgeted performance.

OZ = "Line of equality": where actual and forecasted performance are equal.

CASE 2. Control over deviation from forecast by *constant amount.*

AB = Upper control limit when actual performance exceeds forecast by constant amount.

CD = Lower control limit when actual performance falls short of forecast by constant amount.

CASE 3. Control over deviation from forecast by *constant percentage.*

OA = Upper control limit when actual performance exeeds forecast by constant percentage of 25%.

OB = Lower control limit when actual performance falls short of forecast by constant percentage of 25%.

Applications of statistical control techniques

BUDGET CONTROL

Control charts are particularly applicable to budgetary control. Forecasts of sales, whether formal or informal, serve as the foundation for plans of future business operations. Integration of all phases of a firm's operations to the sales forecast may be accomplished by budgeting. A budget may be thought of as a plan for future operations expressed in financial terms; actually, this requires that plans first be expressed in physical terms, such as units of sales, production, rental space, and number of personnel. A complete and integrated budget plan would probably include the following budgets:

Sales budget
Inventory budget
Production budget
Purchasing budget
Various expense budgets
Capital expenditure budget
Financial budgets

The close relationship existing among the above budgets is obvious. Adequate inventories must be maintained to meet forecast sales. Manufacturing firms must purchase raw materials and plan production to meet inventory and sales requirements. Nonmanufacturing firms must purchase inventories to meet sales requirements. Manufacturing, selling, and administrative expenses must be budgeted for the forecast level of business activity. Expenditures for building and equipment required for anticipated expansion and replacement must be carefully scheduled. Financial budgets are of prime importance. A cash budget reflecting receipts, expenditures, and cash balances is essential to good administration. Also important are budgets reflecting projected statements of profit and loss and financial condition; these statements reflect the financial results which will be realized if forecast operating plans materialize.

Annual budgets are customarily supported by quarterly and monthly budgets. Sales budgets are often prepared for even shorter periods. Company budgets are supported by budgets for branches, departments, divisions, and sections—following the organizational pattern of responsibility.

Budgetary control refers to the control of a firm's operations by a continuous comparison of actual and budgeted operations. Constant review of operations permits executives to take immediate action whenever actual results deviate significantly from budgeted results. All too often budgets are filed away until the end of the year, when they may be referred to principally as a point of departure for preparation of the succeeding year's budget. Such a procedure loses virtually all the benefits available from a sound budgeting program. Budgets must be continually analyzed and reviewed if maximum potential benefits are to be realized. Budgetary control is the cornerstone of a sound program of administrative control. Budgeting familiarizes executives with the relationships among the several phases of a firm's operations and thereby enables them to adjust operations more readily to meet changed conditions.

SALES CONTROL

The scatter diagram control chart can also be applied to the control of sales. The purpose of sales control is to determine the difference between actual sales and budgeted sales at the earliest possible date in order that operational plans may be adjusted accordingly. Depending upon the kind of business and the type of organizational structure, controls may be established for sales classified by branches, territories, products, salesmen, and even customers. Also, the major classifications may be cross-classified a number of ways.

Analysis of sales by customers may reveal that a high percentage of total sales may be to a relatively small percentage of total customers; and conversely, that a large percentage of total customers account for but a small percentage of total sales. Further analysis may indicate that the expense of handling large numbers of small sales exceeds the income from such sales. Under such circumstances executives should consider the advisability of discontinuing sales to small customers. This problem may be a complex one; the sales potential of this class of customer may be expected to increase, or sales income may be exceeding variable direct expenses and hence contributing some revenue (though not its proportionate share) to offset fixed expenses. In this latter instance, elimination of sales to these customers would serve to reduce company profits further (or increase losses). Other related factors are the level of current operations—above or below capacity of facilities—and the alternative uses of existing facilities.

Whenever possible *order* control should precede sales control. For example, backlogs of unfilled orders are significant indicators of future sales. A decline in this backlog should be a warning to management to increase sales efforts and/or initiate steps to curtail production and reduce expenses. On the other hand, an increase in order backlog may justify authorization for expansion and increased expenditures in order to meet future demands.

PRODUCTION AND INVENTORY CONTROLS

Production plans and inventory levels must be integrated with sales levels. Manufacturing firms which experience sharp seasonal fluctuations in sales must choose between a policy of steady employment and accumulation of inventories during slack sales periods or a policy of gearing production to the seasonal sales pattern and reduc-

CHART 47. Sales, inventory, and production

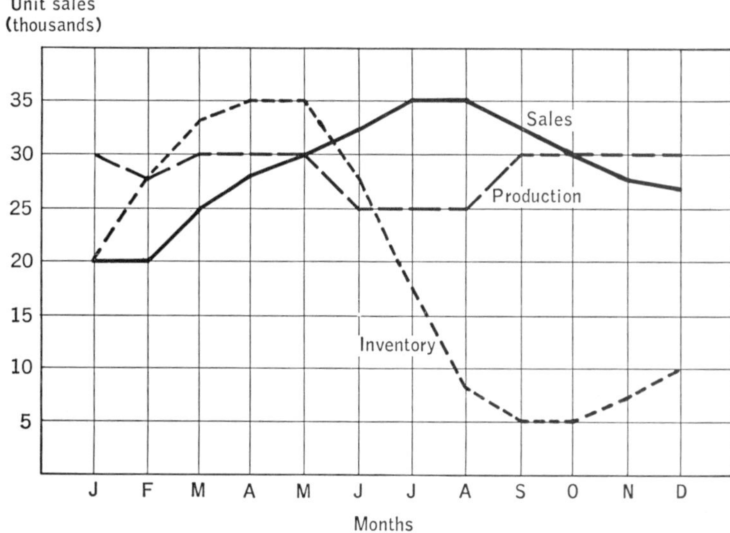

Source: Hypothetical

ing employment in the off seasons. The latter policy may lead to loss of skilled employees and to other labor problems. The former policy may lead to disastrous inventory losses arising from sudden drops in demand. In some instances such dilemmas may be solved by adding product lines which have complementary seasonal patterns. A simple graph of experience such as that shown in Chart 47 can be useful in controlling the relationships among production, inventory, and sales.

Inventory control may also be maintained on company equipment and supplies. Complete inventory counts are frequently time-consuming and costly. Some companies have recently discovered that sampling techniques can reduce inventory costs markedly and also can improve on the accuracy of a total count of items. This surprising result apparently is due to the fact that employees exercise more care in recording a statistical sample of a relatively few items than they do when burdened with the tiresome routine of a complete enumeration.

EXPENSE CONTROL

Expense budgets should be supplemented by the use of expense and performance standards for as many expense items as possible. Actual expenses and performances should be compared regularly with the expense budgets and standards. Control charts can be used to advantage in this area.

Expenses should be classified according to whether they vary or remain fixed when changes occur in the level of operations. Accordingly, expense standards may need to be variable, semi-variable, or fixed.

A number of investigations have revealed that total expenses tend to vary in a straight-line relationship with volume. When this condition holds true for a company, this relationship may be used to control expenses at those levels which are appropriate for specific levels of activity.

A thorough analysis of sales and expenses will enable a firm to construct a break-even chart. Such a chart illustrates the profit or loss which will result at various volumes of sales over a period of time, *provided* expenses are controlled according to plans and provided significant fluctuations do not occur in prices of material, labor, supplies, and finished goods. A break-even chart is illustrated in Chart 48. The break-even point occurs at sales of 125,000 units where sales and costs both equal \$187,617. Sales of below 125,000 units will result in a loss and sales above 125,000 units will result in a profit. This relationship at the break-even point may be expressed algebraically as follows:

$$\text{sales} = \text{variable costs} + \text{fixed costs}$$

In the above illustration variable expense of \$0.70 are required on the average for each unit produced. Fixed cost is \$100,000. Units are sold for \$1.50 each. The break-even volume (X) can be found as follows:

$$\begin{aligned} 1.50X &= 0.70X + 100{,}000 \\ 1.50X - 0.70X &= 100{,}000 \\ 0.80X &= 100{,}000 \\ X &= \mathbf{125{,}000\ units} \end{aligned}$$

It is possible to compute the break-even point in dollar sales. In the above illustration variable expenses of \$0.467 are required for each \$1.00 of sales (\$0.70 ÷ \$1.50). Using the symbol X for sales and zero for the break-even point:

$$\begin{aligned} 0 &= X - 0.467X - 100{,}000 \\ 0.533X &= 100{,}000 \\ X &= \mathbf{\$187{,}617} \end{aligned}$$

CHART 48. Break-even chart

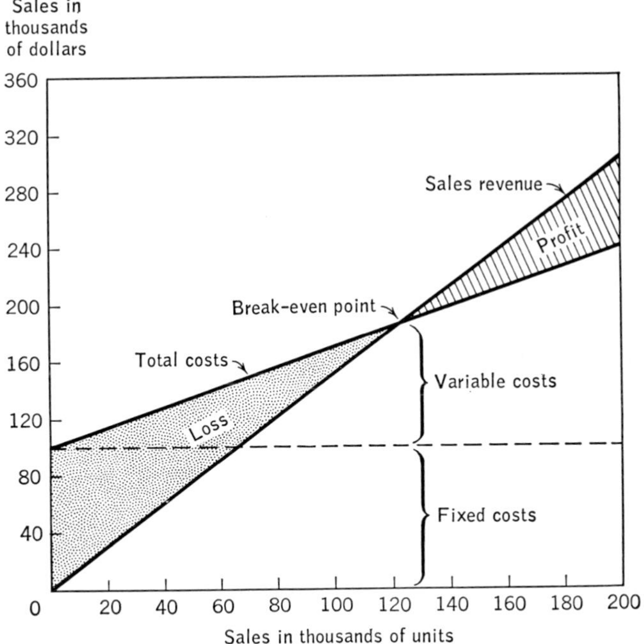

Source: Hypothetical

The physical volume of sales necessary to attain a specified level of profit is found by substituting the desired profit amount (P) into an equation like the following:

$$P = 1.50X - 0.70X - 100{,}000$$

Thus for profits of \$20,000,

$$20{,}000 = 1.50X - 0.70X - 100{,}000$$

$$120{,}000 = 0.80X$$

$$X = \mathbf{150{,}000\ units}$$

The dollar volume of sales necessary to attain a particular profit level is found by substituting the desired profit amount (P) into the following equation:

$$P = X - 0.467X - \$100{,}000$$

Thus for profits of \$20,000,

$$20{,}000 = X - 0.467X - 100{,}000$$
$$0.533X = 120{,}000$$
$$X = \mathbf{\$225{,}141}$$

PERSONNEL CONTROL

The following data may be regularly compiled as an aid to personnel management and control:

Rate of personal turnover
Sick leave rate
Absence and tardy rates
Accident rates
Reasons for resignations, releases, and transfers
Merit and efficiency ratings
Records of promotions and demotions

Application of trend analysis and statistical control to the above data and comparison with other companies may be informative and helpful to management. High turnover and absence rates can be costly through reduced production and increased training costs. Lack of sound performance ratings may contribute to promotion by favoritism with consequent dissension among employees. Future personnel problems may be reduced by testing all job applicants with tests scientifically constructed so that test results have a high correlation with job performance. Employee opinion surveys may reveal points of tension and thereby enable management to prevent the occurrence of many serious disturbances.

REPORTS CONTROL

Internal administrative control is largely dependent upon preparation and analysis of reports on all phases of operations. However, a burdensome reporting system can easily defeat the purpose for which it was intended, namely, effective administrative control. In 1810 the Duke of Wellington, infuriated by seemingly endless requests for reports, penned the following letter to the British Secretary of War, Lord Bradford:

My Lord,

If I attempted to answer the mass of futile correspondence that surrounds me, I should be debarred from all serious business of compaigning.

I must remind your Lordship—for the last time—that so long as I retain an independent position, I shall see that no officer under my command is debarred by attending to the futile drivelling of mere quill driving in your Lordship's Office—from attending to his first duty—which is, and always has been, so to train the private men under his command that they may, without question, beat any force opposed to them in the field.

I am,
My Lord,
Your obedient Servant
(Wellington)

In order to eliminate preparation of duplicate or unnecessary reports, it is often desirable to appoint a reports control officer or a reports control committee whose functions might be as follows:

1. Analyze and edit all requests for new reports;
2. Issue control numbers to all reports which are approved;
3. Periodically review existing reports to determine whether they should be continued, revised, or discontinued.

Data should be reported only if they serve a specific control purpose; data should not be collected merely because they are "interesting" or because they *might* "come in handy sometime." Consideration should always be given to the workload required by reports. Workload required by a particular report may outweigh the potential value of the report. All requests for reports should be accompanied by clear and concise instructions. Inadequate instructions may result in the collection of useless information. Finally, personnel should be instructed to reject requests for reports which do not bear control numbers issued by the reports control officer or committee.

SUMMARY

Statistical techniques are almost indistinguishably interwoven with accounting and reporting techniques in the area of internal administrative control. This chapter has been designed to indicate briefly the broad scope of internal administrative control and to highlight a few of the applications of statistical methods. The treatment has by no means been exhaustive.

Statistical techniques which have useful applications in administrative control include measures of central tendency, measures of variation, ratios, rates, percentages, index numbers, trend analysis, correlation, and sampling. Although internal administrative control involves much more than the application of statistical methods, it is difficult to conceive of an area of control where some statistical techniques could not be employed to advantage.

Administrative and statistical controls, properly designed, highlight essential information which otherwise would remain forever obscured in the mass of detail which necessarily characterizes accounting and administrative records.

Questions and Exercises

1. Briefly describe the statistical control techniques which may be utilized for administrative control purposes.
2. Discuss the internal administrative controls listed below, indicating the role of managerial statistics in each control.
   (a) Budgetary control
   (b) Sales control
   (c) Inventory control
   (d) Production control
   (e) Expense control
   (f) Financial control
   (g) Personnel control
   (h) Reports control
3. Study Chart 43. At what points would the quality of production be "out of control"? Why is there an upper control limit but no lower control limit in the "Standard Deviation Chart"?
4. A small firm with annual fixed expenses of $12,000 has variable expenses which absorb 70 cents out of each sales dollar. What annual dollar volume of sales is required to break even? To realize a profit of $9,000?
5. A large university is interested in purchasing 4,000 padlocks. Several different makes are under consideration. If the university purchasing agent determines which brand is of highest quality on the basis of

the proportion of defective locks in samples of 100, what two types of error can he make?

6. In control of a sales forecast why would management desire an upper control limit? A lower control limit? How might such limits be determined?

12 *Statistics and managerial control*

The preceding chapters have outlined the scope of managerial statistics as including (1) the collection of data from internal records, published sources, and sampling; (2) the computation of meaningful averages and measures of dispersion; (3) the interpretation of sampling results; (4) the preparation of forecasts of general business conditions and individual company sales; (5) the communication of significant findings by carefully prepared tables and charts; and (6) the application of statistical techniques for purposes of internal administrative control. The size and organization of staff required to perform these functions varies a great deal among companies according to their size, type of business, and the preferences of senior executives. This, of course, is also true of the organization and staffing of most departments within a firm. Some organizations have large, centralized statistical sections; others have small sections which act in a staff or advisory capacity to persons performing statistical functions in the several departments of the organization. In small firms the responsibility for discharging these functions often rests with one or more key officers or employees, frequently the president, manager, controller, or chief accountant.

In large and small companies alike, many persons perform statistical functions in addition to other functions and therefore hold position titles such as accountant, analyst, or engineer rather than statistician. Because the application of statistical techniques to management planning and control is a relatively new development, many companies possess neither a formal organizational unit nor a formal plan for achieving the potential benefits of managerial statistics. The purpose of this chapter is to illustrate some of the ways in which statistical functions may be accomplished in both large and small organizations.

Organizational structure and statistical control

ESSENTIAL RELATIONSHIP BETWEEN ORGANIZATIONAL STRUCTURE AND ACCOUNTING SYSTEM

All too often accounting records are maintained solely to provide data required for payrolls, customers' accounts, and for reports to stockholders, creditors, various regulatory bodies, and the Internal Revenue Service. Under these circumstances effective administrative control is an impossibility except perhaps for those firms whose size is so small and whose operations are so simple that the principal executive can be constantly informed concerning all aspects of operations.

A firm's accounting records should be geared to its organizational structure in order that data drawn from the accounts may readily reflect the degree to which executives and supervisors have discharged their responsibilities. This type of accounting is sometimes referred to as "responsibility," "functional," or "managerial" accounting. Accounting systems designed on a responsibility basis yield data required by nonmanagement groups, and in addition, facilitate preparation of reports required for internal administrative control.

> "It is a prerequisite of management reporting that operating results be shown on a responsibility basis, in order that weak performances may be corrected, talented executives may be discovered, and future activity may be built around a combination of plans and the abilities of people." [1]

[1] K. C. Tiffany, "Reports for Management," *The Accounting Review*, XXV, No. 2 (April, 1950), 144.

RELATIONSHIP BETWEEN RESPONSIBILITY ACCOUNTING AND MANAGERIAL STATISTICS

Accounting and statistics have long been recognized as primary tools of the business administrator. To be sure, accounting is much more firmly established than is business statistics. Nevertheless, increasing recognition has been given to the importance of statistics, and the relationship between accounting and statistics has become more evident. This was noticeable first in the development of cost accounting and more recently in the shift toward responsibility or managerial accounting, in which accounts are used to provide data to measure executive or departmental accomplishments in relation to some desired standard.

Business administrators require a variety of reports which often can be obtained only from several classifications of the same data. For example, management often desires reports on sales classified by products, territories, salesmen, and customers. The cost of maintaining a set of accounts which would provide directly all such classifications would be prohibitive. Rather, *primary classification* of accounts should be on the basis of responsibility. Required *secondary classifications* may be obtained easily by the use of electric or manual sorting devices.

Analyses of trends of profits, sales, and expenses by various pertinent classifications may be described as a function of either the accountant or the statistician. The important point is that whoever makes such analyses should be well grounded in both accounting and managerial statistics. Statistical analysis can substantially extend the scope and penetration of accountants' services in aid to management.

Managerial statistics in the large organization

The position of the statistical unit in the business organization is perhaps most frequently found to be in the office or department of the controller.[2] Other organizational plans place the statistical unit in the office of business research, the accounting department, or in a staff capacity under the president or executive committee. Each firm should solve this organizational problem in a manner which best

[2] The reader should be aware that the organization and functions of controller's offices vary widely among different companies.

suits its particular needs. A primary consideration should be to provide the statistical unit with the opportunity to serve management effectively. The statistical unit should always perform as a service unit to executives; it should never be established as an agency for policing and dictating to executives. On the other hand, management must be receptive to assistance from the statistical unit in planning and controlling business operations. A high degree of cooperation should prevail between management and the statistical unit.

ORGANIZATION OF A STATISTICAL DIVISION

The statistical division of the Pacific Telephone Company (Figure 2) has been selected for purposes of illustration in this chapter.[3] This division is part of the accounting department, which is headed by an officer with the title of vice-president and controller. The integration of accounting and statistical divisions in the controller's department has many advantages. Unnecessary duplication of effort, closer harmony among statisticians and accountants, and more meaningful reports for management are among the potential benefits from this organizational plan. Although this plan is an excellent one, the reader should realize that other companies have somewhat different organizational patterns which are also excellent; furthermore, the organization of the Pacific Telephone Company Statistical Division

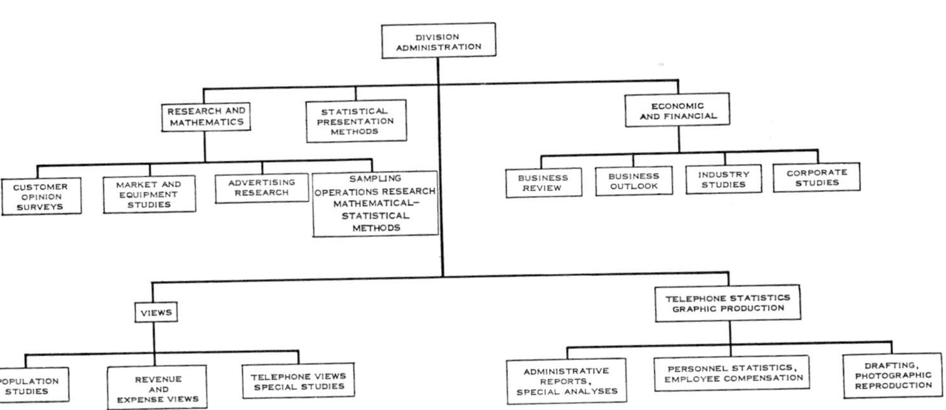

Fig. 2. Present organization of functions, Statistical Division, Pacific Telephone Company.

[3] The discussion of Figure 2 in this chapter is based on information provided by the Pacific Telephone and Telegraph Company.

may be modified from time to time when required to meet changed conditions.

The internal organization of the statistics division illustrated in Figure 2 consists of five separate units; namely, (1) Research and Mathematics, (2) Statistical Presentation Methods, (3) Economic and Financial, (4) Views, and (5) Telephone Statistics—Graphic Reproduction. Each of these sections, except Statistical Presentation Methods, consists of sub-groups as indicated in the figure.

FUNCTIONS OF A STATISTICAL DIVISION

The several sections and units in a large statistical division must work together as a team, just as the statistical division as a whole works for and with the executive management team. In addition, close cooperation must prevail between employees of the statistical division and the many employees in other departments who, regardless of job title, also are performing statistical functions. Major functions of the several sections illustrated in Figure 2 will be described briefly in the following paragraphs.

Economic and financial section. As indicated, this section consists of four groups, (1) Business Review, (2) Business Outlook, (3) Industry Studies, and (4) Corporate Studies. The section is responsible for making a continuing study of general business conditions. As pointed out in Chapter 6, the analysis of current business conditions and the estimate of probable future trends serve as the foundation for forecasts of demands for a company's product or services. This latter forecast, in turn, serves as the basis for development of operational plans which are expressed in a system of integrated budgets.

The Economic and Financial Section computes a monthly index of business activity for each of the four areas in the Pacific Region which are served by the Pacific Telephone Company. Components of the index include department store sales, bank debits, non-manufacturing employment, and a combination of manufacturing employment and electrical power sales. This index is published monthly in a *Business Review*, which is distributed to executives at headquarters and in each area office. The section's forecasts of business conditions are reviewed quarterly and are revised as required by changed conditions.

Continuing studies are made of the rate of return on capital, debt ratios, ratios of surplus to total capital, dividend payments, earnings per share, and other significant items. These data are used for comparative studies of other telephone companies, utilities, and industrial concerns. Such analyses are essential in connection with rate determination proceedings before the regulatory commissions.

Views section. The summary of business conditions and the business forecasts prepared by the Economic and Financial Section aid the executives in the four operating areas who are responsible for making periodic forecasts of operating revenues and expenses. These forecasts present the expected operating results by months, quarters, and years. The Views Section assists the several departments in the respective areas and coordinates their activities. Area forecasts are routed to the Views Section, which assembles the Company forecast and presents it to management. Management must then determine whether the proposed programs as reflected by forecast operations are sound and are consistent with general policies. If the forecast or budgeted operations meet these requirements they are approved by management; if they do not satisfy these requirements they must be revised accordingly. This is an excellent illustration of team-work between statistical personnel and operating people, both at company headquarters and in the field.

The Views Section continually studies short-term and long-term trends of demand, toll messages, and revenues and the relationships of these items to external business activity as indicated by purchasing power, gross national product, personal income, population and households, and changes in general business conditions.

Telephone statistics—graphic reproduction section. This section maintains statistical files on pertinent operating data derived from internal records. From this storehouse of data it issues numerous reports to management, some weekly, others monthly, quarterly, or annually. These reports enable management to compare actual results of current operations with forecast or planned results and also with results for previous periods. Company officials are provided with copies of a statistical manual reflecting historical operating trends presented in both tabular and graphic form.

Another function of this section is to make a variety of special analyses requested by executives in the various Company departments, such as commercial, personnel, public relations, revenue requirements, plant or traffic. This section also works closely with the various accounting divisions.

The personnel and wage study activities of this section consist, first, of gathering force data and, second, of evaluating wage and associated programs in terms of the force data. These data include distribution of employees by occupation, age, location, service and basic salary rate, force movement data, payroll and overtime payments. These data are summarized in periodic reports to management. This activity requires close liaison with Company bargaining teams which must negotiate with over a dozen unions.

The graphics production group of this section has the responsibility for preparing charts and other copy for the visual presentation of data. Much of the Company's results of operation, special studies, and surveys are graphically portrayed.

Research and mathematics section. This section undertakes customer opinion surveys, employee opinion surveys, advertising effectiveness studies, and market surveys. Obviously, the maintenance of favorable customer relations is of utmost importance to a telephone company. Surveys reveal the trends of customer opinion and indicate ways in which a company can improve its service to customers. Employee opinion surveys help to keep management informed of employees' reactions to company policies and procedures, and thereby serve to promote good employee relations.

Examples of studies to evaluate the effectiveness of advertising include (1) newspaper readership studies to determine the proportions of people reading advertisements in a given paper, (2) copy testing to learn which features in an ad do or do not get the message across, and (3) which of the subjects advertised are remembered by most people. This section works closely with the marketing department and conducts surveys which aid in testing new products and services and measuring the extent of market for a service or product. This activity involves sample design, arrangements for field work, preparation of questionnaires, training of interviewers, and preparation of reports.

The mathematical-statistical methods group is concerned with scientific sampling, operations research, and statistical problems and methods. Sampling problems involving the operations of practically every department in the Company have been handled by this group. The application of scientific sampling has resulted in many cost savings and has permitted the analysis of some operations which otherwise would not be physically or economically feasible.

Statistical presentation methods section. This activity operates as a consulting or advisory service on ways to improve content and format of statistical presentations. While it is primarily concerned with presentations of the Statistical Division, it also renders service to other divisions and departments in the Company.

summary

The Pacific Telephone Company has a well-integrated statistical division which works in close cooperation with management, area offices, and the several operating and staff departments. The preparation of Company forecasts is largely the responsibility of operating officials although the Statistical Division provides assistance and assembles the final Company forecast.

No doubt possible variations in organizational structure may have occurred to the reader. Some companies place responsibility for analyses of general business conditions with an economist who is independent of the statistical division. Other companies engage private research organizations to perform this service or rely on their senior executives.

Responsibility for forecasts may rest with a unit of the sales department insofar as revenue is concerned and with each department insofar as expenses are concerned. Consolidation of estimates may be performed by a budget or executive committee.

Results and analyses of operations may be made by accounting units, inasmuch as accounting records are the source for much of the required data.

Surveys and graphics are almost always the function of a statistical unit unless outside agencies are engaged to perform these services. The photostat or reproduction unit, however, is frequently a part of the publications or printing divisions.

The exact organizational pattern employed for performing the managerial statistics functions is not a matter of great concern. Of prime importance, however, is that management avail itself of the tremendous assistance in planning and controlling business operations which may be obtained from a sound program of managerial statistics.

Managerial statistics in the small organization

A common observation of small businessmen is that they cannot afford the frills of a formal statistical division. In some cases this is no doubt true, but in other cases improved planning and control resulting from a statistical program would bring returns far in excess of its cost. Be that as it may, executives of small businesses can profit from an application of the rudiments of managerial statistics.

STAFF AND TIME REQUIREMENTS

Neither of these requirements need be excessive. A single statistician with one or two clerks can accomplish a great deal. Many of the important functions can be assumed as collateral duties by executives and key employees. The president, manager, treasurer, controller, and other senior officers and employees should keep abreast of general business conditions regardless of whether or not they have available the services of a statistician or economist. Sales executives should utilize the best methods possible in forecasting sales. Operating and administrative departments, assisted by the accounting department, should prepare realistic estimates of planned expenditures. Top management should integrate the sales and expense estimates into a budgeted plan of operations. Reports from the accounting department should reflect the trends of actual operations with planned and past operations. Often the required data are available in existing records or can be made available with minor modification of recording procedures.

Responsible executives and employees should also utilize the concepts and techniques of managerial statistics when special investigations are required. Clerks may be self-trained to prepare acceptable charts in a surprisingly short period of time. This may be accomplished by reference to books on graphic presentation and procurement of some simple and inexpensive drafting equipment and supplies. Private agencies may be engaged for preparation of more polished charts, if needed, and for reproduction of graphic material and reports.

Executives who are at a loss as to how to institute a program of managerial statistics may engage a consulting business statistician to assist them. Once installed, the regular company personnel may be able to operate the program. At periodic intervals the consulting statistician may be requested to review the program and also to render assistance on special analyses and surveys.

VALUE OF KNOWLEDGE OF STATISTICAL CONCEPTS

The reader will remember the general nature and significance of statistical methods long after he has forgotten the exact details of computation. Further, the reader will be able to locate sources which provide these details and formulas when needed. However, it is the knowledge of the nature and limitations of statistical techniques which will be of most frequent use to the businessman. This knowledge will enable the businessman to better interpret the significance of averages, ratios, percentages, and measures of variation. Changes in business indexes and comparisons of movements in related series can be more meaningful to the executive who possesses some understanding of index number construction, time series analysis, and correlation. Each of these techniques, properly employed, can contribute to the validity of forecasts upon which all business plans are dependent. Much information useful in forecasting is published regularly in readily available sources; the businessman with little or no appreciation of managerial statistics cannot possibly discern the strengths and weaknesses of these reports.

It is important to note that a business statistician must possess two things: (1) a knowledge of the business and the industry of which it is a part and (2) a knowledge of statistical methods useful to management. Both of these are prerequisites to the exercise of sound judgment. Frequently, experienced businessmen can acquire an understanding of basic statistical methods more rapidly than a person trained in statistical methods can acquire a thorough knowledge of the business.

VALUE OF KNOWLEDGE OF SOURCES OF PUBLISHED DATA

Perhaps the greatest single stumbling block to executives requiring data from external sources is their lack of knowledge of available sources. Although librarians and others may be helpful, there is no substitute for personal knowledge of source material and guides to source material. A great many of these were mentioned specifically in Chapter 2. Often knowledge of existing data serves to suggest solutions to problems which otherwise would perhaps be met inadequately and then only after much waste in time and effort. Businessmen may discover that very little time is required to keep posted on significant data which appears regularly in such publications as the *Survey of Current Business* published by the U. S. Department of Commerce.

SUMMARY

Managerial statistics properly employed can be a powerful tool for planning and controlling business operations. Knowledge of statistical concepts and sources of data can be of real value to executives of large and small firms alike. This is not to deny the danger of misuse of statistical methods and techniques. The computation of meaningless averages, index numbers, correlations, and other measures, and the preparation of tables and charts presenting unnecessary information can be of no possible value to management. Judgment and cooperation on the part of both management and the business statistician are essential to the realization of the maximum benefits possible from managerial statistics.

Questions and Exercises

1. Expand, in detail, your previous answer to question 3, Chapter 1.
2. Consider your previous answer to question 4, Chapter 1; make any modifications which may be required.
3. Of what value to businessmen is a knowledge of statistical concepts and sources of data? Is this value likely to increase or decrease in the future?

APPENDIX A

Mathematical review

1. Rounding and significant numbers 

Numbers are either approximate or exact. Numbers which are *estimates* are obviously approximate. *Measurements* are also approximate because all measuring devices lack precision beyond some degree, and because humans using measuring devices introduce varying degrees of error. However, *counts* may be exact. For example, a firm may at any given time determine the exact number of employees on its payrolls, the number of employees who are absent, the quantity of a given item in inventory, the number of overdue accounts, the number of items of various kinds of equipment and machines—to mention only a few illustrations. Counts tend to be exact, but it is virtually impossible to avoid the occurrence of errors when the data to be counted are large in number. Although the 1950 census was based on a supposedly complete count, it is highly improbable that the 1950 population was exactly 150,697,361 as reported.

ROUNDING

It is common practice to *round* numbers when accuracy to final digits is not essential for a specific purpose, or when the accuracy of a number beyond certain digits is questionable. Little if anything is lost by such rounding, and the resulting numbers are easier to tabulate and easier for the mind to grasp. For example, for many purposes it is just as meaningful to state that the U. S. population in 1950 was almost 151 million as to state that the U. S. population was 150,697,361. Most statistical reports present large numbers in "millions," "thousands," "hundreds," or some other appropriate rounded amount.

Three basic rules should be observed when rounding numbers.

1. When the left digit of the portion to be dropped is greater than 5, the preceding digit is increased. The 1950 population figure, rounded to millions would be 151,000,000; the left digit of the portion to be dropped was 6.
2. When the left digit of the portion to be dropped is less than 5 the preceding digit is left unchanged. The 1950 population figure rounded to thousands would be 150,697,000; the left digit of the portion to be dropped was 3.
3. When the portion to be rounded commences with 5 and is followed only by zeros, the preceding digit is increased if it is an odd digit but is left unchanged if it is an even digit. For example, 6.350, rounded to one decimal place would become 6.4, whereas 6.250 would become 6.2. However, it should be observed that 6.2501 rounded to one decimal place would become 6.3 since the portion following the 5 is greater than zero.

Observance of the above rules provides reasonable assurance that the total of a series of rounded data will be approximately the same as the total of unrounded data. If all numbers were increased in the rounding process, the total would be too large; if none of the numbers were increased the total would be too small. The following tabulation illustrates these points.

	Rounded data, 000 omitted		
Original data	Rounded by rules	All increased	None increased
62,532	63	63	62
49,498	49	50	49
56,271	56	57	56
64,718	65	65	64
75,935	76	76	75
33,364	33	34	33
342,318	342	345	339

In actual practice, where hundreds, thousands, or more items are involved, the error introduced by improper rounding procedures could be large. However, the reader is cautioned not to rely fully on the above rules, particularly when dealing with a short series. Just as a few tosses of a coin may result in all heads or all tails, so may rounding by rules result in all increases or all decreases. Probabilities are based on a large number of items. Occasionally, even in a large series, portions to be dropped by rounding tend to be either predominantly high or low. Sale prices tend to include a high number of cents; for example, $12.95, $199.85, etc. In such cases personal inspection is required to determine appropriate rounding techniques.

SIGNIFICANT DIGITS

Any digit which correctly measures a value or quantity is said to be significant. When measured to the nearest foot, a distance may be recorded as 157 feet; this number has three significant digits. If measurement has been made to the nearest tenth of a foot, the distance may have been 157.4; this number has four significant digits. In each of these cases the value of the right-hand digit was determined by measuring the value of an additional decimal place and then rounding to the desired degree of accuracy. In other words, 157.4 was rounded to 157; in the second case, the measurement in hundreds, 157.36, was rounded to 157.4.

Zeros are troublesome to beginning students because they may be used either to indicate a specific value—like any other digit—or to indicate the magnitude of a number. The 1950 population figure rounded to thousands was 150,697,000. The six left-hand digits of this number are significant—each of them, including the zero, measure a value. The three right-hand digits are zeros which merely indicate the magnitude of the number—in this case millions. This point may be further illustrated by the following list of estimates and measurements, each of which is of different magnitude but each of which has only one significant digit.

1,000
100
10
0.01
0.001
0.0001

The following estimates each contain two significant digits.

10.
1.0
0.010
0.0010

Note that where there is a decimal in a number, any zero which has a non-zero digit located anywhere to the left of it would be considered a significant digit.

Occasionally, data required for an investigation must be drawn from a variety of sources where they have been recorded with varying degrees of precision. Specific rules must be observed when such data are to be added, subtracted, multiplied, or divided.

The rule for addition and subtraction is that the answer may contain no more significant digits *to the right* than is contained in the least accurate figure. Consider the addition of three numbers drawn from three sources, the first of which reported data in millions, the second in thousands, and the third in units.

163,000,000
217,985,000
96,432,768
477,417,768

The above total indicates a preciseness which is not valid. The numbers should be first rounded to one more right-hand significant digit than is contained in the least accurate number, as illustrated below.[1]

163,000,000
218,000,000
96,400,000
477,400,000

The above answer should then be rounded to 477,000,000. The reader should observe the result of rounding the second number, 217,985,000; since the digit to the right of 217,9 was greater than 5 the 9 had to be raised to 10, thereby resulting in the number 218,000,000.

The rule for multiplication and division is that the product or quotient may contain no more significant digits than are contained in the number with the fewest significant digits used in the multiplication or division. Note the difference between this rule and the rule

[1] Errors of rounding may be reduced by rounding to one more right-hand significant digit than is contained in the least accurate number. In this illustration the same rounded total (477,000,000) could have been obtained from (1) rounding each number immediately to the nearest million, (2) rounding the sum of the numbers after each had been rounded to the nearest hundred thousand, or (3) rounding the sum of the original numbers. However, the latter method would have resulted in much needless addition and work, particularly if the series of numbers to be added was of great length.

for addition and subtraction; the addition rule merely requires rounding of digits which lie to the right of the last position of accuracy in the least *accurate* number; the multiplication and division rule requires rounding the result to the least number of significant digits in either number used in the operation. The following illustration highlights this difference.

Multiplication:

$$113.2 \times 1.43 = 161.876, \quad \text{rounded to } \mathbf{162}$$

Division:

$$113.2 \div 1.43 = 79.16, \quad \text{rounded to } \mathbf{79.2}$$

Addition:

$$113.2 + 1.43 = 114.63, \quad \text{rounded to } \mathbf{114.6}$$

Subtraction:

$$113.2 - 1.43 = 111.77, \quad \text{rounded to } \mathbf{111.8}$$

The above product and quotient are limited to three significant digits since 1.43 contains only three significant digits. In contrast, the answers in the addition and subtraction examples contain four significant digits.

One final point concerning significant numbers is worthy of brief mention. Numbers used in the above illustrations have all been estimates or measurements. Numbers which are exact counts are treated as though they consisted of an infinite number of significant digits. When a count is used in computation with a measurement the number of significant digits in the answer is the same as the number of significant digits in the measurement. If a count of 40 is multiplied by a measurement of 10.2, the product is 408. However, if 40 were an estimate accurate only to the nearest 10—and hence contained but one significant digit—the product would be 400.

2. Ratios and percentages

A ratio is a multiple or fraction which expresses the relationship of the size of the two numbers. The ratio of 300 to 100 is 3/1, or 3:1; the ratio of 40 to 50 is 4/5, or 0.8:1. Ratios are widely used in business. A few illustrations are inventory turnover ratios, loss ratios, ratios of current assets to current liabilities, ratios of sales to working capital, and ratios of earnings to investment. The application of these and other ratios is discussed in Chapter 11.

The significance or meaning of a number may be comprehended more easily if expressed as a ratio to some convenient base. For example, automobile gas consumption is expressed as miles per gallon; speed may be expressed as miles per hour; agricultural crop yields may be expressed as bushels, boxes, or tons per acre; industrial production may be expressed as units per hour or other time intervals. Deaths and births are usually expressed per 1,000 of population; deaths from specific diseases may be expressed per 100,000 population in order to avoid use of a small decimal figure. A ratio of 5 deaths per 100,000 is more easily understood than is a ratio of 0.05 death per 1,000.

A per cent is the type of ratio most commonly used; it is the ratio of one number to another expressed in hundredth parts, that is, per cent, percentum, or per hundred. For example, the number 8 is 16 per cent of 50; similarly, 32 is 16 per cent of 200. In each case the computation was made by dividing the number to be expressed as a per cent by the number used as a base or point of reference; this quotient was then multiplied by 100 to arrive at the *per cent*. This may be illustrated as follows:

$$\frac{8}{50} = 0.16, \quad \text{and} \quad 0.16 \times 100 = \mathbf{16\%}$$

$$\frac{32}{200} = 0.16, \quad \text{and} \quad 0.16 \times 100 = \mathbf{16\%}$$

The first illustration may be thought of as increasing 50 to 100 and correspondingly increasing 8 to 16. In the second illustration 200 was reduced to 100 and 32 was reduced to 16. In each case the numerators were expressed as hundredth parts of the denominators.

In computing percentages great care must be exercised to select the proper base. Consider the percentage change involved when a store's sales increase from $400,000 in 1958 to $500,000 in 1959. Sales in 1959 were 125 per cent of sales in 1958.

$$\frac{500{,}000}{400{,}000} = 1.25, \quad \text{or} \quad \mathbf{125\%}$$

Since 1958 is the base or point of reference, sales in 1958 must be placed in the denominator. In effect we are saying that if we make sales in 1958 equal to 100 per cent, then sales in 1959 equal 125 per cent. Obviously sales in 1959 were 25 per cent higher than in 1958. This can be determined either by subtracting 100 per cent from 125 per cent or by the following computation:

$$\frac{500{,}000 - 400{,}000}{400{,}000} = \frac{100{,}000}{400{,}000} = 0.25, \quad \text{or} \quad \mathbf{25\%}$$

If we wish to compare 1958 sales to 1959 sales we reverse the above procedure by placing 1959 sales in the base position, that is, in the denominator.

$$\frac{400{,}000}{500{,}000} = 0.80, \quad \text{or} \quad \mathbf{80\%}$$

Note that whereas 1959 sales were 25 per cent higher than 1958 sales, 1958 sales were 20 per cent lower than in 1959 (100 − 80 = 20).

It should be observed that no limit exists for increases in per cent, but decreases in per cent normally cannot exceed 100. This is true because a number can increase an infinite amount from its base, but it can decrease no further than to zero, unless negative amounts are possible. For example, sales of $400,000 might continue to increase indefinitely in succeeding years, but they could decrease no further than to zero. Suppose sales in 1954 had been zero. Then the percentage decrease would be computed as follows:

$$\frac{400{,}000 - 0}{400{,}000} = \frac{400{,}000}{400{,}000} = 1, \quad \text{or} \quad \mathbf{100\%}$$

Suppose sales in 1954 had decreased to $100,000. Then

$$\frac{400{,}000 - 100{,}000}{400{,}000} = \frac{300{,}000}{400{,}000} = 0.75, \quad \text{or} \quad \mathit{75\%}$$

A common error in comparable situations is to select an incorrect base, which in this case would be the 1954 sales of $100,000. If this were done the following computation would result:

$$\frac{400{,}000 - 100{,}000}{100{,}000} = \frac{300{,}000}{100{,}000} = 3, \quad \text{or} \quad \mathbf{300\%}$$

A 300 per cent decrease is not possible in this case, but intelligent persons often commit similar errors.

Although use of percentages can be helpful in making comparisons, they also can be concealing and even misleading. A statement that a firm's employment has increased 10 per cent suggests the occurrence of a substantial change. This may or may not be the case. An increase from 10 employees to 11 employees is not nearly so significant as an increase from 10,000 to 11,000 employees. Salesmen for small insurance companies sometimes point with pride to the fact that the assets, dividends, policyholders, and insurance outstanding in their company have experienced greater *percentage* increases than similar items in leading, nationally recognized companies. It should be apparent that a 50 per cent increase (*e.g.*, 1,000 to 1,500) of policyholders in a small company may be much smaller in absolute terms than a 10 per cent increase (*e.g.*, 500,000 to 550,000) in a larger company. The above illustrations indicate the necessity for publishing *absolute numbers* along with *percentages.* If the number which served as the base is published, the reader can intelligently evaluate the significance of the percentage.

3. Computation of square root

Whenever possible, square roots should be determined by reference to a table such as that in Table I of Appendix B. In the absence of such tables, square roots may be computed easily with the aid of slide rules or machine calculators. In the absence of all such devices, square roots may be computed by the following longhand method. This method appears quite complex when first introduced to a reader. Fortunately, the procedure becomes simple to those persons who will devote but a few minutes of their time to actual application of the method to short problems.

The longhand method of computing square root differs from the longhand method of division in two important respects: first, the divisor changes after each division step, and second, digits in the dividend are treated as pairs rather than as individual digits. The steps required for computation are as follows:

1. Mark off pairs in the number (dividend) whose square root is to be found. This is done by marking off every second figure, both to the right and to the left of a decimal point. For example, 4237.6273 would be marked 42′37′.62′73; 172 would be marked 1′72, or 01′72; 172.4 would be marked 1′72′.40.
2. Select a divisor which when multiplied by itself will result in a product no greater than the first left-hand pair of values. For example, the first divisor for 593.8 would be 2. The problem may be set up as follows:

```
                 2
(Divisor)  2 | 5′93′.80
             | 4
```

3. Subtract the product computed in step 2 from the first pair (5, or 05) and also bring down the next pair of digits to the right.

```
      2
  2 | 5'93'.80
    | 4
    --------
      1 93
```

4. To determine the next and subsequent divisors, double the root thus far obtained (for the second divisor, $2 \times 2 = 4$); to this amount annex a right-hand digit, which when multiplied times the whole amount will result in a product no greater than the remainder. Hence, the second divisor in our illustration would be 44 which divides into 193 by 4 times plus a fraction; consequently, the digit 4 is also annexed to the portion of the root previously obtained (2). At this point we know that the square root is 24 plus a fraction.

```
       2  4.
   2 | 5'93'.80
     | 4
  ---|--------
  44 | 1 93
       1 76
```

5. Continue the operations described in step 4 until the square root has been determined.

```
          2  4. 3  6  8
      2 | 5'93'.80'00'00
        | 4
   -----|----
     44 | 1 93
        | 1 76
   -----|--------
    483 |   17 80
        |   14 49
   -----|-----------
   4866 |    3 31 00
        |    2 91 96
   -----|--------------
  48728 |       39 04 00
        |       38 98 24
        |--------------
        |           5 76
```

The square root of 593.8 is 24.37, or 24.4. The preceding operation was continued to 24.368 merely to determine whether or not the digit 6 should be rounded to 7; in computing statistical measures it is sometimes desirable to include one more decimal place in the measure than was contained in the basic data.

The reader may observe that divisors subsequent to the first divisor (2) could have been computed by a method different from the first part of step 4. The alternate method, which obtains identical results, consists of adding to the preceding divisor the amount of its right-hand digit. For example, the second divisor (44) could have been obtained by doubling the right-hand digit of the first divisor (2) and annexing a right-hand digit (4) as explained in step 4. Similarly, the third divisor (483) could have been determined by increasing the second divisor (44) by the amount of its right-hand digit (4) and annexing the final right-hand digit (3) as explained in step 4.

Although most persons forget the longhand method when frequent use is not required, the method may be "rediscovered" when needed simply by "solving" for a known root. For example, the square root of 144 is known to be 12. A bit of experimentation will soon lead to the following method of solution:

$$\begin{array}{r|r} & 1\ \ 2 \\ \hline 1 & 1'44 \\ & 1 \\ \hline 22 & 44 \\ & 44 \\ \hline \end{array}$$

This method, "rediscovered," may then be applied to the specific problem.

Questions and Exercises

REVIEW OF ELEMENTARY ALGEBRA AND ARITHMETIC

Place a plus sign at the left of each statement which you believe to be true and a zero at the left of each statement you believe to be false. Be prepared to support your answer.[2]

______ 1. $3 + 5 - 2 = 3 - 2 + 5$

______ 2. $6 + 42 \div 8 = 6$

______ 3. $12\left(\frac{5}{6}\right) = \frac{5(12)}{6}$

______ 4. $36 \div 4 + 2 = 6$

______ 5. $\left(\frac{3}{8}\right)\left(\frac{4}{7}\right)\left(\frac{1}{5}\right) = \left(\frac{4}{7}\right)\left(\frac{1}{5}\right)\left(\frac{3}{8}\right)$

______ 6. $\left(\frac{3}{8}\right)\left(\frac{4}{7}\right)\left(\frac{1}{5}\right) = \left(\frac{1}{7}\right)\left(\frac{3}{5}\right)\left(\frac{4}{8}\right)$

[2] If you have trouble with many of the problems in this section of the review, it would be wise to spend a few hours with the review text by Helen M. Walker, *Mathematics Essential for Elementary Statistics*, Rev. ed., New York, Henry Holt and Company, 1951.

______ 7. $5 + 63 \div 3 = \frac{68}{3}$

______ 8. $\frac{4 + 6}{3 \times 2} = \frac{4}{3} + \frac{6}{2}$

______ 9. $\frac{4 \times 6}{3 \times 2} = \frac{4}{3} \times \frac{6}{2}$

______ 10. $\frac{4 + 6}{3 + 2} = \frac{4}{3} + \frac{6}{2}$

______ 11. $\frac{(15 \times 4 \times 7)}{3} = 5 \times 4 \times 7$

______ 12. $\frac{5 \times 6}{4} = \frac{5}{4} \times \frac{6}{4}$

______ 13. $\frac{12 + 2}{4} = 3\frac{1}{2}$

______ 14. $\sqrt{49 - 16} = 7 - 4$

______ 15. $2 - (0.2)^2 = 1.6$

______ 16. $36 \div 12 + 3 \times 6 = 21$

______ 17. $\left(\frac{3}{7}\right)^2 = \frac{9}{49}$

______ 18. $\left(\frac{46 - 16}{8 - 2}\right) = 5$

______ 19. $\frac{1}{3}(5 \times 7) = \frac{5}{3} \times \frac{7}{3}$

______ 20. $\frac{(0.06)(0.03)}{0.02} = .9$

______ 21. $\frac{3(18 - 3)}{(12 + 3)} = 3$

______ 22. $\frac{x}{y} + \frac{az}{b} = \frac{bx + ayz}{by}$

______ 23. $\frac{y}{x} + 1 = \frac{y + x}{x}$

______ 24. $(0.3)^3 = 0.27$

______ 25. $3 \div \frac{2}{5} = \frac{5}{6}$

FRACTIONS, DECIMALS AND PER CENTS

A. What per cent is equivalent to each of the following:

1. 0.0546__________
2. 1.567__________
3. 0.0008__________
4. 1.5__________
5. $\frac{9}{36}$__________
6. $\frac{45}{72}$__________
7. $\frac{3}{18}$__________
8. $\frac{1}{6}$__________
9. $3\frac{2}{3}$__________
10. $\frac{34}{678}$__________

B. What decimal fraction is equivalent to each of the following per cents?

1. $\frac{162}{3}\%$__________
2. 203%__________
3. 6%__________
4. 0.12%__________
5. 0.02%__________
6. 95%__________
7. 1,300%__________
8. 2.7%__________
9. 106%__________
10. 14%__________

C. Compute answers for the following (show computations):

1. Find what per cent 18 is of 72.
2. Find what per cent 496 is of 192.
3. Find 2.6% of 6400
4. Find 106% of 400
5. Find 0.3% of 15.
6. City A had 156,000 inhabitants in 1950 and 169,000 inhabitants in 1957. What was the percentage change in number of inhabitants?
7. City B had 146,000 inhabitants in 1950 and 127,000 inhabitants in 1957. What was the percentage change in number of inhabitants?
8. In 1950, City A's population was what per cent of City B's population?

9. In 1950, City B's population was what per cent of City A's population?

10. What was the percentage loss in population for City C if its 1957 population were only two thirds of its 1950 population?

SIGNIFICANT DIGITS

Using the rules for significant digits set forth in Appendix A, answer the following:

A. Indicate which of the following are exactly equal:

______ 1. 2.6 = 2.60

______ 2. 43.00 = 43

______ 3. 0.05 = 0.050

______ 4. 2,300. = 2,300

B. Indicate the number of significant digits in each of the following:

______ 1. 4,302 ______ 6. 43.02

______ 2. 3.000 ______ 7. 3,000

______ 3. 6,420 ______ 8. 64.20

______ 4. 2,679 ______ 9. 0.02679

______ 5. 0.002679 ______ 10. 2,679.0

C. Perform the indicated operations and show the *correct* answer assuming the numbers used are approximations. (Show your computations.)

1. 6.53(76)
2. $76 \div 6.53$
3. $4200 + 10.35 + 18 + 365 + 2.74$
4. $(41.6)^2$
5. (25)(896)

D. Round each of the following to three significant digits.

1. 32.750______ 6. 66.349______

2. 13.650______ 7. 13,001______

3. 77.299______ 8. 59,950______

4. 27.991______ 9. 1.2851______

5. 87.429______ 10. 1.2950______

SQUARE ROOT

A. Compute the square root of the following numbers by hand, show your computations. Watch your significant digits.

1. 5651
2. 565.1
3. 0.05651
4. 0.5651

B. Using the table of squares and square roots in Appendix B look up the square root of the following numbers: Explain your procedure in each case, *i.e.*, what columns you use and how you adjust the decimal.

1. 4163
2. 0.4163
3. 41.63
4. 4.163
5. 0.04163
6. 416.3
7. 7.260
8. 7.269
9. 72.69
10. 0.00007269

APPENDIX B

Statistical Tables

Squares, square roots, and reciprocals

Squares and square roots are most easily determined by reference to a table such as appears on the pages which follow. The first column contains a series of numbers from 1 to 1,000. The second column contains the squares of the numbers which appear in the first column. For example, the square of 37 is 1,369. The third column contains the square roots of the numbers in the first column. Hence, the square root of 37 is found to be 6.082763. The fourth column contains the square root of the number which is 10 times the corresponding number in the first column. In our illustration, $10 \times 37 = 370$ and the square root of 370 is 19.23538.

Square roots of decimal numbers may also be determined by reference to this table. Consider the following tabulation:

Number	*Square Root*
144.	12.00000
14.40	3.79473
1.44	1.20000
0.1440	0.37947

The square root of 144 may be read directly from the third column. The square root of 1.44 may be determined by shifting the square root of 144 one decimal place to the left. The square roots of 14.4 and 0.144 may be derived from the fourth column by appropriately shifting the decimal point in the square root of 1,440. A thorough grasp of Appendix A, Part III will enable the reader to understand this process.

Reciprocals, which appear in the right column of each table section, are particularly useful in machine calculations. A reciprocal of a number is the quotient of unity (one) divided by that number. For example, the reciprocal of 35 is 1 ÷ 35 which equals 0.02857143. When each of a series of numbers is to be divided by the same number, such as 35, the process is facilitated by placing the reciprocal in the calculator and then making successive multiplications of each number in the series. This method is illustrated in the following example:

	Thousands of Dollars	*Per cent*
Sales	$35	100.0
Cost of Goods Sold	20	57.1
Selling Expenses	7	20.0
Administrative Expenses	5	14.3
Profit	3	8.6

where some major components of a profit and loss statement have been expressed as percentages of sales. Respective percentages were obtained as follows:

$$20 \times .02857143 = 57.1\%$$
$$7 \times .02857143 = 20.0\%$$
$$5 \times .02857143 = 14.3\%$$
$$3 \times .02857143 = 8.6\%$$

During the above process the reciprocal remained in the calculating machine, thereby reducing the labor required for the computations. This is in contrast to the long method where each of the components is divided in turn by the base; each of these computations would require a separate complete set-up in the calculator.

TABLE I. Squares, Square Roots, and Reciprocals

1–1,000

N	N^2	$\sqrt{N}$	$\sqrt{10N}$	$1/N$
1	1	1.000 000	3.162 278	1.0000000
2	4	1.414 214	4.472 136	.5000000
3	9	1.732 051	5.477 226	.3333333
4	16	2.000 000	6.324 555	.2500000
5	25	2.236 068	7.071 068	.2000000
6	36	2.449 490	7.745 967	.1666667
7	49	2.645 751	8.366 600	.1428571
8	64	2.828 427	8.944 272	.1250000
9	81	3.000 000	9.486 833	.1111111
10	100	3.162 278	10.00000	.1000000
11	121	3.316 625	10.48809	.09090909
12	144	3.464 102	10.95445	.08333333
13	169	3.605 551	11.40175	.07692308
14	196	3.741 657	11.83216	.07142857
15	225	3.872 983	12.24745	.06666667
16	256	4.000 000	12.64911	.06250000
17	289	4.123 106	13.03840	.05882353
18	324	4.242 641	13.41641	.05555556
19	361	4.358 899	13.78405	.05263158
20	400	4.472 136	14.14214	.05000000
21	441	4.582 576	14.49138	.04761905
22	484	4.690 416	14.83240	.04545455
23	529	4.795 832	15.16575	.04347826
24	576	4.898 979	15.49193	.04166667
25	625	5.000 000	15.81139	.04000000
26	676	5.099 020	16.12452	.03846154
27	729	5.196 152	16.43168	.03703704
28	784	5.291 503	16.73320	.03571429
29	841	5.385 165	17.02939	.03448276
30	900	5.477 226	17.32051	.03333333
31	961	5.567 764	17.60682	.03225806
32	1 024	5.656 854	17.88854	.03125000
33	1 089	5.744 563	18.16590	.03030303
34	1 156	5.830 952	18.43909	.02941176
35	1 225	5.916 080	18.70829	.02857143
36	1 296	6.000 000	18.97367	.02777778
37	1 369	6.082 763	19.23538	.02702703
38	1 444	6.164 414	19.49359	.02631579
39	1 521	6.244 998	19.74842	.02564103
40	1 600	6.324 555	20.00000	.02500000
41	1 681	6.403 124	20.24846	.02439024
42	1 764	6.480 741	20.49390	.02380952
43	1 849	6.557 439	20.73644	.02325581
44	1 936	6.633 250	20.97618	.02272727
45	2 025	6.708 204	21.21320	.02222222
46	2 116	6.782 330	21.44761	.02173913
47	2 209	6.855 655	21.67948	.02127660
48	2 304	6.928 203	21.90890	.02083333
49	2 401	7.000 000	22.13594	.02040816
50	2 500	7.071 068	22.36068	.02000000

N	N^2	$\sqrt{N}$	$\sqrt{10N}$	$1/N$ .0
50	2 500	7.071 068	22.36068	2000000
51	2 601	7.141 428	22.58318	1960784
52	2 704	7.211 103	22.80351	1923077
53	2 809	7.280 110	23.02173	1886792
54	2 916	7.348 469	23.23790	1851852
55	3 025	7.416 198	23.45208	1818182
56	3 136	7.483 315	23.66432	1785714
57	3 249	7.549 834	23.87467	1754386
58	3 364	7.615 773	24.08319	1724138
59	3 481	7.681 146	24.28992	1694915
60	3 600	7.745 967	24.49490	1666667
61	3 721	7.810 250	24.69818	1639344
62	3 844	7.874 008	24.89980	1612903
63	3 969	7.937 254	25.09980	1587302
64	4 096	8.000 000	25.29822	1562500
65	4 225	8.062 258	25.49510	1538462
66	4 356	8.124 038	25.69047	1515152
67	4 489	8.185 353	25.88436	1492537
68	4 624	8.246 211	26.07681	1470588
69	4 761	8.306 624	26.26785	1449275
70	4 900	8.366 600	26.45751	1428571
71	5 041	8.426 150	26.64583	1408451
72	5 184	8.485 281	26.83282	1388889
73	5 329	8.544 004	27.01851	1369863
74	5 476	8.602 325	27.20294	1351351
75	5 625	8.660 254	27.38613	1333333
76	5 776	8.717 798	27.56810	1315789
77	5 929	8.774 964	27.74887	1298701
78	6 084	8.831 761	27.92848	1282051
79	6 241	8.888 194	28.10694	1265823
80	6 400	8.944 272	28.28427	1250000
81	6 561	9.000 000	28.46050	1234568
82	6 724	9.055 385	28.63564	1219512
83	6 889	9.110 434	28.80972	1204819
84	7 056	9.165 151	28.98275	1190476
85	7 225	9.219 544	29.15476	1176471
86	7 396	9.273 618	29.32576	1162791
87	7 569	9.327 379	29.49576	1149425
88	7 744	9.380 832	29.66479	1136364
89	7 921	9.433 981	29.83287	1123596
90	8 100	9.486 833	30.00000	1111111
91	8 281	9.539 392	30.16621	1098901
92	8 464	9.591 663	30.33150	1086957
93	8 649	9.643 651	30.49590	1075269
94	8 836	9.695 360	30.65942	1063830
95	9 025	9.746 794	30.82207	1052632
96	9 216	9.797 959	30.98387	1041667
97	9 409	9.848 858	31.14482	1030928
98	9 604	9.899 495	31.30495	1020408
99	9 801	9.949 874	31.46427	1010101
100	10 000	10.00000	31.62278	1000000

TABLE I. Squares, Square Roots, and Reciprocals (cont.)

N	N^2	$\sqrt{N}$	$\sqrt{10N}$	$1/N$ .0
100	10 000	10.00000	31.62278	10000000
101	10 201	10.04988	31.78050	09900990
102	10 404	10.09950	31.93744	09803922
103	10 609	10.14889	32.09361	09708738
104	10 816	10.19804	32.24903	09615385
105	11 025	10.24695	32.40370	09523810
106	11 236	10.29563	32.55764	09433962
107	11 449	10.34408	32.71085	09345794
108	11 664	10.39230	32.86335	09259259
109	11 881	10.44031	33.01515	09174312
110	12 100	10.48809	33.16625	09090909
111	12 321	10.53565	33.31666	09009009
112	12 544	10.58301	33.46640	08928571
113	12 769	10.63015	33.61547	08849558
114	12 996	10.67708	33.76389	08771930
115	13 225	10.72381	33.91165	08695652
116	13 456	10.77033	34.05877	08620690
117	13 689	10.81665	34.20526	08547009
118	13 924	10.86278	34.35113	08474576
119	14 161	10.90871	34.49638	08403361
120	14 400	10.95445	34.64102	08333333
121	14 641	11.00000	34.78505	08264463
122	14 884	11.04536	34.92850	08196721
123	15 129	11.09054	35.07136	08130081
124	15 376	11.13553	35.21363	08064516
125	15 625	11.18034	35.35534	08000000
126	15 876	11.22497	35.49648	07936508
127	16 129	11.26943	35.63706	07874016
128	16 384	11.31371	35.77709	07812500
129	16 641	11.35782	35.91657	07751938
130	16 900	11.40175	36.05551	07692308
131	17 161	11.44552	36.19392	07633588
132	17 424	11.48913	36.33180	07575758
133	17 689	11.53256	36.46917	07518797
134	17 956	11.57584	36.60601	07462687
135	18 225	11.61895	36.74235	07407407
136	18 496	11.66190	36.87818	07352941
137	18 769	11.70470	37.01351	07299270
138	19 044	11.74734	37.14835	07246377
139	19 321	11.78983	37.28270	07194245
140	19 600	11.83216	37.41657	07142857
141	19 881	11.87434	37.54997	07092199
142	20 164	11.91638	37.68289	07042254
143	20 449	11.95826	37.81534	06993007
144	20 736	12.00000	37.94733	06944444
145	21 025	12.04159	38.07887	06896552
146	21 316	12.08305	38.20995	06849315
147	21 609	12.12436	38.34058	06802721
148	21 904	12.16553	38.47077	06756757
149	22 201	12.20656	38.60052	06711409
150	22 500	12.24745	38.72983	06666667

N	N^2	$\sqrt{N}$	$\sqrt{10N}$	$1/N$ .00
150	22 500	12.24745	38.72983	6666667
151	22 801	12.28821	38.85872	6622517
152	23 104	12.32883	38.98718	6578947
153	23 409	12.36932	39.11521	6535948
154	23 716	12.40967	39.24283	6493506
155	24 025	12.44990	39.37004	6451613
156	24 336	12.49000	39.49684	6410256
157	24 649	12.52996	39.62323	6369427
158	24 964	12.56981	39.74921	6329114
159	25 281	12.60952	39.87480	6289308
160	25 600	12.64911	40.00000	6250000
161	25 921	12.68858	40.12481	6211180
162	26 244	12.72792	40.24922	6172840
163	26 569	12.76715	40.37326	6134969
164	26 896	12.80625	40.49691	6097561
165	27 225	12.84523	40.62019	6060606
166	27 556	12.88410	40.74310	6024096
167	27 889	12.92285	40.86563	5988024
168	28 224	12.96148	40.98780	5952381
169	28 561	13.00000	41.10961	5917160
170	28 900	13.03840	41.23106	5882353
171	29 241	13.07670	41.35215	5847953
172	29 584	13.11488	41.47288	5813953
173	29 929	13.15295	41.59327	5780347
174	30 276	13.19091	41.71331	5747126
175	30 625	13.22876	41.83300	5714286
176	30 976	13.26650	41.95235	5681818
177	31 329	13.30413	42.07137	5649718
178	31 684	13.34166	42.19005	5617978
179	32 041	13.37909	42.30839	5586592
180	32 400	13.41641	42.42641	5555556
181	32 761	13.45362	42.54409	5524862
182	33 124	13.49074	42.66146	5494505
183	33 489	13.52775	42.77850	5464481
184	33 856	13.56466	42.89522	5434783
185	34 225	13.60147	43.01163	5405405
186	34 596	13.63818	43.12772	5376344
187	34 969	13.67479	43.24350	5347594
188	35 344	13.71131	43.35897	5319149
189	35 721	13.74773	43.47413	5291005
190	36 100	13.78405	43.58899	5263158
191	36 481	13.82027	43.70355	5235602
192	36 864	13.85641	43.81780	5208333
193	37 249	13.89244	43.93177	5181347
194	37 636	13.92839	44.04543	5154639
195	38 025	13.96424	44.15880	5128205
196	38 416	14.00000	44.27189	5102041
197	38 809	14.03567	44.38468	5076142
198	39 204	14.07125	44.49719	5050505
199	39 601	14.10674	44.60942	5025126
200	40 000	14.14214	44.72136	5000000

TABLE I. Squares, Square Roots, and Reciprocals (cont.)

N	N^2	$\sqrt{N}$	$\sqrt{10N}$	$1/N$ .00
200	40 000	14.14214	44.72136	5000000
201	40 401	14.17745	44.83302	4975124
202	40 804	14.21267	44.94441	4950495
203	41 209	14.24781	45.05552	4926108
204	41 616	14.28286	45.16636	4901961
205	42 025	14.31782	45.27693	4878049
206	42 436	14.35270	45.38722	4854369
207	42 849	14.38749	45.49725	4830918
208	43 264	14.42221	45.60702	4807692
209	43 681	14.45683	45.71652	4784689
210	44 100	14.49138	45.82576	4761905
211	44 521	14.52584	45.93474	4739336
212	44 944	14.56022	46.04346	4716981
213	45 369	14.59452	46.15192	4694836
214	45 796	14.62874	46.26013	4672897
215	46 225	14.66288	46.36809	4651163
216	46 656	14.69694	46.47580	4629630
217	47 089	14.73092	46.58326	4608295
218	47 524	14.76482	46.69047	4587156
219	47 961	14.79865	46.79744	4566210
220	48 400	14.83240	46.90416	4545455
221	48 841	14.86607	47.01064	4524887
222	49 284	14.89966	47.11688	4504505
223	49 729	14.93318	47.22288	4484305
224	50 176	14.96663	47.32864	4464286
225	50 625	15.00000	47.43416	4444444
226	51 076	15.03330	47.53946	4424779
227	51 529	15.06652	47.64452	4405286
228	51 984	15.09967	47.74935	4385965
229	52 441	15.13275	47.85394	4366812
230	52 900	15.16575	47.95832	4347826
231	53 361	15.19868	48.06246	4329004
232	53 824	15.23155	48.16638	4310345
233	54 289	15.26434	48.27007	4291845
234	54 756	15.29706	48.37355	4273504
235	55 225	15.32971	48.47680	4255319
236	55 696	15.36229	48.57983	4237288
237	56 169	15.39480	48.68265	4219409
238	56 644	15.42725	48.78524	4201681
239	57 121	15.45962	48.88763	4184100
240	57 600	15.49193	48.98979	4166667
241	58 081	15.52417	49.09175	4149378
242	58 564	15.55635	49.19350	4132231
243	59 049	15.58846	49.29503	4115226
244	59 536	15.62050	49.39636	4098361
245	60 025	15.65248	49.49747	4081633
246	60 516	15.68439	49.59839	4065041
247	61 009	15.71623	49.69909	4048583
248	61 504	15.74802	49.79960	4032258
249	62 001	15.77973	49.89990	4016064
250	62 500	15.81139	50.00000	4000000
250	62 500	15.81139	50.00000	4000000
251	63 001	15.84298	50.09990	3984064
252	63 504	15.87451	50.19960	3968254
253	64.009	15.90597	50.29911	3952569
254	64 516	15.93738	50.39841	3937008
255	65 025	15.96872	50.49752	3921569
256	65 536	16.00000	50.59644	3906250
257	66 049	16.03122	50.69517	3891051
258	66 564	16.06238	50.79370	3875969
259	67 081	16.09348	50.89204	3861004
260	67 600	16.12452	50.99020	3846154
261	68 121	16.15549	51.08816	3831418
262	68 644	16.18641	51.18594	3816794
263	69 169	16.21727	51.28353	3802281
264	69 696	16.24808	51.38093	3787879
265	70 225	16.27882	51.47815	3773585
266	70 756	16.30951	51.57519	3759398
267	71 289	16.34013	51.67204	3745318
268	71 824	16.37071	51.76872	3731343
269	72 361	16.40122	51.86521	3717472
270	72 900	16.43168	51.96152	3703704
271	73 441	16.46208	52.05766	3690037
272	73 984	16.49242	52.15362	3676471
273	74 529	16.52271	52.24940	3663004
274	75 076	16.55295	52.34501	3649635
275	75 625	16.58312	52.44044	3636364
276	76 176	16.61325	52.53570	3623188
277	76 729	16.64332	52.63079	3610108
278	77 284	16.67333	52.72571	3597122
279	77 841	16.70329	52.82045	3584229
280	78 400	16.73320	52.91503	3571429
281	78 961	16.76305	53.00943	3558719
282	79 524	16.79286	53.10367	3546099
283	80 089	16.82260	53.19774	3533569
284	80 656	16.85230	53.29165	3521127
285	81 225	16.88194	53.38539	3508772
286	81 796	16.91153	53.47897	3496503
287	82 369	16.94107	53.57238	3484321
288	82 944	16.97056	53.66563	3472222
289	83 521	17.00000	53.75872	3460208
290	84 100	17.02939	53.85165	3448276
291	84 681	17.05872	53.94442	3436426
292	85 264	17.08801	54.03702	3424658
293	85 849	17.11724	54.12947	3412969
294	86 436	17.14643	54.22177	3401361
295	87 025	17.17556	54.31390	3389831
296	87 616	17.20465	54.40588	3378378
297	88 209	17.23369	54.49771	3367003
298	88 804	17.26268	54.58938	3355705
299	89 401	17.29162	54.68089	3344482
300	90 000	17.32051	54.77226	3333333

TABLE I. Squares, Square Roots, and Reciprocals (cont.)

N	N^2	$\sqrt{N}$	$\sqrt{10N}$	$1/N$ .00
300	90 000	17.32051	54.77226	3333333
301	90 601	17.34935	54.86347	3322259
302	91 204	17.37815	54.95453	3311258
303	91 809	17.40690	55.04544	3300330
304	92 416	17.43560	55.13620	3289474
305	93 025	17.46425	55.22681	3278689
306	93 636	17.49286	55.31727	3267974
307	94 249	17.52142	55.40758	3257329
308	94 864	17.54993	55.49775	3246753
309	95 481	17.57840	55.58777	3236246
310	96 100	17.60682	55.67764	3225806
311	96 721	17.63519	55.76737	3215434
312	97 344	17.66352	55.85696	3205128
313	97 969	17.69181	55.94640	3194888
314	98 596	17.72005	56.03570	3184713
315	99 225	17.74824	56.12486	3174603
316	99 856	17.77639	56.21388	3164557
317	100 489	17.80449	56.30275	3154574
318	101 124	17.83255	56.39149	3144654
319	101 761	17.86057	56.48008	3134796
320	102 400	17.88854	56.56854	3125000
321	103 041	17.91647	56.65686	3115265
322	103 684	17.94436	56.74504	3105590
323	104 329	17.97220	56.83309	3095975
324	104 976	18.00000	56.92100	3086420
325	105 625	18.02776	57.00877	3076923
326	106 276	18.05547	57.09641	3067485
327	106 929	18.08314	57.18391	3058104
328	107 584	18.11077	57.27128	3048780
329	108 241	18.13836	57.35852	3039514
330	108 900	18.16590	57.44563	3030303
331	109 561	18.19341	57.53260	3021148
332	110 224	18 22087	57.61944	3012048
333	110 889	18.24829	57.70615	3003003
334	111 556	18.27567	57.79273	2994012
335	112 225	18.30301	57.87918	2985075
336	112 896	18.33030	57.96551	2976190
337	113 569	18.35756	58.05170	2967359
338	114 244	18.38478	58.13777	2958580
339	114 921	18.41195	58.22371	2949853
340	115 600	18.43909	58.30952	2941176
341	116 281	18.46619	58.39521	2932551
342	116 964	18.49324	58.48077	2923977
343	117 649	18.52026	58.56620	2915452
344	118 336	18.54724	58.65151	2906977
345	119 025	18.57418	58.73670	2898551
346	119 716	18.60108	58.82176	2890173
347	120 409	18.62794	58.90671	2881844
348	121 104	18.65476	58.99152	2873563
349	121 801	18.68154	59.07622	2865330
350	122 500	18.70829	59.16080	2857143
350	122 500	18.70829	59.16080	2857143
351	123 201	18.73499	59.24525	2849003
352	123 904	18.76166	59.32959	2840909
353	124 609	18.78829	59.41380	2832861
354	125 316	18.81489	59.49790	2824859
355	126 025	18.84144	59.58188	2816901
356	126 736	18.86796	59.66574	2808989
357	127 449	18.89444	59.74948	2801120
358	128 164	18.92089	59.83310	2793296
359	128 881	18.94730	59.91661	2785515
360	129 600	18.97367	60.00000	2777778
361	130 321	19.00000	60.08328	2770083
362	131 044	19.02630	60.16644	2762431
363	131 769	19.05256	60.24948	2754821
364	132 496	19.07878	60.33241	2747253
365	133 225	19.10497	60.41523	2739726
366	133 956	19.13113	60.49793	2732240
367	134 689	19.15724	60.58052	2724796
368	135 424	19.18333	60.66300	2717391
369	136 161	19.20937	60.74537	2710027
370	136 900	19.23538	60.82763	2702703
371	137 641	19.26136	60.90977	2695418
372	138 384	19.28730	60.99180	2688172
373	139 129	19.31321	61.07373	2680965
374	139 876	19.33908	61.15554	2673797
375	140 625	19.36492	61.23724	2666667
376	141 376	19.39072	61.31884	2659574
377	142 129	19.41649	61.40033	2652520
378	142 884	19.44222	61.48170	2645503
379	143 641	19.46792	61.56298	2638522
380	144 400	19.49359	61.64414	2631579
381	145 161	19.51922	61.72520	2624672
382	145 924	19.54483	61.80615	2617801
383	146 689	19.57039	61.88699	2610966
384	147 456	19.59592	61.96773	2604167
385	148 225	19.62142	62.04837	2597403
386	148 996	19.64688	62.12890	2590674
387	149 769	19.67232	62.20932	2583979
388	150 544	19.69772	62.28965	2577320
389	151 321	19.72308	62.36986	2570694
390	152 100	19.74842	62.44998	2564103
391	152 881	19.77372	62.52999	2557545
392	153 664	19.79899	62.60990	2551020
393	154 449	19.82423	62.68971	2544529
394	155 236	19.84943	62.76942	2538071
395	156 025	19.87461	62.84903	2531646
396	156 816	19.89975	62.92853	2525253
397	157 609	19.92486	63.00794	2518892
398	158 404	19.94994	63.08724	2512563
399	159 201	19.97498	63.16645	2506266
400	160 000	20.00000	63.24555	2500000

TABLE I. Squares, Square Roots, and Reciprocals (cont.)

N	N^2	$\sqrt{N}$	$\sqrt{10N}$	1/N .00
400	160 000	20.00000	63.24555	2500000
401	160 801	20.02498	63.32456	2493766
402	161 604	20.04994	63.40347	2487562
403	162 409	20.07486	63.48228	2481390
404	163 216	20.09975	63.56099	2475248
405	164 025	20.12461	63.63961	2469136
406	164 836	20.14944	63.71813	2463054
407	165 649	20.17424	63.79655	2457002
408	166 464	20.19901	63.87488	2450980
409	167 281	20.22375	63.95311	2444988
410	168 100	20.24846	64.03124	2439024
411	168 921	20.27313	64.10928	2433090
412	169 744	20.29778	64.18723	2427184
413	170 569	20.32240	64.26508	2421308
414	171 396	20.34699	64.34283	2415459
415	172 225	20.37155	64.42049	2409639
416	173 056	20.39608	64.49806	2403846
417	173 889	20.42058	64.57554	2398082
418	174 724	20.44505	64.65292	2392344
419	175 561	20.46949	64.73021	2386635
420	176 400	20.49390	64.80741	2380952
421	177 241	20.51828	64.88451	2375297
422	178 084	20.54264	64.96153	2369668
423	178 929	20.56696	65.03845	2364066
424	179 776	20.59126	65.11528	2358491
425	180 625	20.61553	65.19202	2352941
426	181 476	20.63977	65.26868	2347418
427	182 329	20.66398	65.34524	2341920
428	183 184	20.68816	65.42171	2336449
429	184 041	20.71232	65.49809	2331002
430	184 900	20.73644	65.57439	2325581
431	185 761	20.76054	65.65059	2320186
432	186 624	20.78461	65.72671	2314815
433	187 489	20.80865	65.80274	2309469
434	188 356	20.83267	65.87868	2304147
435	189 225	20.85665	65.95453	2298851
436	190 096	20.88061	66.03030	2293578
437	190 969	20.90454	66.10598	2288330
438	191 844	20.92845	66.18157	2283105
439	192 721	20.95233	66.25708	2277904
440	193 600	20.97618	66.33250	2272727
441	194 481	21.00000	66.40783	2267574
442	195 364	21.02380	66.48308	2262443
443	196 249	21.04757	66.55825	2257336
444	197 136	21.07131	66.63332	2252252
445	198 025	21.09502	66.70832	2247191
446	198 916	21.11871	66.78323	2242152
447	199 809	21.14237	66.85806	2237136
448	200 704	21.16601	66.93280	2232143
449	201 601	21.18962	67.00746	2227171
450	202 500	21.21320	67.08204	2222222

N	N^2	$\sqrt{N}$	$\sqrt{10N}$	1/N .00
450	202 500	21.21320	67.08204	2222222
451	203 401	21.23676	67.15653	2217295
452	204 304	21.26029	67.23095	2212389
453	205 209	21.28380	67.30527	2207506
454	206 116	21.30728	67.37952	2202643
455	207 025	21.33073	67.45369	2197802
456	207 936	21.35416	67.52777	2192982
457	208 849	21.37756	67.60178	2188184
458	209 764	21.40093	67.67570	2183406
459	210 681	21.42429	67.74954	2178649
460	211 600	21.44761	67.82330	2173913
461	212 521	21.47091	67.89698	2169197
462	213 444	21.49419	67.97058	2164502
463	214 369	21.51743	68.04410	2159827
464	215 296	21.54066	68.11755	2155172
465	216 225	21.56386	68.19091	2150538
466	217 156	21.58703	68.26419	2145923
467	218 089	21.61018	68.33740	2141328
468	219 024	21.63331	68.41053	2136752
469	219 961	21.65641	68.48357	2132196
470	220 900	21.67948	68.55655	2127660
471	221 841	21.70253	68.62944	2123142
472	222 784	21.72556	68.70226	2118644
473	223 729	21.74856	68.77500	2114165
474	224 676	21.77154	68.84766	2109705
475	225 625	21.79449	68.92024	2105263
476	226 576	21.81742	68.99275	2100840
477	227 529	21.84033	69.06519	2096436
478	228 484	21.86321	69.13754	2092050
479	229 441	21.88607	69.20983	2087683
480	230 400	21.90890	69.28203	2083333
481	231 361	21.93171	69.35416	2079002
482	232 324	21.95450	69.42622	2074689
483	233 289	21.97726	69.49820	2070393
484	234 256	22.00000	69.57011	2066116
485	235 225	22.02272	69.64194	2061856
486	236 196	22.04541	69.71370	2057613
487	237 169	22.06808	69.78539	2053388
488	238 144	22.09072	69.85700	2049180
489	239 121	22.11334	69.92853	2044990
490	240 100	22.13594	70.00000	2040816
491	241 081	22.15852	70.07139	2036660
492	242 064	22.18107	70.14271	2032520
493	243 049	22.20360	70.21396	2028398
494	244 036	22.22611	70.28513	2024291
495	245 025	22.24860	70.35624	2020202
496	246 016	22.27106	70.42727	2016129
497	247 009	22.29350	70.49823	2012072
498	248 004	22.31591	70.56912	2008032
499	249 001	22.33831	70.63993	2004008
500	250 000	22.36068	70.71068	2000000

TABLE I. Squares, Square Roots, and Reciprocals (cont.)

N	N^2	$\sqrt{N}$	$\sqrt{10N}$	$1/N$ .00
500	250 000	22.36068	70.71068	2000000
501	251 001	22.38303	70.78135	1996008
502	252 004	22.40536	70.85196	1992032
503	253 009	22.42766	70.92249	1988072
504	254 016	22.44994	70.99296	1984127
505	255 025	22.47221	71.06335	1980198
506	256 036	22.49444	71.13368	1976285
507	257 049	22.51666	71.20393	1972387
508	258 064	22.53886	71.27412	1968504
509	259 081	22.56103	71.34424	1964637
510	260 100	22.58318	71.41428	1960784
511	261 121	22.60531	71.48426	1956947
512	262 144	22.62742	71.55418	1953125
513	263 169	22.64950	71.62402	1949318
514	264 196	22.67157	71.69379	1945525
515	265 225	22.69361	71.76350	1941748
516	266 256	22.71563	71.83314	1937984
517	267 289	22.73763	71.90271	1934236
518	268 324	22.75961	71.97222	1930502
519	269 361	22.78157	72.04165	1926782
520	270 400	22.80351	72.11103	1923077
521	271 441	22.82542	72.18033	1919386
522	272 484	22.84732	72.24957	1915709
523	273 529	22.86919	72.31874	1912046
524	274 576	22.89105	72.38784	1908397
525	275 625	22.91288	72.45688	1904762
526	276 676	22.93469	72.52586	1901141
527	277 729	22.95648	72.59477	1897533
528	278 784	22.97825	72.66361	1893939
529	279 841	23.00000	72.73239	1890359
530	280 900	23.02173	72.80110	1886792
531	281 961	23.04344	72.86975	1883239
532	283 024	23.06513	72.93833	1879699
533	284 089	23.08679	73.00685	1876173
534	285 156	23.10844	73.07530	1872659
535	286 225	23.13007	73.14369	1869159
536	287 296	23.15167	73.21202	1865672
537	288 369	23.17326	73.28028	1862197
538	289 444	23.19483	73.34848	1858736
539	290 521	23.21637	73.41662	1855288
540	291 600	23.23790	73.48469	1851852
541	292 681	23.25941	73.55270	1848429
542	293 764	23.28089	73.62065	1845018
543	294 849	23.30236	73.68853	1841621
544	295 936	23.32381	73.75636	1838235
545	297 025	23.34524	73.82412	1834862
546	298 116	23.36664	73.89181	1831502
547	299 209	23.38803	73.95945	1828154
548	300 304	23.40940	74.02702	1824818
549	301 401	23.43075	74.09453	1821494
550	302 500	23.45208	74.16198	1818182

N	N^2	$\sqrt{N}$	$\sqrt{10N}$	$1/N$ .00
550	302 500	23.45208	74.16198	1818182
551	303 601	23.47339	74.22937	1814882
552	304 704	23.49468	74.29670	1811594
553	305 809	23.51595	74.36397	1808318
554	306 916	23.53720	74.43118	1805054
555	308 025	23.55844	74.49832	1801802
556	309 136	23.57965	74.56541	1798561
557	310 249	23.60085	74.63243	1795332
558	311 364	23.62202	74.69940	1792115
559	312 481	23.64318	74.76630	1788909
560	313 600	23.66432	74.83315	1785714
561	314 721	23.68544	74.89993	1782531
562	315 844	23.70654	74.96666	1779359
563	316 969	23.72762	75.03333	1776199
564	318 096	23.74868	75.09993	1773050
565	319 225	23.76973	75.16648	1769912
566	320 356	23.79075	75.23297	1766784
567	321 489	23.81176	75.29940	1763668
568	322 624	23.83275	75.36577	1760563
569	323 761	23.85372	75.43209	1757469
570	324 900	23.87467	75.49834	1754386
571	326 041	23.89561	75.56454	1751313
572	327 184	23.91652	75.63068	1748252
573	328 329	23.93742	75.69676	1745201
574	329 476	23.95830	75.76279	1742160
575	330 625	23.97916	75.82875	1739130
576	331 776	24.00000	75.89466	1736111
577	332 929	24.02082	75.96052	1733102
578	334 084	24.04163	76.02631	1730104
579	335 241	24.06242	76.09205	1727116
580	336 400	24.08319	76.15773	1724138
581	337 561	24.10394	76.22336	1721170
582	338 724	24.12468	76.28892	1718213
583	339 889	24.14539	76.35444	1715266
584	341 056	24.16609	76.41989	1712329
585	342 225	24.18677	76.48529	1709402
586	343 396	24.20744	76.55064	1706485
587	344 569	24.22808	76.61593	1703578
588	345 744	24.24871	76.68116	1700680
589	346 921	24.26932	76.74634	1697793
590	348 100	24.28992	76.81146	1694915
591	349 281	24.31049	76.87652	1692047
592	350 464	24.33105	76.94154	1689189
593	351 649	24.35159	77.00649	1686341
594	352 836	24.37212	77.07140	1683502
595	354 025	24.39262	77.13624	1680672
596	355 216	24.41311	77.20104	1677852
597	356 409	24.43358	77.26578	1675042
598	357 604	24.45404	77.33046	1672241
599	358 801	24.47448	77.39509	1669449
600	360 000	24.49490	77.45967	1666667

TABLE I. Squares, Square Roots, and Reciprocals (cont.)

N	N^2	$\sqrt{N}$	$\sqrt{10N}$	$1/N$ .00
600	360 000	24.49490	77.45967	1666667
601	361 201	24.51530	77.52419	1663894
602	362 404	24.53569	77.58866	1661130
603	363 609	24.55606	77.65307	1658375
604	364 816	24.57641	77.71744	1655629
605	366 025	24.59675	77.78175	1652893
606	367 236	24.61707	77.84600	1650165
607	368 449	24.63737	77.91020	1647446
608	369 664	24.65766	77.97435	1644737
609	370 881	24.67793	78.03845	1642036
610	372 100	24.69818	78.10250	1639344
611	373 321	24.71841	78.16649	1636661
612	374 544	24.73863	78.23043	1633987
613	375 769	24.75884	78.29432	1631321
614	376 996	24.77902	78.35815	1628664
615	378 225	24.79919	78.42194	1626016
616	379 456	24.81935	78.48567	1623377
617	380 689	24.83948	78.54935	1620746
618	381 924	24.85961	78.61298	1618123
619	383 161	24.87971	78.67655	1615509
620	384 400	24.89980	78.74008	1612903
621	385 641	24.91987	78.80355	1610306
622	386 884	24.93993	78.86698	1607717
623	388 129	24.95997	78.93035	1605136
624	389 376	24.97999	78.99367	1602564
625	390 625	25.00000	79.05694	1600000
626	391 876	25.01999	79.12016	1597444
627	393 129	25.03997	79.18333	1594896
628	394 384	25.05993	79.24645	1592357
629	395 641	25.07987	79.30952	1589825
630	396 900	25.09980	79.37254	1587302
631	398 161	25.11971	79.43551	1584786
632	399 424	25.13961	79.49843	1582278
633	400 689	25.15949	79.56130	1579779
634	401 956	25.17936	79.62412	1577287
635	403 225	25.19921	79.68689	1574803
636	404 496	25.21904	79.74961	1572327
637	405 769	25.23886	79.81228	1569859
638	407 044	25.25866	79.87490	1567398
639	408 321	25.27845	79.93748	1564945
640	409 600	25.29822	80.00000	1562500
641	410 881	25.31798	80.06248	1560062
642	412 164	25.33772	80.12490	1557632
643	413 449	25.35744	80.18728	1555210
644	414 736	25.37716	80.24961	1552795
645	416 025	25.39685	80.31189	1550388
646	417 316	25.41653	80.37413	1547988
647	418 609	25.43619	80.43631	1545595
648	419 904	25.45584	80.49845	1543210
649	421 201	25.47548	80.56054	1540832
650	422 500	25.49510	80.62258	1538462

N	N^2	$\sqrt{N}$	$\sqrt{10N}$	$1/N$ .00
650	422 500	25.49510	80.62258	1538462
651	423 801	25.51470	80.68457	1536098
652	425 104	25.53429	80.74652	1533742
653	426 409	25.55386	80.80842	1531394
654	427 716	25.57342	80.87027	1529052
655	429 025	25.59297	80.93207	1526718
656	430 336	25.61250	80.99383	1524390
657	431 649	25.63201	81.05554	1522070
658	432 964	25.65151	81.11720	1519757
659	434 281	25.67100	81.17881	1517451
660	435 600	25.69047	81.24038	1515152
661	436 921	25.70992	81.30191	1512859
662	438 244	25.72936	81.36338	1510574
663	439 569	25.74879	81.42481	1508296
664	440 896	25.76820	81.48620	1506024
665	442 225	25.78759	81.54753	1503759
666	443 556	25.80698	81.60882	1501502
667	444 889	25.82634	81.67007	1499250
668	446 224	25.84570	81.73127	1497006
669	447 561	25.86503	81.79242	1494768
670	448 900	25.88436	81.85353	1492537
671	450 241	25.90367	81.91459	1490313
672	451 584	25.92296	81.97561	1488095
673	452 929	25.94224	82.03658	1485884
674	454 276	25.96151	82.09750	1483680
675	455 625	25.98076	82.15838	1481481
676	456 976	26.00000	82.21922	1479290
677	458 329	26.01922	82.28001	1477105
678	459 684	26.03843	82.34076	1474926
679	461 041	26.05763	82.40146	1472754
680	462 400	26.07681	82.46211	1470588
681	463 761	26.09598	82.42272	1468429
682	465 124	26.11513	82.58329	1466276
683	466 489	26.13427	82.64381	1464129
684	467 856	26.15339	82.70429	1461988
685	469 225	26.17250	82.76473	1459854
686	470 596	26.19160	82.82512	1457726
687	471 969	26.21068	82.88546	1455604
688	473 344	26.22975	82.94577	1453488
689	474 721	26.24881	83.00602	1451379
690	476 100	26.26785	83.06624	1449275
691	477 481	26.28688	83.12641	1447178
692	478 864	26.30589	83.18654	1445087
693	480 249	26.32489	83.24662	1443001
694	481 636	26.34388	83.30666	1440922
695	483 025	26.36285	83.36666	1438849
696	484 416	26.38181	83.42661	1436782
697	485 809	26.40076	83.48653	1434720
698	487 204	26.41969	83.54639	1432665
699	488 601	26.43861	83.60622	1430615
700	490 000	26.45751	83.66600	1428571

TABLE I. Squares, Square Roots, and Reciprocals (cont.)

N	N^2	$\sqrt{N}$	$\sqrt{10N}$	$1/N$ .00
700	490 000	26.45751	83.66600	1428571
701	491 401	26.47640	83.72574	1426534
702	492 804	26.49528	83.78544	1424501
703	494 209	26.51415	83.84510	1422475
704	495 616	26.53300	83.90471	1420455
705	497 025	26.55184	83.96428	1418440
706	498 436	26.57066	84.02381	1416431
707	499 849	26.58947	84.08329	1414427
708	501 264	26.60827	84.14274	1412429
709	502 681	26.62705	84.20214	1410437
710	504 100	26.64583	84.26150	1408451
711	505 521	26.66458	84.32082	1406470
712	506 944	26.68333	84.38009	1404494
713	508 369	26.70206	84.43933	1402525
714	509 796	26.72078	84.49852	1400560
715	511 225	26.73948	84.55767	1398601
716	512 656	26.75818	84.61678	1396648
717	514 089	26.77686	84.67585	1394700
718	515 524	26.79552	84.73488	1392758
719	516 961	26.81418	84.79387	1390821
720	518 400	26.83282	84.85281	1388889
721	519 841	26.85144	84.91172	1386963
722	521 284	26.87006	84.97058	1385042
723	522 729	26.88866	85.02941	1383126
724	524 176	26.90725	85.08819	1381215
725	525 625	26.92582	85.14693	1379310
726	527 076	26.94439	85.20563	1377410
727	528 529	26.96294	85.26429	1375516
728	529 984	26.98148	85.32292	1373626
729	531 441	27.00000	85.38150	1371742
730	532 900	27.01851	85.44004	1369863
731	534 361	27.03701	85.49854	1367989
732	535 824	27.05550	85.55700	1366120
733	537 289	27.07397	85.61542	1364256
734	538 756	27.09243	85.67380	1362398
735	540 225	27.11088	85.73214	1360544
736	541 696	27.12932	85.79044	1358696
737	543 169	27.14774	85.84870	1356852
738	544 644	27.16616	85.90693	1355014
739	546 121	27.18455	85.96511	1353180
740	547 600	27.20294	86.02325	1351351
741	549 081	27.22132	86.08136	1349528
742	550 564	27.23968	86.13942	1347709
743	552 049	27.25803	86.19745	1345895
744	553 536	27.27636	86.25543	1344086
745	555 025	27.29469	86.31338	1342282
746	556 516	27.31300	86.37129	1340483
747	558 009	27.33130	86.42916	1338688
748	559 504	27.34959	86.48699	1336898
749	561 001	27.36786	86.54479	1335113
750	562 500	27.38613	86.60254	1333333

N	N^2	$\sqrt{N}$	$\sqrt{10N}$	$1/N$ .00
750	562 500	27.38613	86.60254	1333333
751	564 001	27.40438	86.66026	1331558
752	565 504	27.42262	86.71793	1329787
753	567 009	27.44085	86.77557	1328021
754	568 516	27.45906	86.83317	1326260
755	570 025	27.47726	86.89074	1324503
756	571 536	27.49545	86.94826	1322751
757	573 049	27.51363	87.00575	1321004
758	574 564	27.53180	87.06320	1319261
759	576 081	27.54995	87.12061	1317523
760	577 600	27.56810	87.17798	1315789
761	579 121	27.58623	87.23531	1314060
762	580 644	27.60435	87.29261	1312336
763	582 169	27.62245	87.34987	1310616
764	583 696	27.64055	87.40709	1308901
765	585 225	27.65863	87.46428	1307190
766	586 756	27.67671	87.52143	1305483
767	588 289	27.69476	87.57854	1303781
768	589 824	27.71281	87.63561	1302083
769	591 361	27.73085	87.69265	1300390
770	592 900	27.74887	87.74964	1298701
771	594 441	27.76689	87.80661	1297017
772	595 984	27.78489	87.86353	1295337
773	597 529	27.80288	87.92042	1293661
774	599 076	27.82086	87.97727	1291990
775	600 625	27.83882	88.03408	1290323
776	602 176	27.85678	88.09086	1288660
777	603 729	27.87472	88.14760	1287001
778	605 284	27.89265	88.20431	1285347
779	606 841	27.91057	88.26098	1283697
780	608 400	27.92848	88.31761	1282051
781	609 961	27.94638	88.37420	1280410
782	611 524	27.96426	88.43076	1278772
783	613 089	27.98214	88.48729	1277139
784	614 656	28.00000	88.54377	1275510
785	616 225	28.01785	88.60023	1273885
786	617 796	28.03569	88.65664	1272265
787	619 369	28.05352	88.71302	1270648
788	620 944	28.07134	88.76936	1269036
789	622 521	28.08914	88.82567	1267427
790	624 100	28.10694	88.88194	1265823
791	625 681	28.12472	88.93818	1264223
792	627 264	28.14249	88.99438	1262626
793	628 849	28.16026	89.05055	1261034
794	630 436	28.17801	89.10668	1259446
795	632 025	28.19574	89.16277	1257862
796	633 616	28.21347	89.21883	1256281
797	635 209	28.23119	89.27486	1254705
798	636 804	28.24889	89.33085	1253133
799	638 401	28.26659	89.38680	1251564
800	640 000	28.28427	89.44272	1250000

TABLE I. Squares, Square Roots, and Reciprocals (cont.)

N	N^2	$\sqrt{N}$	$\sqrt{10N}$	$1/N$ .00
800	640 000	28.28427	89.44272	1250000
801	641 601	28.30194	89.49860	1248439
802	643 204	28.31960	89.55445	1246883
803	644 809	28.33725	89.61027	1245330
804	646 416	28.35489	89.66605	1243781
805	648 025	28.37252	89.72179	1242236
806	649 636	28.39014	89.77750	1240695
807	651 249	28.40775	89.83318	1239157
808	652 864	28.42534	89.88882	1237624
809	654 481	28.44293	89.94443	1236094
810	656 100	28.46050	90.00000	1234568
811	657 721	28.47806	90.05554	1233046
812	659 344	28.49561	90.11104	1231527
813	660 969	28.51315	90.16651	1230012
814	662 596	28.53069	90.22195	1228501
815	664 225	28.54820	90.27735	1226994
816	665 856	28.56571	90.33272	1225490
817	667 489	28.58321	90.38805	1223990
818	669 124	28.60070	90.44335	1222494
819	670 761	28.61818	90.49862	1221001
820	672 400	28.63564	90.55385	1219512
821	674 041	28.65310	90.60905	1218027
822	675 684	28.67054	90.66422	1216545
823	677 329	28.68798	90.71935	1215067
824	678 976	28.70540	90.77445	1213592
825	680 625	28.72281	90.82951	1212121
826	682 276	28.74022	90.88454	1210654
827	683 929	28.75761	90.93954	1209190
828	685 584	28.77499	90.99451	1207729
829	687 241	28.79236	91.04944	1206273
830	688 900	28.80972	91.10434	1204819
831	690 561	28.82707	91.15920	1203369
832	692 224	28.84441	91.21403	1201923
833	693 889	28.86174	91.26883	1200480
834	695 556	28.87906	91.32360	1199041
835	697 225	28.89637	91.37833	1197605
836	698 896	28.91366	91.43304	1196172
837	700 569	28.93095	91.48770	1194743
838	702 244	28.94823	91.54234	1193317
839	703 921	28.96550	91.59694	1191895
840	705 600	28.98275	91.65151	1190476
841	707 281	29.00000	91.70605	1189061
842	708 964	29.01724	91.76056	1187648
843	710 649	29.03446	91.81503	1186240
844	712 336	29.05168	91.86947	1184834
845	714 025	29.06888	91.92388	1183432
846	715 716	29.08608	91.97826	1182033
847	717 409	29.10326	92.03260	1180638
848	719 104	29.12044	92.08692	1179245
849	720 801	29.13760	92.14120	1177856
850	722 500	29.15476	92.19544	1176471

N	N^2	$\sqrt{N}$	$\sqrt{10N}$	$1/N$ .00
850	722 500	29.15476	92.19544	1176471
851	724 201	29.17190	92.24966	1175088
852	725 904	29.18904	92.30385	1173709
853	727 609	29.20616	92.35800	1172333
854	729 316	29.22328	92.41212	1170960
855	731 025	29.24038	92.46621	1169591
856	732 736	29.25748	92.52027	1168224
857	734 449	29.27456	92.57429	1166861
858	736 164	29.29164	92.62829	1165501
859	737 881	29.30870	92.68225	1164144
860	739 600	29.32576	92.73618	1162791
861	741 321	29.34280	92.79009	1161440
862	743 044	29.35984	92.84396	1160093
863	744 769	29.37686	92.89779	1158749
864	746 496	29.39388	92.95160	1157407
865	748 225	29.41088	93.00538	1156069
866	749 956	29.42788	93.05912	1154734
867	751 689	29.44486	93.11283	1153403
868	753 424	29.46184	93.16652	1152074
869	755 161	29.47881	93.22017	1150748
870	756 900	29.49576	93.27379	1149425
871	758 641	29.51271	93.32738	1148106
872	760 384	29.52965	93.38094	1146789
873	762 129	29.54657	93.43447	1145475
874	763 876	29.56349	93.48797	1144165
875	765 625	29.58040	93.54143	1142857
876	767 376	29.59730	93.59487	1141553
877	769 129	29.61419	93.64828	1140251
878	770 884	29.63106	93.70165	1138952
879	772 641	29.64793	93.75500	1137656
880	774 400	29.66479	93.80832	1136364
881	776 161	29.68164	93.86160	1135074
882	777 924	29.69848	93.91486	1133787
883	779 689	29.71532	93.96808	1132503
884	781 456	29.73214	94.02127	1131222
885	783 225	29.74895	94.07444	1129944
886	784 996	29.76575	94.12757	1128668
887	786 769	29.78255	94.18068	1127396
888	788 544	29.79933	94.23375	1126126
889	790 321	29.81610	94.28680	1124859
890	792 100	29.83287	94.33981	1123596
891	793 881	29.84962	94.39280	1122334
892	795 664	29.86637	94.44575	1121076
893	797 449	29.88311	94.49868	1119821
894	799 236	29.89983	94.55157	1118568
895	801 025	29.91655	94.60444	1117318
896	802 816	29.93326	94.65728	1116071
897	804 609	29.94996	94.71008	1114827
898	806 404	29.96665	94.76286	1113586
899	808 201	29.98333	94.81561	1112347
900	810 000	30.00000	94.86833	1111111

TABLE I. Squares, Square Roots, and Reciprocals (cont.)

N	N^2	$\sqrt{N}$	$\sqrt{10N}$	$1/N$ .00
900	810 000	30.00000	94.86833	1111111
901	811 801	30.01636	94.92102	1109878
902	813 604	30.03331	94.97368	1108647
903	815 409	30.04996	95.02631	1107420
904	817 216	30.06659	95.07891	1106195
905	819 025	30.08322	95.13149	1104972
906	820 836	30.09983	95.18403	1103753
907	822 649	30.11644	95.23655	1102536
908	824 464	30.13304	95.28903	1101322
909	826 281	30.14963	95.34149	1100110
910	828 100	30.16621	95.39392	1098901
911	829 921	30.18278	95.44632	1097695
912	831 744	30.19934	95.49869	1096491
913	833 569	30.21589	95.55103	1095290
914	835 396	30.23243	95.60335	1094092
915	837 225	30.24897	95.65563	1092896
916	839 056	30.26549	95.70789	1091703
917	840 889	30.28201	95.76012	1090513
918	842 724	30.29851	95.81232	1089325
919	844 561	30.31501	95.86449	1088139
920	846 400	30.33150	95.91663	1086957
921	848 241	30.34798	95.96874	1085776
922	850 084	30.36445	96.02083	1084599
923	851 929	30.38092	96.07289	1083424
924	853 776	30.39737	96.12492	1082251
925	855 625	30.41381	96.17692	1081081
926	857 476	30.43025	96.22889	1079914
927	859 329	30.44667	96.28084	1078749
928	861 184	30.46309	96.33276	1077586
929	863 041	30.47950	96.38465	1076426
930	864 900	30.49590	96.43651	1075269
931	866 761	30.51229	96.48834	1074114
932	868 624	30.52868	96.54015	1072961
933	870 489	30.54505	96.59193	1071811
934	872 356	30.56141	96.64368	1070664
935	874 225	30.57777	96.69540	1069519
936	876 096	30.59412	96.74709	1068376
937	877 969	30.61046	96.79876	1067236
938	879 844	30.62679	96.85040	1066098
939	881 721	30.64311	96.90201	1064963
940	883 600	30.65942	96.95360	1063830
941	885 481	30.67572	97.00515	1062699
942	887 364	30.69202	97.05668	1061571
943	889 249	30.70831	97.10819	1060445
944	891 136	30.72458	97.15966	1059322
945	893 025	30.74085	97.21111	1058201
946	894 916	30.75711	97.26253	1057082
947	896 809	30.77337	97.31393	1055966
948	898 704	30.78961	97.36529	1054852
949	900 601	30.80584	97.41663	1053741
950	902 500	30.82207	97.46794	1052632

N	N^2	$\sqrt{N}$	$\sqrt{10N}$	$1/N$ .00
950	902 500	30.82207	97.46794	1052632
951	904 401	30.83829	97.51923	1051525
952	906 304	30.85450	97.57049	1050420
953	908 209	30.87070	97.62172	1049318
954	910.116	30.88689	97.67292	1048218
955	912 025	30.90307	97.72410	1047120
956	913 936	30.91925	97.77525	1046025
957	915 849	30.93542	97.82638	1044932
958	917 764	30.95158	97.87747	1043841
959	919 681	30.96773	97.92855	1042753
960	921 600	30.98387	97.97959	1041667
961	923 521	31.00000	98.03061	1040583
962	925 444	31.01612	98.08160	1039501
963	927 369	31.03224	98.13256	1038422
964	929 296	31.04835	98.18350	1037344
965	931 225	31.06445	98.23441	1036269
966	933 156	31.08054	98.28530	1035197
967	935 089	31.09662	98.33616	1034126
968	937 024	31.11270	98.38699	1033058
969	938 961	31.12876	98.43780	1031992
970	940 900	31.14482	98.48858	1030928
971	942 841	31.16087	98.53933	1029866
972	944 784	31.17691	98.59006	1028807
973	946 729	31.19295	98.64076	1027749
974	948 676	31.20897	98.69144	1026694
975	950 625	31.22499	98.74209	1025641
976	952 576	31.24100	98.79271	1024590
977	954 529	31.25700	98.84331	1023541
978	956 484	31.27299	98.89388	1022495
979	958 441	31.28898	98.94443	1021450
980	960 400	31.30495	98.99495	1020408
981	962 361	31.32092	99.04544	1019368
982	964 324	31.33688	99.09591	1018330
983	966 289	31.35283	99.14636	1017294
984	968 256	31.36877	99.19677	1016260
985	970 225	31.38471	99.24717	1015228
986	972 196	31.40064	99.29753	1014199
987	974 169	31.41656	99.34787	1013171
988	976 144	31.43247	99.39819	1012146
989	978 121	31.44837	99.44848	1011122
990	980 100	31.46427	99.49874	1010101
991	982 081	31.48015	99.54898	1009082
992	984 064	31.49603	99.59920	1008065
993	986 049	31.51190	99.64939	1007049
994	988 036	31.52777	99.69955	1006036
995	990 025	31.54362	99.74969	1005025
996	992 016	31.55947	99.79980	1004016
997	994 009	31.57531	99.84989	1003009
998	996 004	31.59114	99.89995	1002004
999	998 001	31.60696	99.94999	1001001
1000	1 000 000	31.62278	100.00000	1000000

Areas under the normal curve

The table of areas under the normal curve gives the proportion of the area under the normal curve that is located between the mean and any given point, where the location of the point is given in terms of standard (Z) units. This is useful in analysis because the proportion of area under the curve corresponds to the proportion of the total number of items which is included in that same interval. The table can be used only with Z values. All non-standardized values must first be transformed into Z values by the methods described in Chapter 5. The general transformation formula is:

$$Z = \frac{X - \bar{X}}{\sigma}$$

To find out what proportion of the area lies between the mean and a standard (Z) value of 1.90 look down the left column till 1.9 is found, across to the column 0.00 and there the figure 0.4713 is found. This indicates that 47.13 per cent of the area under the normal curve lies between the mean and a point 1.90 standard deviations from the mean on one side of the mean.

To find out what proportion of the area lies between the mean and a point $+1.93$ Z's way, (or -1.93 Z's, since the proportion would be the same), again look down the left hand column till 1.9 is found. Now look across the row to the right of 1.9 to the column headed 0.03. The number at the intersection of row 1.9 and column 0.03 is 0.4732. This indicates that 47.32 per cent of the area under the normal curve lies between the mean and a point 1.93 standard deviations from the mean (in only one direction).

The table can be used to find the per cent of the area between any two points in a normal distribution by adding or subtracting the figures found in the body of the table.

The table is used in reverse to find the Z units equivalent to given percentages of area. Thus, to find the interval in the standard units that includes 35 per cent of the area, measuring above the mean only, look for 0.3500 in the body of the table. The closest number is 0.3508: its coordinates are 1.0 and 0.04. Therefore, to include approximately 35

TABLE II. Areas under the normal curve

(Proportion of total area within stated interval away from the mean on one side of the mean.)

$(X - \overline{X})/\sigma$ or Z	0.00	0.01	0.02	0.03	0.04	0.05	0.06	0.07	0.08	0.09
0.0	0.0000	0.0040	0.0080	0.0120	0.0160	0.0199	0.0239	0.0279	0.0319	0.0359
.1	.0398	.0438	.0478	.0517	.0557	.0596	.0636	.0675	.0714	.0753
.2	.0793	.0832	.0871	.0910	.0948	.0987	.1026	.1064	.1103	.1141
.3	.1179	.1217	.1255	.1293	.1331	.1368	.1406	.1443	.1480	.1517
.4	.1554	.1591	.1628	.1664	.1700	.1736	.1772	.1808	.1844	.1879
.5	.1915	.1950	.1985	.2019	.2054	.2088	.2123	.2157	.2190	.2224
.6	.2257	.2291	.2324	.2357	.2389	.2422	.2454	.2486	.2518	.2649
.7	.2580	.2612	.2642	.2673	.2704	.2734	.2764	.2794	.2823	.2852
.8	.2881	.2910	.2939	.2967	.2995	.3023	.3051	.3078	.3106	.3133
.9	.3159	3186	.3212	.3238	.3264	.3289	.3315	.3340	.3365	.3389
1.0	.3413	.3438	.3461	.3485	.3508	.3531	.3554	.3577	.3599	.3621
1.1	.3643	.3665	.3686	.3708	.3729	.3749	.3770	.3790	.3810	.3830
1.2	.3849	.3869	.3888	.3907	.3925	.3944	.3962	.3980	.3997	.4015
1.3	.4032	.4049	.4066	.4082	.4099	.4115	.4131	.4147	.4162	.4177
1.4	.4192	.4207	.4222	.4236	.4251	.4264	.4279	.4292	.4306	.4319
1.5	.4332	.4345	.4357	.4370	.4382	.4394	.4406	.4418	.4429	.4441
1.6	.4452	.4463	.4474	.4484	.4495	.4505	.4515	.4525	.4535	.4545
1.7	.4554	.4564	.4573	.4582	.4591	.4599	.4608	.4616	.4625	.4633
1.8	.4641	.4649	.4656	.4664	.4671	.4678	.4686	.4693	.4699	.4706
1.9	.4713	.4719	.4726	.4732	.4738	.4744	.4750	.4756	.4761	.4767
2.0	.4772	.4778	.4783	.4788	.4793	.4798	.4803	.4808	.4812	.4817
2.1	.4821	.4826	.4830	.4834	.4838	.4842	.4846	.4850	.4854	.4857
2.2	.4861	.4864	.4868	.4871	.4875	.4878	.4881	.4884	.4887	.4890
2.3	.4893	.4896	.4898	.4901	.4904	.4906	.4909	.4911	.4913	.4916
2.4	.4918	.4920	.4922	.4925	.4927	.4929	.4931	.4932	.4934	.4936
2.5	.4938	.4940	.4941	.4943	.4945	.4946	.4948	.4949	.4951	.4952
2.6	.4953	.4955	.4956	.4957	.4959	.4960	.4961	.4962	.4963	.4964
2.7	.4965	.4966	.4967	.4968	.4969	.4970	.4971	.4972	.4973	.4974
2.8	.4974	.4975	.4976	.4977	.4977	.4978	.4979	.4979	.4980	.4981
2.9	.4981	.4982	.4982	.4983	.4984	.4984	.4985	.4985	.4986	.4986
3.0	.49865	.4987	.4987	.4988	.4988	.4989	.4989	.4989	.4990	.4990
3.1	.49903	.4991	.4991	.4991	.4992	.4992	.4992	.4992	.4993	.4993
3.2	.4993129									
3.3	.4995166									
3.4	.4996631									
3.5	.4997674									
3.6	.4998409									
3.7	.4998922									
3.8	.4999277									
3.9	.4999519									
4.0	.4999683									
4.5	.4999966									
5.0	.4999997133									

per cent of the area under the curve in an interval above the mean, establish an interval from the mean to the mean plus 1.04 standard deviations ($\bar{X}$ to $\bar{X} + 1.04\sigma$).

The table is reprinted from Croxton and Cowden, *Applied General Statistics*, 2nd ed., Englewood Cliffs, N. J., Prentice-Hall, Inc., 1955, by permission of the publisher, and by permission of Houghton Mifflin Company, publishers of Rugg's *Statistical Methods Applied to Education*, the original source for the table.

Minimum values of t

A given standard error is divided into a difference to obtain t. The table below gives the minimum values of t required for significance at the 10, 5, and 1 per cent levels. The table is entered with the number of degrees of freedom determined for the problem. If the value of t obtained through calculation is equal to or exceeds the value given in a column of the table, the observed difference may be considered to be significant at the level of significance indicated at the top of the column. The level of significance expresses the probability of obtaining a t value of the size indicated purely by chance. The table indicates the probabilities of the difference being so large in either a positive or negative direction. The probabilities for one direction only are obtained by dividing the given probability values by 2.

TABLE III. Table of *t*

Degrees of freedom	Probability 0.10	0.05	0.01
1	6.31	12.71	63.66
2	2.92	4.30	9.92
3	2.35	3.18	5.84
4	2.13	2.78	4.60
5	2.02	2.57	4.03
6	1.94	2.45	3.71
7	1.90	2.36	3.50
8	1.86	2.31	3.36
9	1.83	2.26	3.25
10	1.81	2.23	3.17
11	1.80	2.20	3.11
12	1.78	2.18	3.06
13	1.77	2.16	3.01
14	1.76	2.14	2.98
15	1.75	2.13	2.95
16	1.75	2.12	2.92
17	1.74	2.11	2.90
18	1.73	2.10	2.88
19	1.73	2.09	2.86
20	1.72	2.09	2.84
21	1.72	2.08	2.83
22	1.72	2.07	2.82
23	1.71	2.07	2.81
24	1.71	2.06	2.80
25	1.71	2.06	2.79
26	1.71	2.06	2.78
27	1.70	2.05	2.77
28	1.70	2.05	2.76
29	1.70	2.04	2.76
30	1.70	2.04	2.75
60	1.67	2.00	2.66
120	1.66	1.98	2.62
∞	1.64	1.96	2.58

Source: This table adapted from Table III, p. 44 of Fisher and Yates, *Statistical Tables for Biological, Agricultural, and Medical Research*, 5th ed., Edinburgh, Oliver and Boyd Ltd., 1957, by permission of the authors and publishers.

APPENDIX C

Selected references

General references

Croxton, Frederick E. and Dudley J. Cowden, *Applied General Statistics*, 2nd ed., Englewood Cliffs, N. J., Prentice-Hall, Inc., 1955.

Neiswanger, William A., *Elementary Statistical Methods*, 2nd ed., New York, The Macmillan Company, 1956.

Neter, John and William Wasserman, *Fundamental Statistics for Business and Economics*, New York, Allyn and Bacon, Inc., 1956.

Sources of data

Cole, A. H., *Measures of Business Change*, Homewood, Illinois, Richard D. Irwin, Inc., 1952.

Coman, Edwin T. Jr., *Sources of Business Information*, Englewood Cliffs, N. J., Prentice-Hall, Inc., 1949.

Hauser, P. M. and W. R. Leonard, *Government Statistics for Business*, New York, John Wiley & Sons, Inc., 1946.

Johnson and McFarland, *How to Use the Business Library, With Sources of Business Information*, 2nd ed., Cincinnati, South-Western Publishing Company, 1957.

Also see Chapter 2 for sources of recorded data.

Sampling methods and theory

Deming, William Edwards, *Some Theory of Sampling*, New York, John Wiley & Sons, Inc., 1950.

Hansen, Morris H., William N. Hurwitz, William G. Madow, *Sample Survey Methods and Theory*, Vol. I, *Methods and Applications*, New York, John Wiley & Sons, Inc., 1953.

Parten, Mildred, *Surveys, Polls and Samples: Practical Procedures*, New York, Harper & Brothers, 1950.

Business forecasting

Controllership Foundation, Inc., *Business Forecasting: a Survey of Business Practices and Methods*, New York, 1950.

Newbury, Frank D., *Business Forecasting: Principles and Practices*, New York, McGraw-Hill Book Company, Inc., 1952.

Prochnow, Herbert V., ed., *Determining the Business Outlook*, New York, Harper & Brothers, 1954.

Wright, Wilson, *Forecasting for Profit. A Technique for Business Management*, New York, John Wiley & Sons, Inc., 1947.

Marketing research

Ferber, Robert, *Statistical Techniques in Market Research*, New York, McGraw-Hill Book Company, Inc., 1949.

Luck, David J. and Hugh G. Wales, *Marketing Research*, Englewood Cliffs, N. J., Prentice-Hall, Inc., 1952.

Internal administrative control

Anderson, David R., *Practical Controllership*, Homewood, Illinois, Richard D. Irwin, Inc., 1949.

Doris, Lillian, editor, *Corporate Treasurer's and Controller's Handbook*, Prentice-Hall, Inc., 1950.

Heckert, J. Brooks and James D. Willson, *Controllership, the Work of the Accounting Executive*, New York, The Ronald Press Company, 1952.

Presentation of data

Lutz, R. R., *Graphic Presentation Simplified*, New York, Funk & Wagnalls Company, 1949.

Schmid, Calvin F., *Handbook of Graphic Presentation*, New York, The Ronald Press Company, 1954.

Spear, Mary Eleanor, *Charting Statistics*, New York, McGraw-Hill Book Company, Inc., 1952.

Statistical inference

Bross, Irwin D. J., *Design for Decision*, New York, The Macmillan Company, 1953.

Grant, Eugene L., *Statistical Quality Control*, 2nd ed., New York, McGraw-Hill Book Company, Inc., 1952.

Lindgren, B. W. and G. W. McElrath, *Introduction to Probability and Statistics*, New York, The Macmillan Company, 1959.

Index